BINDING

THE binding on this volume is a facsimile of the original on exhibition among the Treasures of the Vatican, and is here reproduced, by special permission, for the first time.

It is an Italian binding of the first half of the sixteenth century, executed for the famous Italian collector Tommaso Maioli.

This is a very chaste and elegant arabesque design, and is a good example of the excellence of fine Italian bindings at the time of its execution.

The inscription at the bottom of the cover (THO. MAIOLI. ET. AMICOR) means "For Tho. Maioli and his friends."

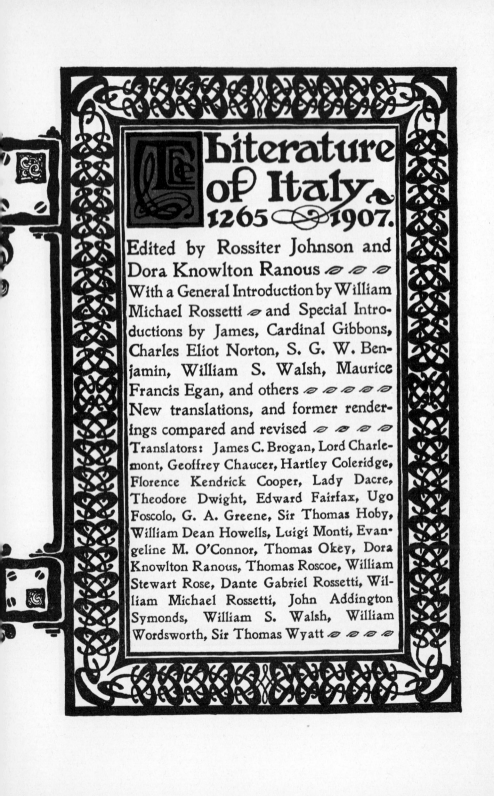

Literature of Italy 1265 ⌘ 1907.

Edited by Rossiter Johnson and Dora Knowlton Ranous *◈ ◈ ◈* With a General Introduction by William Michael Rossetti *◈* and Special Introductions by James, Cardinal Gibbons, Charles Eliot Norton, S. G. W. Benjamin, William S. Walsh, Maurice Francis Egan, and others *◈ ◈ ◈ ◈* New translations, and former renderings compared and revised *◈ ◈ ◈ ◈* Translators: James C. Brogan, Lord Charlemont, Geoffrey Chaucer, Hartley Coleridge, Florence Kendrick Cooper, Lady Dacre, Theodore Dwight, Edward Fairfax, Ugo Foscolo, G. A. Greene, Sir Thomas Hoby, William Dean Howells, Luigi Monti, Evangeline M. O'Connor, Thomas Okey, Dora Knowlton Ranous, Thomas Roscoe, William Stewart Rose, Dante Gabriel Rossetti, William Michael Rossetti, John Addington Symonds, William S. Walsh, William Wordsworth, Sir Thomas Wyatt *◈ ◈ ◈ ◈*

CELLINI IMPRISONED IN THE CASTLE OF ST. ANGELO

From a Painting by Robert Henry

CELLINI IMPRISONED IN THE CASTLE OF ST. ANGELO

From a Painting by Robert Henry

MEMOIRS

OF

BENVENUTO CELLINI

WRITTEN BY HIMSELF

TRANSLATED BY THOMAS ROSCOE

THE NATIONAL ALUMNI

CONTENTS

ILLUSTRATIONS

INTRODUCTION

Benvenuto Cellini had four characters—a goldsmith, a sculptor, a soldier, a courtier—and in view of his *Memoirs*, which have won a place in permanent literature, we may also class him as an author. This book has a double value as the frank, unreserved story of a genius whose life was full of adventure, and as a picture of the state of European society in the Sixteenth Century. He was born at the beginning of that century, when Michelangelo, of whom he speaks as his master in the arts, was twenty-six years old. Raphael, Vasari, Andrea del Sarto, and other artists were his contemporaries, for some of whom he had, or professed to have, little respect. And it is a significant fact that time has corroborated his judgment of them. He contended with several for patronage, and learned the little value of a prince's promise. He both enjoyed the favor and encountered the animosity of kings, dukes, popes and cardinals; at times made his way by his skill as a swordsman, and again submitted tamely to be cheated in a lawsuit. At the siege of Rome he commanded a battery on the Castle of St. Angelo, and afterward he was a prisoner within its walls. He produced works of exquisite beauty in gold and silver, and met with the shabbiest treatment from those who should have encouraged and paid him. He was boastful beyond all men that have written memoirs, but his boasts were usually made good. He did not hesitate to redress a personal grievance with a murder, and his domestic morals were of the worst, but he considered himself highly chivalrous. Death came very near him when he

made a desperate escape from prison, and again when
a farmer's wife poisoned him with the food that he ate
at her table; yet he lived through all sorts of dangers
and murderous plots and reached the allotted three score
and ten. He represented, perhaps in excess, the spirit of
his age, and it is that spirit displayed on every page
of his book that gives it its value for all future times.

Cellini's father was determined to make a musician
of him, but the boy detested the flute, and followed his
true bent toward the arts of design. As a goldsmith he
surpassed all, and as a sculptor he attained a high rank,
though later critics are disposed to abate somewhat of
this. At the age of sixty he married the woman that
had nursed him through the fearful illness that followed
the poisoning—thus also meeting an obligation that
could be discharged in no other way.

In his day Italy was still ruled by popes and dukes
in separate principalities; Francis I of France was building the wonderful Castle of Fontainebleau; Charles V
(born in the same year with Cellini) became Emperor
of Germany; Rome was stormed and sacked; his lifetime
included the reigns of Henry VIII and Mary in England,
and twelve years of Elizabeth's. Columbus discovered
the new world eight years before Cellini was born, and
Shakespeare was six years old when he died.

At the age of fifty-four Cellini was made a member
of the Florentine nobility. Four years later he began the
writing of his *Memoirs,* most of which he dictated to an
amanuensis. This task occupied his leisure four years,
when for an unknown reason he abruptly ended it.
However great was his self-esteem as an artist, he was
sufficiently modest as an author, and in submitting his
manuscript to the criticism of a friend he expressed apparently sincere doubts of its value. The book has been
translated into the principal European languages, and
has appeared in many editions. Cellini wrote treatises

on sculpture and the goldsmith's art, and a few of his
letters also have been preserved. He died February 15,
1570, and was buried, in accordance with his own wish,
in the chapter-house of the Annunziata, where he had
intended to build himself a costly tomb; but his famous
book is a more significant and durable monument than
anything that even he could have constructed of bronze
or marble.

Augustine Birrell, one of the keenest of modern critics,
in an analysis of the unique book, writes thus:

"What a liar was Benvenuto Cellini!—who can believe a word he says? To hang a dog on his oath would
be a judicial murder. Yet when we lay down his Memoirs
and let our thought travel back to those far-off days he
tells us of, there we see him standing, in bold relief,
against the black sky of the past, the very man he was.
Not more surely did he, with that rare skill of his,
stamp the image of Clement VII on the papal currency
than he did the impress of his own singular personality
upon every word he spoke and every sentence he wrote.
We ought, of course, to hate him, but do we? A murderer he has written himself down. A liar he stands
self-convicted of being. Were anyone in the nether world
bold enough to call him thief, it may be doubted whether
Rhadamanthus would award him the damages for which
we may be certain he would loudly clamor. Why do
we hate him? Listen to him: 'Upon my uttering these
words, there was a general outcry, the noblemen affirming that I promised too much. But one of them, who
was a great philosopher, said in my favor: "From the
admirable symmetry of shape and happy physiognomy
of this young man, I venture to engage that he will perform all he promises, and more." The Pope replied, "I
am of the same opinion"; then calling Trajano, his gentleman of the bedchamber, he ordered him to fetch me
five hundred ducats.'

"And so it always ended; suspicions, aroused most reasonably, allayed most unreasonably, and then—ducats! He deserved hanging, but he died in his bed. He wrote his own *Memoirs* after a fashion that should have brought posthumous justice upon him, and made them a literary gibbet, on which he should swing, a creaking horror, for all time; but nothing of the sort has happened. The rascal is so symmetrical, and his physiognomy, as it gleams upon us through the centuries, so happy, that we cannot withhold our ducats, though we may accompany the gift with a shower of abuse.

"You open his book—a Pharisee of the Pharisees. Lying indeed! Why, you hate prevarication. As for murder, your friends know you too well to mention the subject in your hearing, except in immediate connection with capital punishment. You are, of course, willing to make some allowance for Cellini's time and place—the first half of the sixteenth century, and Italy. 'Yes,' you remark, 'Cellini shall have strict justice at my hands.' So you say as you settle yourself in your chair and begin to read. We seem to hear the rascal laughing in his grave. His spirit breathes upon you from his book —peeps at you roguishly as you turn the pages. His atmosphere surrounds you; you smile when you ought to frown, chuckle when you should groan, and—Oh, final triumph!—laugh aloud when, if you had a rag of principle left, you would fling the book into the fire.

"That such a man as this encountered suffering in the course of his life should be a matter for satisfaction to every well-regulated mind; but, somehow or another, you find yourself pitying the fellow as he narrates the hardships he endured in the Castle of St. Angelo. He is so symmetrical a rascal! Just hear him! 'Having at length recovered my strength and vigor, after I had composed myself and resumed my cheerfulness, I continued to read my Bible, and so accustomed my eyes to that darkness that, though I was at first able to read only an hour and a half, I could at length read three hours. I then reflected on the wonderful power of the Almighty upon the hearts of simple men, who had carried their enthusiasm so far as to believe firmly that God would indulge them in all they wished for; and I promised myself the assistance of the Most High, as well through His mercy as on account of my innocence. Thus turning constantly to the Supreme Being, sometimes in prayer, sometimes in silent meditation on the divine goodness, I was totally engrossed by these heavenly reflections, and came to take such delight in pious meditations that I no longer thought of past misfortunes. On the contrary, I was all day long singing psalms and many other compositions of mine, in which I celebrated and praised the Deity.'

"Thus torn from their context, these passages may seem to supply the best possible falsification of the previous statement that Cellini told the truth about himself. Judged by these passages alone, he may appear a hypocrite of an unusually odious description. But it is only necessary to read his book to dispel that notion. He tells lies about other people; he repeats long conversations, sounding his own praises, during which, as his own narrative shows, he was not present; he exaggerates his own exploits, his sufferings—even, it may be, his crimes; but when we lay down his book, we feel we are saying good-by to a man whom we know. He has introduced himself to us, and though doubtless we prefer saints to sinners, we may be forgiven for liking the company of a live rogue better than that of the lay-figures and empty clock-cases, labeled with distinguished names, who are to be found doing duty for men in the works of our standard historians. What would we not give to know Julius Cæsar one half as well as we know this outrageous rascal? The saints of the earth, too, how shadowy they are! Which of them do we really know? Excepting one or two ancient and modern Quietists, there is hardly one among the whole number who being dead yet speaketh.

"On laying down Cellini's *Memoirs,* let us be careful to recall our banished moral sense, and make peace with her, by passing a final judgment on this desperate sinner, which perhaps, after all, we cannot do better than by employing language of his own concerning a monk, a fellow-prisoner of his, who never, so far as appears, murdered anybody, but of whom Cellini none the less felt himself entitled to say: 'I admired his shining qualities, but his odious vices I freely censured and held in abhorrence.'"

Various critics have analyzed this remarkable character, and though they all arrive virtually at the same conclusion, few have expressed it so forcibly as Birrell.

R. J.

CHAPTER I

THE AUTHOR'S MOTIVES

IT is a duty incumbent on upright and credible men of all ranks, who have performed anything noble or praiseworthy, to record, in their own writing, the events of their lives; yet they should not begin this honorable task before they have passed their fortieth year. Such, at least, is my opinion, now that I have completed my fifty-eighth year, and am settled in Florence, where, considering the numerous ills that constantly attend human life, I perceive that I have never been so free from vexations and calamities, or possessed of so great a share of content and health, as at this period. Looking back on some delightful and happy events of my life, and on many misfortunes so overwhelming that the appalling retrospect makes me wonder how I have reached this age in vigor and prosperity, through God's goodness, I have resolved to publish an account of my life. And although men whose exertions have been crowned with any degree of honor, and who have rendered themselves conspicuous to the world, ought, perhaps, to regard only that personal merit to which they owe their celebrity; yet as in this world it is necessary to live like other people, I must, in beginning my narrative, satisfy the public on some few points to which its curiosity is usually directed; the first of which is to ascertain whether a man is descended from a virtuous and ancient family.

My name, then, is Benvenuto Cellini, and I am the son of Maestro Giovanni, the son of Andrea, the son of Cristofano Cellini; my mother was Maria Lisabetta, daughter

1

to Stefano Granacci: and both my parents were citizens
of Florence. It appears from the ancient chronicles com-
piled by natives of that city, men highly deserving of
credit, that it was built after the model of Rome. This
is evident from the vestiges of the Colosseum, and the
hot baths, near the Holy Cross: the capitol was an ancient market-place: the rotunda, which is still entire,
was built for a temple of Mars, and is now called San
Giovanni's church. This is so evident that it cannot be
denied; but the above-mentioned structures are of much
smaller dimensions than those of Rome. It is said that
they were erected by Julius Cæsar, in conjunction with
some other Roman patricians, who, having subdued and
taken Fiesole, in this very place founded a city, and each
of them undertook to erect one of these remarkable
edifices. Julius Cæsar had a gallant officer of high rank
in his army, named Florentius of Cellino, which is a
castle within two miles of Monte Fiascone. This Florentius having taken up his quarters under Fiesole, where
Florence at present stands, to be near the river Arno for
the convenience of his army, all the soldiers and others
who had any business with that officer used to say, "Let
us go to Florence;" as well because the name of the
officer was Florentius, as because on the spot where he
had fixed his headquarters there was great plenty of
flowers. Thus in the infancy of the town the elegant
appellation of Florence seeming to Julius Cæsar appropriate, and its allusion to flowers appearing auspicious,
he gave it the name of Florentia; at the same time paying a compliment to his valiant officer, to whom he was
the more attached because he had promoted him from a
very humble station and considered his merit as in some
measure a creation of his own. The other name of
Fluentia, which the learned inventors and investigators
of the connexion of names pretend that Florence obtained
on account of the Arno's *flowing* through the town, can-

not be admitted. I believe the matter to be as I have stated, and am of opinion that this city takes its name from the valiant captain Florentius.

My ancestors lived in retirement in the valley of Ambra, where they were lords of considerable domains: they were all trained to arms, and distinguished for military prowess. One of the family, a youth named Cristofano, had a fierce dispute with some of their neighbors and friends; and because the chief relations on both sides had engaged in the dispute, and it seemed likely that the flames of discord would end in the destruction of the two families, the eldest people, having maturely considered the matter, unanimously agreed to remove the two young men who began the quarrel out of the way. The opposite party obliged their kinsman to withdraw to Siena, and Cristofano's parents sent him to Florence, where they purchased a small house for him in the Via Chiara, from the monastery of St. Ursula, with a pretty good estate near the bridge of Rifredi. This Cristofano married in Florence, and had several sons and daughters: the daughters were portioned off; and the sons divided the remainder of their father's substance between them. After his decease, the house of Via Chiara, with some other property of no great amount, fell to one of the above-mentioned sons, whose name was Andrea. He took a wife, by whom he had four male children: the name of the first was Girolamo, that of the second Bartolommeo; the third was Giovanni, my father; the fourth was Francesco.

Andrea Cellini, my grandfather, was tolerably well versed in the architecture of those days, and made it his profession. Giovanni, my father, cultivated it more than any of his brothers; and since, according to the opinion of Vitruvius, those who are desirous of succeeding in this art, should know something of music and drawing, Giovanni, having acquired great proficiency in the art of designing, began to apply himself to music. He learned to play admirably upon the viol and flute; and being of a very studious disposition, he hardly ever went abroad.

His next-door neighbor was Stefano Granacci, who had several daughters of extraordinary beauty. Giovanni soon became sensible to the charms of one of them, named Lisabetta; and at length grew so deeply enamored that he asked her in marriage. Their fathers being intimate, it was no difficult matter to bring about the match, as both parties thought they found their account in it. First of all, the two old men concluded the marriage, and then began to talk of the portion; but they could not agree on that point, for Andrea said to Stefano, "My son Giovanni is the best youth in Florence, and even in all Italy; and if I had thought of procuring him a wife before, I might have obtained for him the best portion in Florence amongst persons of our rank." Stefano answered, "You have a thousand reasons on your side, but I have five daughters and several sons; so that, all things duly considered, it is as much as I can afford." Giovanni had stood some time listening to their conversation unperceived by them, but on hearing this he suddenly interrupted them, saying, "Ah! father, it is the girl that I love and desire, and not her money. Wretched is he who marries to repair his fortune by means of his wife's dowry. You boast that I am possessed of some talents; is it then to be supposed that I am unable to maintain my wife and supply her necessities? I want nothing of you but your consent; and I must give you to understand that the girl shall be mine; as to the portion, you may take it yourself." Andrea Cellini, who was somewhat eccentric, was not a little displeased at this; but in a few days Giovanni took his wife home, and never required any portion of her father.

They enjoyed their consecrated love for eighteen years; but had no children, which they ardently desired.

At the expiration of the eighteenth year, however, Giovanni's wife miscarried of two male children, through the unskilfulness of her medical attendants. Later she gave birth to a girl, who was called Rosa, after my father's mother. Two years after, she was once more with child, and, as women in her condition are liable to certain longings, hers being exactly the same upon this occasion as before, it was generally thought that she would have another girl, and it had been already agreed to give her the name of Reparata, after my mother's mother. It happened that she was brought to bed precisely the night of All-Saints-day, in the year 1500, at half past four. The midwife, who was sensible that the family expected the birth of a female, as soon as she had washed the child and wrapped it in fine swaddling-clothes, came softly up to my father, and said to him, "I here bring you a fine present, which you little expected." My father, who was of a philosophical disposition, and happened to be then walking about, said, "What God gives me, I shall always receive thankfully;" but, taking off the clothes, he saw with his own eyes the unexpected boy. Clasping his hands together, he lifted up his eyes to heaven, saying: "Lord, I thank thee from the bottom of my heart for this present, which is very dear and welcome to me." The standers-by asked him, joyfully, how he proposed to call the child: he made them no other answer than, "He is Welcome." And this name of Welcome (Benvenuto) he resolved to give me at the font; and so I was christened accordingly.

Andrea Cellini was still living when I was about three years of age; and he was then more than a hundred. As they were one day removing a water-pipe, a large scorpion, which they had not perceived, came out of it. The scorpion descended to the ground and had got under a great bench, when I, seeing it, ran and caught it in my hand. This scorpion was of such a size, that while I held it in my little hand it put out its tail on one side, and on the other darted its two mouths. I ran overjoyed to my grandfather, crying, "Grandfather, look at my pretty little crab!" The good old man, who knew it to be a scorpion, was so frightened, and so apprehensive for my safety, that he seemed ready to drop dead, and begged me with great eagerness to give the creature to him; but I grasped it the harder, and cried, for I did not choose to part with it. My father, who was in the house, ran to us upon hearing the noise; but, stupefied with terror at the sight of that venomous reptile, he could think of no means of rescuing me from my perilous situation. But happening just at that instant to espy a pair of scissors, he laid hold of them, and by caressing and playing with me, he contrived to cut off the tail and head of the scorpion. Then, finding I had received no harm, he pronounced it a happy omen.

When I was about five years of age, my father happened to be in a little room in which they had been washing, and where there was a good oak fire. With a violin he sang and played near the fire, the weather being exceedingly cold. Looking into the fire, he saw a little animal resembling a lizard, which lived and enjoyed itself in the hottest flames. Instantly perceiving what it was, he called for my sister, and after he had shown us the creature, he gave me a box on the ear. I fell a-crying, while he, soothing me with caresses, said, "My dear child, I don't give you that blow for any fault you have committed, but that you may remember that the little lizard which you see in the fire is a salamander; a creature that no one that I have heard of ever beheld before." So saying, he embraced me, and gave me some money."

My father began to teach me to play upon the flute, and to sing by note; and though I was very young, at an age when children, generally speaking, are highly pleased with piping and such amusements, I had the utmost aversion for it, and played and sang merely in obedience to his authority. My father at that time made the most curious organs with pipes of wood, the finest and best harpsichords that were to be seen in those days, and most beautiful and excellent viols, lutes, and harps. He was an engineer, and constructed a variety of machines, such as draw-bridges and fulling-mills. He worked admirably in ivory, and was the first artist of his time in that line. But as he was also musically inclined, insomuch that this art had engrossed his whole thoughts and attention, he was requested by the court musicians to join with them; and as he was willing to oblige them, they made him one of their band. Lorenzo de' Medici, and Pietro, his son, who were very much his friends, seeing afterward that he attached himself entirely to music, and neglected his business as an engineer, and his admirable art of working in ivory, removed him from that place. This my father highly resented, and thought himself very ill used by his patrons. He therefore on a sudden applied again to his business, and made a looking-glass, about a cubit in diameter, of bone and ivory, adorned with carved figures and foliages, with the finest polish and the most admirable elegance of design. It was in the form of a wheel; the mirror was in the center; round it were seven circles, in which the seven virtues were carved in ivory and bone; and both the mirror and the figures of the virtues were balanced in such a manner that, the wheel turning round, all the virtues moved at the same time, and had a weight at their feet to counterpoise them, which kept them perpendicular. As he had a smattering of the Latin language, he carved a verse round the mirror, the purport of which was, that "on which side soever the wheel of fortune turns, virtue stands upon her feet."

A short time afterward his place of court-musician was

restored to him. At that period (which was before I was born) these musicians were all eminent artizans; some of them, being manufacturers of wool, and others of silk, belonged to the *Arti Maggiori*. Hence my father did not think this profession beneath him; and his first desire with regard to me was, that I should become a great player on the flute. I was never more offended than when he touched upon this subject, and when he told me that, if I had a mind, I might become the best musician in the world. As I have already observed, my father was a staunch friend to the house of Medici, so that when Pietro was banished from Florence [1494], he entrusted him with many affairs of consequence. The illustrious Pietro Soderini afterward being elected to the government, when my father was in his service as a musician, that great statesman, discovering his extraordinary genius, began to have recourse to him in many matters of importance.

At this time my father, as I was of a tender age, once caused me to be carried upon a person's shoulders to play upon the flute before the senate, and one of their servants supported me all the time. After the music was over, Soderini, then gonfalonier, or chief magistrate, amused himself with my prattle, and, giving me sweetmeats, said to my father, "Giovanni, you must teach him your other two elegant arts, as well as that of music." My father replied that he did not intend I should follow any other business but that of playing upon the flute, and composing; for if it pleased God to spare his days, he hoped to make me the first man in the world in that profession. To this one of the old gentleman present replied, "Ah, Master Cellini, mind what the gonfalonier says; why should the boy aim at nothing higher all his life than being a good musician?"

Thus some time passed before the Medici family was restored. The Cardinal de' Medici, who was afterward

Pope Leo X, immediately upon his recall showed the utmost kindness to my father. While the family was in exile, the balls were removed from the coat of arms in the front of their palace; and the citizens had caused to be painted in their place the figure of a red cross, which was the emblem of the republic. But at the sudden return of the Medicean princes the red cross was effaced, and upon the said escutcheon were again painted the red balls, and the golden field was replaced with most beautiful decorations. My father, who had a turn for poetry, with somewhat of a prophetic vein—doubtless, a divine gift—when the new arms were shown him, wrote the following quatrain:—

> "These arms, so long interr'd from human sight,
>   Beneath the image bland of Holy Cross,
>   Renew their glorious ensigns' proud emboss,
> And wait but Peter's sacred mantle bright,"

This epigram was read throughout Florence. A few days later died Pope Julius II, and the Cardinal de' Medici, afterward known as the magnanimous and liberal Leo X, was elected Pope [1513], contrary to the general opinion. My father, having sent him the four verses which contained so happy an augury, was invited by him to repair to the capital, which would have been greatly to his advantage, but he did not choose to leave Florence. Instead of his being rewarded, his place at court was taken from him by Giacopo Salviati, as soon as that nobleman was made gonfalonier.

This was the reason that I applied myself to the goldsmith's business; and while I was learning that trade I was compelled to spend part of my time in practising upon the flute, much against my inclination. For when my father spoke to me in the manner above mentioned, I requested him to let me draw so many hours a day, telling him that I would dedicate the remainder of it to

the flute; upon which he said to me, "Do you not take
pleasure in playing on that instrument?" I answered in
the negative, saying that the profession of a musician
appeared to me base in comparison with that to which
I aspired. My poor father then, in the utmost despair,
placed me with the father of the cavalier Bandinello,
who was called Michelagnolo, goldsmith of Pinzi di
Monte, a man of great skill in his art. He was the
son of a collier. This I do not mention as a reflection on
Bandinello, who, as the founder of a distinguished family, is entitled to respect, provided his success was merited; and however that may be, I have nothing to say
against him. When I had stayed there a few days, my
father took me away from Michelagnolo, being unable to
bear me any longer out of his sight; so that I continued,
much against my will, to play upon the flute till the age
of fifteen.

Having attained the age of fifteen, I engaged myself,
against my father's inclination, with a goldsmith, named
Antonio di Sandro, who was commonly called Marcone.
This was an excellent artist, and a very worthy man,
high-spirited, and generous in every respect. My father would not have him allow me any wages, as was
customary with other workmen; for this reason, that,
since I voluntarily applied myself to this art, I should
likewise have an opportunity to draw whenever I
thought proper. To this arrangement I readily acceded,
and my worthy master was much pleased. He had an
only, but illegitimate son, to whom he often addressed
his orders on purpose to spare me. So great was my
inclination to improve, that in a few months I rivaled
the most skilful journeyman in the business, and began
to reap some fruits from my labor. I continued, however, to play sometimes, through complaisance to my father, either upon the flute or the horn; and I drew tears
and deep sighs from him every time he heard me. From

a feeling of filial piety, I often gave him that satisfaction, endeavoring to persuade him that it gave me also particular pleasure.

CHAPTER II

CHANGES OF RESIDENCE

AT this juncture my brother had an adventure that was attended with serious consequences to us both. He was two years younger than I, of a warm temper and the most undaunted courage, qualities that fitted him for the military school of Signor Giovanni de' Medici, father to Duke Cosmo, where he became an excellent soldier. One Sunday evening, being between the gates of St. Gallo and Pitti, he challenged a young man of twenty, though he was but fourteen himself, and behaved so gallantly that, after wounding the youth dangerously, he was upon the point of either killing or disarming him. A great crowd was present, and amongst others were many of the young man's relatives. Seeing their kinsman hard pressed, they threw stones at my brother's head, who immediately fell to the ground. I, who happened to be present, alone and unarmed, cried out to my brother, as loud as I could, to quit the place. But as soon as I saw him fall, I ran to him, took his sword, and, standing as near him as possible, I confronted a great many swords and stones, till some valiant soldiers, who came from the gate of St. Gallo, saved me from the exasperated multitude. I carried my brother home for dead. He was with great difficulty brought to himself, and afterward cured.

The Council of Eight condemned our adversaries to a few years' imprisonment, and banished me and my brother, for six months, to the distance of ten miles from the city. Thus we took leave of our poor father, who, having no money, gave us his blessing.

I repaired to Siena, in quest of an honest goldsmith, whose name was Francesco Castoro. I had worked with him some time before at my trade, when I had eloped, for some frivolous reason, from my father. Signor Castoro received me very kindly and found me employ, offering me a house for the whole time I should reside at Siena. I accepted his offer, and brought my brother to the house, where I followed my business for several months with close application. My brother, too, had made some progress in Latin, but, being young, he was not equally capable of appreciating the excellence of moral beauty, and led rather a dissipated life.

Soon after this troublesome affair the Cardinal de' Medici, afterward Pope Clement VII, was prevailed upon, by the entreaties of my father, to obtain permission for us to return to Florence. A pupil of my father's, excited by his natural malignity, desired the Cardinal to send me to Bologna, in order to take lessons on the flute of a great master, whose name was Antonio. The Cardinal told my father that if he would send me thither he would give me a letter of recommendation. The old gentleman was extremely desirous that I should go, and I was glad of that opportunity of seeing the world.

Upon my arrival at Bologna I undertook to work under a person named Ercole del Piffero, and I began to make money. At the same time, I went every day to receive a lesson on the flute, and soon gained a considerable emolument by that odious profession; but I got much more by my trade as a goldsmith and jeweler. Having received no assistance from the Cardinal, I went to lodge with a miniature-painter, named Scipio Cavaletti, who lived in the street of Our Lady of Baracani, and there

I worked for Grazia Dio, a Jew, with whom I earned a great deal of money.

Six months afterward I returned to Florence, where Pierino the musician, who had been a pupil to my father, was greatly mortified at my success; but I, through the complaisance of my aged parent, waited upon Pierino, and played both upon the horn and the flute with a brother of his, whose name was Girolamo. He was some years younger than Pierino, and was moreover well disposed, displaying a marked contrast to his brother. My father happening one day to be at the house of this Pierino to hear us play, and being highly pleased with my performance, said, "I am determined to make a great musician of him, in spite of those who would fain prevent such a genius from shining in the world." To this Pierino answered (and what he said was true), "Your son Benvenuto will acquire more profit, as well as honor, by minding his business as a goldsmith, than by blowing the horn, or any other instrument." My father, finding I was of the same opinion, was incensed to the last degree; he therefore said to him in a violent passion, "I was very sensible that you were the person who thwarted me in my design; and it was you that were the cause of my being deprived of the place I held at court, behaving to me with that base ingratitude which is but too frequently the return for the greatest favors. I got you promoted, and you were so base as to undermine me; but mark these words: in less than a few weeks you will rue this black ingratitude." Pierino replied: "Signor Giovanni Cellini, most men when they advance in years begin to dote. This is your case; nor am I surprised at it, as you have already lavished all your substance, without reflecting that your children were likely to want. Now I, for my part, purpose taking quite a different course: I intend to leave so much to my sons that they shall be able to assist yours." To this my father replied, "No bad tree ever brings forth good fruit, but the reverse; and I must tell you that, if you be a bad man, your sons will be fools and indigent, and come to beg of my children, who shall be crowned with affluence." At this they parted, murmuring and railing at each other. I, who, as was reasonable, took my worthy father's part, said to him at quitting the house, that I intended to revenge the affront he had received from that scoundrel, if he would give me leave to dedicate my talents to the art of design. My father made answer, "Dear child, I have been myself, in my time, a master of that art; but will you not, in your turn, promise me by way of recreation, after your noble labors are done, and for my sake, who am your father, educated you, and laid the foundation of so many shining qualifications, sometimes to take in hand your flute and cheerful horn, and play for your pastime and amusement?" I made answer that I would readily comply with his desire. My good father then rejoined, that the virtues I displayed to the world would be the best revenge I could take for the affronts and abusive language he had received from his enemies.

Before the month expired, it happened that Pierino, causing a vault to be made to his house in the street *dello Studio*, and being one day on the ground-floor over the vault, which was then repairing, entered into conversation with some company, and spoke of his master, who was no other than my father, repeating the prophetical words the latter had uttered, concerning his approaching ruin. Hardly had he ended his discourse, when the chamber in which he stood suddenly sank, either because the vault had been unskilfully constructed, or through an effect of the divine vengeance, which, though late, is only deferred to a fitter season. Some of the stones and bricks, falling with him, broke both his legs, while the rest of the company, standing upon the extremities of the vault, received no manner of hurt, but

remained in the utmost astonishment at what they saw;
and most of all at what he had said to them a little before in a scoffing mood. My father, having heard of
this accident, took his sword, and went to see him; and,
in the presence of his father, whose name was Niccolajo
da Volterra, trumpeter to the senate, addressed him in
these words: "My dear pupil Pierino, I am very sorry
for your misfortune; but you may remember that it is
but a short time since I apprised you of it; and my
prophecy will likewise be verified with regard to our
children."

Soon afterward, Pierino died of the consequences of
his fall, and left a wife of bad character, and a son, who
a few years later came to me at Rome, asking charity.
I gave him alms, as well because I am naturally of a
charitable disposition as because I could not without
tears recollect the affluence with which Pierino was surrounded when my father spoke the words quoted above.

Continuing to apply closely to my business as a goldsmith, by the emoluments arising from it I assisted my
good father, as well as my brother Cecchino, whom he
caused to be instructed in Latin; for, as he intended I
should be the best player upon the flute in the world,
it was his design that my younger brother should be a
man of learning. But he was not able to force nature,
which gave me a turn for drawing, and made my brother,
who had a fine person, devote himself to the military
profession. This brother, having in his early youth
learned the rudiments of war under that renowned commander, Giovanni de' Medici, returned to my father's
house, at a time when I happened to be out of the way.
Being much in want of clothing, he applied to my sister,
who, unknown to my father, gave him a new surtout and
cloak that belonged to me; for, besides assisting my father, and my sisters, who were virtuous and deserving
girls, I had, by the profits arising from my extraordinary

application, contrived to purchase this handsome apparel. Finding my clothes gone, and my brother disappeared, I said to my father, "How could you suffer me to be wronged in such a manner, when you see I spare no toil nor trouble to assist the family?" He made answer, that I was his good and worthy son, but that what I thought a loss, I should find to be true gain; adding that it was a duty incumbent on us, and the command of God himself, that he who had property should share it with him who had none; and that, if I would for his sake patiently bear the wrong I had suffered, God would increase my store, and pour down blessings upon me.

I behaved to my poor afflicted father like an inexperienced young man; and, taking with me what little money and clothes I had left, I bent my course toward one of the city gates, and, not knowing which of them led to Rome, I traveled to Lucca, and thence to Pisa. I was now about sixteen years of age. Upon my arrival in the last-mentioned city, I stopped near the middle bridge, hard by the fish-market, at a goldsmith's shop, and looked attentively at the master while he was at work. He asked me my name, and what business I followed. I made answer, that I worked a little in the same branch that he did. The man thereupon bade me come in, and, setting before me some tools, he told me my physiognomy induced him to believe that I was an honest youth. So saying, he laid before me gold, silver, and jewels, and, after I had finished my first day's task, he carried me to his house, where he lived very respectably with his wife and children.

I then called to mind the grief my father must feel on my account, and wrote him that I was at the house of a very worthy tradesman, one Signor Ulivieri dello Chiostra; and that, under him, I was employed in my profession on many great and beautiful works. I therefore desired him to make himself easy, as I was improving in my business, and hoped soon to procure him both profit and honor by my skill. He immediately wrote me an answer, the purport of which was as follows: "My dear son, so great is the love I bear to you, that I should instantly set out for the place where you now reside, were it not that the laws of honor, which I always adhere to, prevent me; for I think myself deprived of the light of my eyes every day that I am without seeing you, as I did formerly, when I gave you the best instructions. I shall keep it in view to incite my family to virtuous enterprise, and pray lead the way in the attainment of good qualities, for which all I wish is that you would keep in mind those few simple words—observe, and never once allow them to escape your memory:—

> 'The man who consults his house's weal
> Lives honest—and lives to work—not steal.' "

This letter fell into the hands of my master Ulivieri, who read it to himself, and then said to me: "Thy good looks, Benvenuto, did not deceive me, as I find by a letter from thy father, which has fallen into my hands. He must, doubtless, be a man of worth; therefore consider thyself as in thine own house, and under the care of thy father."

Whilst I stayed at Pisa I went to see the Campo Santo, where I discovered a great number of antiquities, such as large marble urns; and in many parts of the town I saw other monuments of antiquity, which afforded me constant amusement, whenever I was disengaged from business. As my master came daily, with great good nature, to see me at the little apartment he had assigned to my use, when he found that I spent all my time in laudable and virtuous occupations, he conceived as strong an affection for me as if he had been my father. I improved considerably, during a year's stay in that city, and executed several fine pieces of workmanship, which

2

inspired me with an ardent desire to become more eminent in my profession.

At the expiration of the year, Signor Ulivieri happened
to have occasion to go to Florence, to dispose of some
filings of gold and silver; and, as in that unwholesome
air I had contracted a slight fever, I returned with my
master to Florence; where my father secretly entreated
my master, in the most urgent manner, not to carry me
back to Pisa. My fever still continuing, I kept my bed
about two months, and my father attended me with the
greatest affection imaginable; telling me repeatedly that
he thought it a thousand years till I recovered, that he
might hear me play on the flute; but feeling my pulse he
perceived so great a change in it whenever he mentioned
the flute, that he was often frightened, and left me in
tears. Observing then the concern he was in, I bade one
of my sisters bring me a flute; for, though I had a fever,
the instrument was very easy. I thereupon played with
such skill that my father, entering the room on a sudden,
gave me a thousand blessings, assuring me that I had
made great improvement.

But no sooner had I recovered my health, than I returned to my worthy friend, the goldsmith Marcone,
who put me in a way of making money; and with my
gains I assisted my father and my relatives.

CHAPTER III

CELLINI'S PROGRESS IN ART

ABOUT this time a sculptor named Pietro Torrigiani came to Florence. He had just arrived
from England, where he had resided several
years; and as he was an intimate friend of my
master's, he came to see him every day. This artist,

having seen my drawings and workmanship, said to me:
"I am come to Florence to invite as many young artists
as I can to England, and, having a great work in hand
for the King of England, I should be glad of the assistance of my fellow-citizens of Florence. I perceive
that your manner of working and your designs are rather
those of a sculptor than of a goldsmith; and I have considerable undertakings in bronze, so that, if you will go
with me to England, I will speedily make your fortune."
This Torrigiani was a handsome man, of consummate
assurance, having rather the air of a bravo than of a
sculptor; above all, his fierce gestures and his sonorous
voice, with a peculiar manner of knitting his brows, were
enough to frighten every one that saw him; and he was
continually talking of his valiant feats among those
bears of Englishmen. His conversation one day happened to turn upon Michelangelo Buonarroti, from a
drawing of mine that was taken from one of the cartoons
of that divine artist.

This cartoon was the first in which Michelangelo displayed his extraordinary abilities, as he made this and
another, which were to adorn the hall of the palace
where the senators assembled, in emulation of Leonardo
da Vinci. They represented the taking of Pisa by the
Florentines. The admirable Leonardo had chosen for
his subject a battle fought by cavalry, with the taking
of certain standards, in which he acquitted himself with
a force of genius that cannot be surpassed by conception.
Michelangelo Buonarroti, in his cartoon, exhibited a considerable body of foot, who were bathing in summer-
time in the river Arno; at this very instant he represents
an alarm of battle, and all the naked soldiers rushing to
arms, with gestures so admirably expressive that no ancient or modern performance was ever known to attain
to so high a degree of perfection; and, as I have already
observed, that of the great Leonardo was also a work

of extraordinary beauty. These two cartoons stood, one of them in the palace of the Medici, the other in the Pope's hall. So long as they remained there, they were the school* of the world; and though the divine Michelangelo painted the great chapel of Pope Julius, he never again rose to that pitch of excellence; his genius could not reach the force of those first essays.

Let us now return to Pietro Torrigiani; who, holding my drawing in his hand, spoke thus: "This Buonarroti and I went, when we were boys, to learn to draw at the chapel of Masaccio, in the church of the Carmelites, and it was customary with Buonarroti to rally all those who were learning to draw there. One day, a sarcasm of his having stung me to the quick, I was provoked to an uncommon degree, and gave him so violent a blow upon the nose with my fist, that I felt the bone and cartilage yield under my hand as if they had been made of paste, and the mark I then gave him he will carry to his grave." This speech raised in me such an aversion to the fellow, because I had seen the works of the divine Michelangelo, that, far from having any inclination to go with him to England, I could never more bear the sight of him.

While I was in Florence I did my utmost to learn the exquisite manner of Michelangelo, and never once lost sight of it. About this time I contracted an intimate friendship with a youth of my own age, who, like me, was learning the goldsmith's business: his name was Francesco, son of Filippo, whose father was Frà Filippo, an excellent painter. Our intercourse gave rise to so great an affection between us, that we were never asunder. His house was full of the admirable performances of his father, which consisted of several books of drawings by his own hand, representing the antiquities of Rome. I took great delight in these, and our acquaint-

*These are now lost. That by Buonarroti was engraved by Marc Antonio Raimondi.

ance lasted about two years. At this time I produced a
piece of basso rilievo in silver, about as big as the hand
of a little child; it served for the clasp of a man's belt;
clasps of that size being then in use. Upon it was carved
a group of foliages, made in the antique taste, with several figures of youths, and other beautiful grotesques.
This piece of work I made in the shop of a person named
Francesco Salimbeni; and, upon its coming under the
inspection of the goldsmith's company, I acquired the
reputation of the most expert young man in the trade.

At this time I was also acquainted with one Giovanni
Battista, surnamed Tasso, who was a carver in wood, a
youth of my own age exactly. He one day began to
talk to me about going to Rome, observing that he should
like to accompany me thither (this occurred as we sat
conversing after dinner), and I having had a new difference with my father about learning the flute, said to
Tasso, "You appear to be a man of words and not of
deeds." Tasso answered, "I have had a dispute with my
mother, and, if I had but money sufficient to bear my
charges to Rome, I would never more trouble my head
about my little hole of a shop." To this I replied, that
if there was no other obstruction to our journey, I had
money enough in my pocket to defray our expenses.
Then chatting as we walked along, before we knew
where we were we came to the gate of San Pier Gattolini; when I said to my companion: "My good friend,
Tasso, it is by the direction of God that we have in-
sensibly reached this gate. Since I have proceeded so
far, I think I have performed half the journey."

Matters being thus agreed, we said to each other, as
we were jogging on, "What will the old folks at home
say this evening?" We then came to a resolution to
think no more of them, till we arrived at Rome. So
we buckled on our knapsacks, and proceeded in silence
to Siena. When we reached that city, Tasso said he

had hurt his feet, and did not choose to walk any further, at the same time asking me to lend him money to return home. I answered that I should have none left to bear my expenses to Rome, and that he should have well weighed his project before he left Florence, adding, that if the hurt he received prevented his accompanying me, we should find a return-horse for Rome, and then he would have no excuse. Thus having hired a horse, as I saw he did not answer me, I bent my course toward the gate that led to Rome. Perceiving that I was resolved, he came hopping after me as well as he could, at a distance, grumbling and muttering all the time. When I reached the gate I was touched with compassion for my companion, and, having waited for his coming, took him up behind me, using these words: "What would our friends say of us, if, after beginning a journey to Rome, we had not the courage to push any farther than Siena?" Tasso acknowledged that my observation was just, and, as he had a cheerful disposition, he began to laugh and sing, and in this merry mood we pursued our journey to Rome. I was then in my nineteenth year.

As soon as we reached that capital, I went to work with a master whose name was Firenzuola, of Lombardy, an excellent artist in making vases and other things of a considerable size. When I showed him part of the model I had made at Florence with Salimbeni, he was highly pleased, and spoke thus to a journeyman of his named Gianotto Gianotti, a native of Florence, that had lived with him several years; "This is one of the geniuses of Florence, and thou art one of its dunces." As I knew this Gianotto, I had a mind to have some chat with him. Before he set out for Rome, we often practised drawing in the same school, and had been for several years intimate acquaintances. He was so much nettled at his master's speech that he declared he was not acquainted with me, nor had ever seen me before.

Provoked at his behavior in this manner, I said to him, "Oh, Gianotto! formerly my intimate friend, though we were employed together in drawing, and ate and drank in such and such apartments of your native town, I do not desire that you should bear testimony of my abilities to your master, for I hope, by my own hands, to show what I am, without your assistance." When I had done speaking, Firenzuola, who was a passionate man, turned to Gianotto, and said: "You vile scoundrel, are you not ashamed to behave in such a manner to one that was formerly your intimate acquaintance?" At the same time he addressed himself to me: "Come in, young man," said he, "and do as you proposed; let your own hands prove your abilities."

So saying, he set me upon a fine piece of work in silver, which was intended for a cardinal. This was a small case, in imitation of that of porphyry which stands before the door of the Rotunda. That which I made I adorned with so many fine figures, that my master went about showing it everywhere, and making it his boast that his shop had produced so admirable a piece of art. It was about half a cubit in circumference, and made in such a manner as to hold a salt-cellar at table.

This was the first time I earned money at Rome. Part of it I sent to the relief of my good father, and the remainder I kept to support me while I studied the antiquities of that city, which I did till my money began to fail, and then I was obliged to return to the shop. My fellow-traveler, Battista di Tasso, made but a short stay at Rome, and returned to Florence. For my part, I undertook new commissions, and when I had finished them I took it into my head to change my master, being enticed away by a Milanese, whose name was Signor Pagolo Arsago.

My first master, Firenzuola, had thereupon a great quarrel with this Arsago, and gave him some abusive

language in my presence. I began to speak in defence of my new master; and told Firenzuola that I was born free, and resolved to continue so; that he had no cause of complaint either against Arsago or me; that some money was still due me from him; and that, as I was a free artificer, I would go wherever I thought proper, not being conscious of injuring anybody thereby.

At the expiration of two years I returned to Florence at the request of my good father, and began to work again under Francesco Salembeni with whom I gained a genteel subsistence, taking great pains to become perfect in my profession. Having renewed my acquaintance with Francesco di Filippo, though that odious flute drew me into some pleasurable dissipation, I contrived to dedicate some hours, both of the night and of the day, to my studies. About this time I made a silver clasp girdle, such as were usually worn at that time by new-married ladies. It was three inches broad, and worked in half rilievo, with small round figures in it; this girdle I made for a person named Raffaello Rapaccini. Though I was very ill-paid for my trouble, the work did me so much honor that the reputation I acquired by it was of more service to me than a fair pecuniary recompense.

Having at this time worked with several masters in Florence, among the different goldsmiths I knew in that city I met with some persons of worth, as was Marcone, my first master; while others, who had the reputation of honest men, being envious of my works, and robbing and calumniating me, did me the greatest injustice. When I perceived this, I shook off my connections with them, and looked upon them all as little better than thieves. Among the rest, a goldsmith named Giovanni Battista Sogliani was so complaisant as to lend me part of his shop, which stood at the side of the

new market, hard by Landi's bank. There I executed many little works, and earned a great deal of money.

Envy began then to rankle in the hearts of my former bad masters; they all three kept shops, and had immense business. Seeing that they did me ill offices with men of worth, I complained of it, and said they ought to be satisfied with having robbed me, as they had done, under the mask of benevolence. This coming to their ears, they declared loudly that they would make me repent having uttered such words; but I, being a stranger to fear, little regarded their menaces.

As I happened one day to lean against the shop of one of these men, he called me to him, and in the most abusive language bullied and threatened me. Upon which I said, that if they had done their duty with respect to me, I should have spoken of them as persons or fair character, but as they had behaved in a different manner, they had only themselves to complain of. While I spoke thus, one Gherardo Guasconti, a cousin of theirs, who was in all probability set on by them, took the opportunity, as a beast loaded with bricks happened to pass by, to push it so violently against me that I was very much hurt. Upon which I instantly turned about, and, seeing him laugh, gave him so violent a blow on the tmple that he fell, and lay upon the ground insensible. Then, turning to his cousins, I said to them, "That is the way I use cowardly rascals like you;" and as they, confiding in their number, seemed preparing to take their revenge, I, in a violent passion, drew a little knife, and vented my anger in these words: "If any one of you offers to leave the shop, let another run for a confessor, as there will be no occasion for a surgeon." This declaration struck such terror into them all, that not one of them ventured to stir to the assistance of his cousin.

No sooner had I left the place, than both the fathers

and sons ran to the magistrates, and told them I had violently assailed them with arms, in so audacious a manner that the like had never been known in Florence. The Council of Eight summoned me, and I, without delay, presented myself before them. Here I met with a severe reprimand, as well in consequence of the appearance of my adversaries in long mantles and robes, while I wore only a cloak, as because they had taken care to prepossess them in their favor, a precaution that I, being inexperienced, and trusting to the goodness of my cause, had neglected. I told them, that as I had received such provocation from Gherardo, and had only given him a slap on the face, I did not think I deserved so severe a rebuke. Prinzivalle della Stufa, who was one of that court, hardly suffering me to make an end of the words "slap on the face," exclaimed, "You gave him a violent blow with your fist, and not a slap." The bell having rung, and we being all dismissed, Prinzivalle thus spoke in my favor to the rest of the bench: "Observe, gentlemen, the simplicity of this poor youth, who acknowledges himself to have given a slap on the face, thinking it to be a less offence than a violent blow: whereas there is a penalty of five-and-twenty crowns for giving a person a slap on the face, in the new market, while the penalty for a blow with the fist is little or nothing. This is a very worthy young man, who supports his poor relatives by his industry. Would to God that there were many like him in our city, which can, indeed, boast but a very small number of virtuous citizens."

There were in the court some persons in olded caps, who, moved by the importunities and misrepresentations of my adversaries, because they were of the faction of Fra Girolamo, were for having me sent to prison, and heavily fined; but the good Prinzivalle defeated their malice by getting me fined only four bushels of

meal, which were to be given in charity to the monastery *delle Murate*. This same judge, having called me
into his presence, commanded me not to say a single
word, but obey the orders of the court, upon pain of
incurring their displeasure. They sent us then to the
chancelor, and I muttered the words "slap, and not a
blow, on the face;" the magistrates burst out laughing.
The chancelor commanded us all to give security to
each other for good behavior, and sentenced me only
to pay the four measures of meal. I thought myself
very hardly used, and sent for a cousin of mine, whose
name was Annibale Librodoro, father to Signor Librodoro, the surgeon, that he might be bail for me; but
he refused to appear. This incensed me to the highest
degree, believing my case desperate, and I exclaimed
loudly at his behavior, as he was under great obligations to my family.

Inflamed by this treatment, swelling like an enraged
asp, and being naturally of a very passionate temper,
I waited till the court broke up and the magistrates
were gone to dinner. Finding myself then alone, and
that I was no longer observed by any officers of the
court, I left the place in a violent fury, and went in
all haste to my workshop, where I took up a dagger,
and ran to attack my adversaries, who by that time
were come home. I found them at table, and young
Gherardo, who had been the chief cause of the quarrel,
immediately flew at me. I thereupon gave him a stab
in the breast, which pierced through his cloak and
doublet, without reaching his skin or doing him any
harm. Imagining, however, from the rustling of his
clothes, and from his falling flat upon the ground,
through fright and astonishment, that I had done him
some great hurt, I cried out, "Traitor, this day I shall
be revenged on you all." The father, mother, and
sisters, thinking that the day of judgment was come, fell

prostrate upon their knees, and, with voices full of terror and consternation, implored for mercy. Seeing then
that none of my adversaries stood upon the defensive,
and that Gherardo lay stretched out upon the ground
like a corpse, I scorned to meddle with them, but ran
down stairs like a madman. When I got into the street,
I found the rest of the family, about a dozen in number,
ready to attack me. One of them held a ball of iron,
another a thick iron tube, another a hammer taken from
an anvil, and others again had huge cudgels. Rushing
amongst them like a mad bull, I threw down four or five
and fell to the ground along with them, now aiming
my dagger at one, now at another. Those that continued standing exerted themselves to the utmost, belabor-
ing me with their hammers and cudgels; but, as God
sometimes mercifully interposes upon such occasions,
it so happened that I neither received nor did any harm.
I lost nothing but my cap, which fell into the hands of
some of my adversaries, who at first had fled. Being
assured it was only my cap, each of them struck it with
his weapon. On looking about for the wounded and
slain, it appeared that none of them had sustained any
injury.

The scuffle being over, I bent my course toward the
convent of Santa Maria Novella, and accidentally met
with a friar named Alessio Strozzi. Though I was not
acquainted with the good father, I entreated him to save
my life, saying I had been guilty of a serious offence.
The friar desired me not to be under any apprehensions,
for, whatever crimes I might have committed, I should
be in perfect security in his cell. In about an hour, the
magistrates, having assembled in an extraordinary meeting, published one of the most tremendous edicts that
ever were heard of, threatening the severest penalties to
whosoever should grant me an asylum, or be privy to

my concealment, without any distinction of place or quality of person that harbored me.

My poor afflicted father, appearing before the eight judges, fell prostrate and begged them to show compassion on his young and unfortunate son. Thereupon one of those incensed magistrates, shaking the top of his venerable hood, stood up, and thus angrily expressed himself: "Rise directly, and quit this spot, or, tomorrow morning, we shall send you from the town under a guard!" My father, in answer to these menaces, said, "You will do what God permits you, and nothing more." The magistrate replied that nothing could be more certain than that God had thus ordered matters. My father then said boldly to him, "My comfort is that you are a stranger to the decrees of Providence."

Having thus quitted the court, he came to me with a youth about my age, whose name was Piero, son of Giovanni Landi (we were dearer to each other than brothers); this young man had under his mantle an excellent sword and a coat of mail. My father having acquainted me with the situation of affairs, and what the magistrates had said, embraced me most tenderly, and gave me his blessing, saying, "May the protection of God be with you!" . Then presenting me with the sword, and the coat of mail, he, with his own hands, helped to accouter me, concluding with these words, "My worthy son, with these arms you must either live or die." Piero Landi wept without ceasing, and brought me ten crowns of gold. I desired him to pull off a few hairs from my cheeks, which were the first down that overspread them. Father Alessio dressed me in the habit of a friar, and gave me a lay brother for a companion.

I came out of the convent by the Al Prato gate, and walked by the side of the town walls, as far as the great square, ascending the steep of Montui, where I found, in one of the first houses, a person named Grassuccio, natural brother to Benedetto da Monte Varchi. After I had laid aside my friar's disguise, and resumed my former appearance, we mounted two horses, which there stood ready for us, and galloped away in the night to Siena.

Grassuccio, on his return to Florence, waited on my father, and informed him that I had reached a place of safety. My father, highly rejoiced at these tidings, was impatient to see the magistrate who, the day before, had rebuked him with such severity. As soon as he came into his presence, he said, "You see at last, Antonio, it was God, not you, that knew what was to befall my son." To which the other answered, "I wish I could see him once more before this court." My father replied, "I return thanks to God, that he has rescued him out of your hands."

In the mean time I was waiting at Siena for the Roman Procaccio, or mail, with which I traveled on the rest of my journey; and when we had passed the Paglia, we met a courier that brought intelligence of the election of Pope Clement VII.

CHAPTER IV

EXTRAORDINARY SUCCESS AT ROME

UPON my arrival at Rome I went to work in the shop formerly of Santi the goldsmith, who was dead, and his son continued the business. The latter did not work himself, but employed a young man, whose name was Lucagnolo da Jesi, whom Signor Santi had taken into his service when he was a little country lad. He was low in stature, but very well proportioned. This youth was more expert than any journeyman I had ever seen, possessing great facility and freedom of design. He worked only on a large scale, making beautiful vases, basins, and other things of the kind. Having engaged to work in this shop, I began to make some chandeliers for the Bishop of Salamanca, a Spaniard, which were wrought with as much art as it was possible to bestow upon a work of that nature. A pupil of Raffaello da Urbino, one Giovanni Francesco, surnamed *il Fattore*, who was an excellent painter, and intimate with the bishop, found means to introduce me to his favor, insomuch that he frequently employed me, and I gained considerably by my business.

About this same period I sometimes went to draw at the chapel of Michelangelo, and sometimes at the house of Agostino Chigi of Siena, in which were several admirable paintings by that great master, Raffaello da Urbino; this was only on holidays, because Signor Gismondo, brother of Signor Agostino, was come to live there. The family, however, were greatly pleased when they saw young artists frequenting their house as a school of painting. The wife of the said Signor Gismondo, a most elegant and beautiful lady, having often seen me thus employed under her roof, one day came to look at my drawings, and asked me whether I was a painter or a statuary. I told her I was a goldsmith. She replied that I drew too well for a goldsmith; and having ordered her waiting-maid to bring her a jewel consisting of some very fine diamonds set in gold, she desired me to tell their value. I estimated them at eight hundred crowns. The lady declared that I had judged very rightly, and asked whether I would undertake to set them properly. I answered that I would do it most willingly, and began the design in her presence, in which I was the more successful on account of the pleasure I took in conversing with so fair and agreeable a lady. When I had finished my sketch, another most beautiful Roman lady came down stairs into the room, and asked Porzia (which was the first lady's name) what she was about; to which the latter answered, smiling, "I am amusing myself in seeing this young man draw, who is as good as he is handsome." Though I had acquired some assurance, I still retained a mixture of bashfulness with it; I colored deeply, and said, "Let me be what I may, madam, I shall always be most ready to serve you." The lady, reddening a little herself, replied, "You know I am desirous of your services." She then bade me take the diamonds home with me, and gave me twenty gold crowns, saying, "Set these diamonds according to the design which you have drawn, and preserve me the old gold in which they are mounted." The other lady then said, "If I were the young man, I would go off with what I had got." Signora Porzia rejoined, that virtues are seldom coupled with vices, and that, were I to behave in that manner, I should belie my honest countenance. Then, taking the other lady by the hand, she turned about and said to me with a smile of condescension, "Farewell, Benvenuto."

I stayed some time after I had drawn the design, copying a figure of Jove, the work of Raffaello da Urbino. As soon as I had finished it, I went away, and set about making a little model in wax. This I carried to Signora Porzia, with whom I found the Roman lady. They were highly pleased with my design, and encouraged me by such compliments that I promised them that the work itself should be far superior to the model. I thereupon began my task, and in twelve days set the jewels in the form of a fleur-de-lys, adorning it with little masks, figures of boys and animals, and the finest enamel, so that the diamonds of which the fleur-de-lys was composed appeared with redoubled lustre.

While I was engaged on this work, the worthy
Lucagnolo seemed much dissatisfied, frequently telling
me that it would be more for my interest, as well as
my reputation, to help him in working on pieces of plate,
as I had done at first. I made answer, that I could always obtain that kind of employment, but that such
commissions as that in which I was occupied did not
occur every day; and that they were no less reputable,
and far more profitable, than large silver vessels. Upon
my telling Lucagnolo that they were more lucrative,
he laughed at me, and said, "You'll see that, Benvenuto;
for by the time that you have completed your job I
shall contrive to finish this piece of plate, which I began precisely at the same time when you undertook the
setting of jewels; and experience will convince you of
the difference between the profit accruing to me from my
piece of plate, and to you for your trinkets." I answered,
that I would with pleasure make such a trial of skill with
so consummate an artist, that it might appear which of
us was mistaken, when both our performances were
finished.

Thus, with countenances that betokened some displeasure, we both fell hard to work, eager to finish our
several undertakings; and we labored so industriously
that in about ten days we had completed our tasks in an
elegant and workmanlike style. That of Lucagnolo was
a large silver vase, which was to be placed on the table
of Pope Clement, and to receive bones and the rinds
of various fruits whilst that pontiff was at his meals—
a work rather calculated for magnificence and ostentation than for any real use. This piece of plate was
adorned with two beautiful handles, and likewise with
many masks of different sizes, and several fine foliages
of the most beautiful and ingenious design that could
possibly be conceived. On seeing this performance, I
told Lucagnolo that it was the finest piece of plate I had

3

ever beheld. Lucagnolo, thinking he had convinced me of my error, answered, "Your work appears to me equally admirable; but we shall soon see the difference between them." He then carried his piece of plate to the Pope, who was highly satisfied, and immediately caused him to be paid the ordinary price for works of that kind.

In the mean time I took my performance to Signora Porzia, who expressed great surprise at my having finished it so expeditiously, and told me I had far exceeded my promise to her. She then desired me to ask whatever I thought proper in recompense for my labor, declaring that, were she to make me lord of a castle, she should hardly think she had rewarded me in proportion to my deserts; but since that surpassed her ability, she desired me, with a smile, to ask something in her power to bestow. I answered that the most valued recompense that could crown my endeavors was the satisfaction of having pleased her ladyship. This I said in a cheerful way; and, having made my bow, was departing, assuring her that I desired no other payment. Upon this, Signora Porzia, turning to the other lady, said, "You see the virtues we discovered in him are accompanied by others, and not by vices;" and they both expressed equal admiration. Signora Porzia then said to me, "My good Benvenuto, did you never hear it said that when the poor give to the rich the devil laughs?" I replied that, since he had met with so many vexations, I had a mind he should laugh for once. But as I was going away, she said she did not intend to favor him so much this time.

Upon my return to the shop, Lucagnolo, who had the money he received from the Pope wrapped up in a paper, said to me, "Now compare the payment I have received for my piece of plate, with what you have had for your jewels." I answered that we might let the matter rest for that time, but I hoped the day following to make it appear that, as my work was in its kind as exquisite as his, I should be rewarded with equal munificence. The next day Signora Porzia sent her steward to the shop, who called me out and put into my hands a paper bag of money, which he brought from that lady, telling me, at the same time, it was not his mistress's intention that the devil should laugh at my expense; and that the money she sent me was by no means a reward adequate to my merit, with several other compliments worthy of such a lady.

Lucagnolo, who was impatient to compare his money with mine, that instant rushed into the shop, and, in the presence of twelve workmen, and other neighbors, who were come to see how the contest would end, took his paper, laughing with an air of triumph; then, having pretended to make three or four efforts, he at last poured out the cash, which rattled loudly upon the counter. It amounted to five-and-twenty crowns in silver. I, who was quite stunned and disconcerted with his noise, and with the laughter and scoffs of the bystanders, having just peeped into my paper, and seen it was filled with gold, without any emotion or bustle, held my paper bag up in the air, as I stood on one side of the counter, and emptied it as a miller empties a sack. My coin was double the number of his, so that all the spectators, who before had their eyes fixed upon me with a scornful air, suddenly turned to him, and said, "Lucagnolo, Benvenuto's pieces, being all gold, and twice as many as yours, make the grander appearance of the two."

Such an effect had envy, and the scorn shown by all present upon Lucagnolo, that I thought he would have dropped dead; and though he was to receive a third part of the money, as I was only a journeyman, and he my master, envy prevailed in him over avarice, which one would have expected to be just the contrary, this Lucagnolo tracing his birth to a native of Jesi. He cursed his art, and those from whom he had learned it, declaring

that thenceforth he would renounce it, giving his whole
mind to these toys, since they were so well paid for.
Equally indignant on my part, I said that every bird
considered its own note the sweetest; and that he talked
like a rude, uncultivated fellow, in keeping with the
Bœotian soil from which he had sprung.

The next day I went to return thanks to Signora
Porzia, and told her that her ladyship had done the reverse of what she said she would; that I proposed to
make the devil laugh, and that she had made him once
more renounce God. We both were merry upon the occasion, and she gave me orders for other fine and valuable works.

About this time I contrived, by means of a pupil of
Raffaello da Urbino, to be employed by the Bishop of
Salamanca in making one of those large silver vases for
holding water, which are used in cupboards, and are
usually laid upon them by way of ornament. The
bishop, being desirous of having two of equal size, employed Lucagnolo to make one, and me another. Giovanni Francesco, the painter, gave us a design, to which
we were to conform. I with great alacrity set about
this piece of plate; and a Milanese, Signor Giovanni
Pietro della Tacca, accommodated me with a part of his
shop.

Having begun my work, I laid by money enough for
my own private use, and the remainder I sent to the relief of my poor father.

Whilst I was going on with the Bishop of Salamanca's plate, I had no assistance but that of a little boy,
whom, at the earnest request of his relatives, I had, half
against my will, taken as an apprentice. This boy,
named Paulino, then about fourteen, was son to a citizen
of Rome, who lived upon his fortune. Paulino was one
of the best bred, sweetest tempered and prettiest boys
that I ever saw in my life; and on account of his good

qualities, his extraordinary beauty, and the great love he bore me, I conceived the strongest affection for him that the human breast can conceive.

One of the effects of this great fondness was that, in order to diffuse a ray of cheerfulness over his features, which had naturally a melancholy cast, I from time to time took in hand my flute. He used then to smile in so graceful and affecting a manner, that I am not the least surprised at the fables the Greeks have written concerning their deities. Paulino had a sister named Faustina, of so exquisite a form that she might justly be compared to the renowned Faustina, whose charms are so much vaunted by historians; and as he sometimes took me with him to his father's, so far as I could judge from observation, that worthy man seemed desirous that I should be his son-in-law. This made me set a much higher value upon music than before. It happened about this time that Giovanni Giacomo, a musician of Cesena, who belonged to the Pope's household, and was an excellent performer, sent Lorenzo Trombone, of Lucca, a person who is now in the service of our Duke, to propose to me to assist them with my flute at the Pope's Ferragosto*, in playing some concert music; as he had selected some of the most beautiful compositions for the occasion. Though I had an earnest desire to finish the fine piece of plate that I had begun, yet as music has a secret charm in it, and as I was in some measure desirous of gratifying my aged father, I agreed to make one at their concert; so that for eight days before the Ferragosto we had a rehearsal every two hours.

On the first of August we repaired to Belvedere, and while Pope Clement was at dinner we played those fine compositions we had long practised, insomuch that his Holiness declared he had never been delighted with more exquisite harmony; then, sending for Giovanni

* A feast at Rome on the first of August.

Giacomo, he inquired of him how he had procured so able a master of the flute, and ordered him to give a full and circumstantial account of my person. On Giovanni's mentioning my name, the Pope said, "Is he the son of Giovanni Cellini?" Finding who I was, he added that he would take me into his service and make me one of his band of music. Giacomo answered, "As to his joining your Holiness's band, I believe it when I see it. His business is that of a goldsmith and jeweler, in which he is a complete master, and by working at it constantly he makes a great deal more money than he could ever gain by music." The Pope replied, "I am therefore the more desirous of having him in my service, since he is possessed of one talent more than I expected. Let him have the same salary with the rest of you, and tell him from me that I desire he would become one of my band, and I will find him constant employment in his other business." His Holiness thereupon gave him a handkerchief, which contained a hundred gold crowns, desiring him to divide them amongst the band, and let me have my share.

Giacomo having quitted the Pope, came to us and repeated word for word all that his Holiness had said. Having then divided the money amongst eight of us musicians, and given me what fell to my share, he added, "I have orders to set you down as one of our band." To this I made answer, "Give me a day to consider it, and to-morrow I will let you know my determination."

The night following, my father appeared to me in a dream, and entreated me, with tears, that I would for his sake accept the place of a musician to the Pope; I thought I replied, that it was my firm resolution to do no such thing. He then appeared to me to assume a form so horrible that I was shocked, and he said, "If you do not, you will have your father's curse; but if you conform to my desire, I will bless you forever." No sooner was

I awake, than I ran in a fright to get my name entered
with the Pope's musicians. I then wrote to my aged
father, telling him what I had done. On receiving the
intelligence, he was, through excess of joy, attacked by
a disorder that brought him almost to death's door. Immediately upon his recovery he wrote me word that he
had had exactly the same dream as mine. I therefore
concluded that I had given my father full satisfaction,
and that all things would succeed to my wishes. I then
exerted myself to the utmost to finish the piece of plate,
which I had begun for the Bishop of Salamanca.

This prelate was an extraordinary person, exceedingly
rich and very difficult to please. He sent every day to
inquire how I got on; and as the messenger happened
once not to find me at work, his master came in a great
passion, and said he would take the work out of my
hands, and give to another to finish. This came of my
attaching myself to that odious flute. I therefore continued the work day and night with the most assiduous
application, till I had forwarded it to such a degree that
I thought I might venture to show it to the bishop; but
upon seeing what I had done, he grew so impatient to
have it completed that I heartily repented having ever
shown it to him. In about three months I finished this
grand piece of plate, which I adorned with a surprising
variety of beautiful animals, foliages, and figures. I
then sent my apprentice Paulino to show it to the ingenious Lucagnolo. Paulino delivered his message in
the most graceful manner imaginable, in these terms;
"Signor Lucagnolo, my master, Benvenuto, in pursuance
of his promise, has sent me to show you a piece of work,
which he has made in imitation of your performances,
and he expects in return to see some of your little knick-
knacks." Lucagnolo took the piece of plate in his hand,
and having examined it sufficiently, said to Paulino:

"My pretty youth, tell thy master that he is an excellent artist, and I desire nothing more than his friendship."

The plate was then carried to the bishop, who wanted to have a price set upon it. Just at this juncture Lucagnolo entered the room, and spoke of my work so honorably, and praised it to such a degree, that he even surpassed my own good opinion of it. The bishop having taken the plate into his hands, said, like a true Spaniard, "By G— I will be as slow in paying him as he was in finishing the work." When I heard this, I was highly mortified, and cursed Spain and all that belonged to it.

Among other beautiful ornaments, there was a handle to this silver vase of the most exquisite workmanship, which by means of a spring stood exactly upon the mouth of it. The bishop one day was ostentatiously exhibiting this piece of plate to some Spanish gentlemen of his acquaintance, when it happened that one of them meddled indiscreetly with the handle, and the delicate spring suddenly broke. This occurred after his lordship had left the room. The gentleman, thinking this a most unlucky accident, entreated the person that took care of the cupboard, to carry the vase directly to the artist that had made it, and order him to mend it without delay, promising that he should be paid his own price, in case he proved expeditious. The piece of plate having thus again come into my hands, I promised to mend it without loss of time; and I finished it by ten o'clock that night. The person that left it with me then came in a most violent hurry, for my lord bishop had called for it again, to show it to other gentlemen. The messenger, not giving me time to utter a word, cried, "Quick, quick, bring the plate in all haste." Being determined to take my own time, and not to let him have it, I said I did not choose to make such despatch. The man then flew into a passion, and clapping his hand to his sword, seemed

to be ready to break into the shop by main force; but this I prevented by dint of arms and menacing expressions. "I will not let you have it," said I. "Go tell your master that it shall not be taken out of my shop till I am paid for my trouble." Seeing he could not obtain it by bullying, he began to beg and pray in the most suppliant manner, saying that if I would put it into his hands he would take care to see me satisfied. These words did not in the least shake my resolution; and as I persisted in the same answer, he at last despaired of success, and swearing that he would return with a body of Spaniards and cut me to pieces, thought proper to depart. In the mean time I, who gave some credit to what I had heard of Spanish assassinations, resolved that I would defend myself courageously; and having put in order an excellent fowling-piece, I said to myself, "He that takes both my property and my labor, may as well deprive me of life."

While I thus argued with myself, a crowd of Spaniards made their appearance with the above-mentioned domestic at their head, who with great arrogance bade them break open the shop. At these words I showed them the muzzle of my loaded gun, and cried out, "Miscreants! traitors! cut-throats! are the houses and shops of citizens of Rome to be assailed in this manner? If any thief among you offers to approach this door, I will shoot him dead." Then taking aim at the domestic, and pretending that I was going to fire at him, I cried out, "As for you, you rascal, that set them on, you are the very first I shall make an example of." On hearing this, he clapped spurs to a jennet, upon which he was mounted, and fled at full speed. The disturbance had now brought all the neighbors out of their houses, when some Roman gentlemen passing by said: "Kill the dogs, and we will stand by you." These words had such an effect on the

Spaniards, that they left me in a panic, and told his lordship all that had happened.

The bishop, a proud, haughty man, reprimanded his servants severely, both because they had begun such an act of violence, and because they had not gone through with it. The painter who had been present at the accident, entered at this juncture, and his lordship desired him to go and tell me that, if I did not bring him the piece of plate directly, he would leave no part of my body entire but my ears; but that if I brought it without delay he would instantly satisfy my demand. The proud prelate's menaces did not in the least terrify me, and I sent him word that I should immediately lay the whole affair before the Pope.

In the mean time his anger and my fear having subsided, and some gentlemen of Rome assuring me that I should come to no harm, and should be paid for my trouble, I went, armed with my dagger and coat of mail, to the house of the bishop, who had caused all his servants to be drawn up in line. Paulino followed close behind me with the piece of plate. To make my way through the line of domestics was like passing through the Zodiac; one of them looked like a lion, another like a scorpion, and a third like a crab, till at last we came into the presence of this reverend prelate, who uttered the most priest-like Spanish-like words that I ever heard. All this time I never once looked at him, or so much as answered a single word; at which his lordship seemed to discover more resentment than ever, and having ordered pen, ink, and paper, requested me to write him a receipt. I then looked him full in the face, and told him that I would readily do so after I had received my money. The haughty bishop was then more exasperated than ever; but after a great deal of scolding and hectoring I was paid, and then, having written an acquittance, I left the place in high spirits.

Pope Clement afterward heard the whole affair, having first seen the piece of plate, though it was not shown to him by me. He was highly pleased at what had happened, and said publicly that he approved of my behavior, so that the bishop heartily repented what he had done; and, in order to make atonement, sent me word that he intended to give me many important commissions; to which I made answer, that I was very willing to undertake them, but that I should insist upon being paid beforehand. These words also came to the ear of Pope Clement and made him laugh heartily. Cardinal Cibo was at Rome when the affair happened; and his Holiness told him the whole story of the difference between me and the Bishop of Salamanca, with all the disturbances it had given rise to; upon which he turned to one of his domestics, and bade him find constant employment for me as a goldsmith. Cardinal Cibo sent for me, and after much conversation ordered me to make him a piece of plate, more considerable than that which I had finished for the Bishop of Salamanca. I worked likewise for Cardinal Cornaro, and for many other cardinals, especially Ridolfi and Salviati: I was employed by them all, and earned a great deal of mony. Signora Porzia Chigi advised me to open a shop on my own account. I did so accordingly, and was kept in constant employment by that good lady, so that it was perhaps by her means chiefly that I came to make some figure in the world.

At this time I contracted an intimate acquaintance with Signor Gabriello Cesarini, gonfalonier of Rome, and was frequently employed by him. Among the works that I executed for him, one was particularly remarkable, a large gold medal to be worn upon a hat, on which was engraved Leda with her enamored swan. He was highly pleased with the execution, and said he would have my work examined, in order to pay me its full value. My medal being a masterpiece of art, the connoisseurs set a much higher price upon it than he expected; he kept the medal, and I reaped no benefit from my labor.

CHAPTER V

THE PLAGUE IN ROME

IT HAPPENED once, at our feast of Saint John, to dine with several of my countrymen of different callings, where, among other artists of distinguished reputation, were present one Rosso, a painter, Giovanni Francesco, a pupil of Raffaello da Urbino, and many more. As I had invited them without any ceremony or constraint, they laughed and jested, as is usual with mixed companies, and made merry upon occasion of so great a festival. In the mean time a swaggering, bullying youth, a soldier of Signor Rienzo da Ceri, happening to pass by, thought proper to ridicule the Florentines, and to cast many injurious reflections upon the whole body of the nation. As it was I who had invited all these men of genius and worth to this meeting, I considered myself as the person chiefly insulted; and therefore, unnoticed by any of the company, I went quietly up to the gentleman, who was in company with a woman of the town and continued his gibing to divert her. I asked him whether he was the audacious man that abused the Florentines; and he immediately replied, "I am that man." Scarcely had he uttered these words, when I gave him a slap on the face, saying, "And I am *this* man." We both instantly drew our swords in a violent rage. But we had hardly made three passes when several bystanders interposed, most of them seem-

ing to take my part, perceiving, from what they had
heard and seen, that I was in the right. The next day
I received a written challenge from my adversary, which
I accepted with great cheerfulness, declaring that I
thought this an affair of much more urgent importance
than the business of my art. I instantly consulted an
old man named Bevilacqua, who had the reputation of
being the best swordsman in Italy, having fought more
than twenty duels, and always come off with honor.
This worthy man was my particular friend. He said to
me, "My good friend, Benvenuto, if you were to cope
with Mars himself, I have not the least doubt that you
would acquire honor; for though I have been acquainted
with you so many years, I never knew you in the wrong
in any quarrel." He consented to be my second, and,
having repaired to the place appointed, in arms, I came
off with much credit. My opponent yielded, though
no blood was shed.

At this time there was in Rome a native of Perugia,
of great abilities, named Lautizio; the only man that
worked in his branch of the business, which was that of a
seal-engraver. Every cardinal at Rome has a seal on
which his title is engraved; it is as large as the hand of
a child ten years old, and the title is embellished with a
variety of figures. One of these seals, well executed, costs
a hundred crowns or more. I could not help desiring to
rival so eminent an artist, though this business widely
differs from that of the jeweler and goldsmith; but Lautizio, who was master of the art, seemed to be confined
to that, and knew nothing of any other. I therefore set
about learning this business, and though I found it extremely difficult, I never was wearied by any labor it
cost me, but steadily pursued the objects of gain and
improvement. There was likewise, in Rome, another
eminent artist, a native of Milan, who went by the name
of Caradosso. This man worked only in medals, en-

graved with a chisel, upon thin plates of metal and many other materials. He made some Scripture pieces in mezzo rilievo, and figures of Christ, a palm long, of thin plates of gold, and of such admirable workmanship that I thought him one of the greatest masters in this art that I had ever known; and I envied him more than any of the rest. There were likewise other masters there, who worked in medals engraved on steel. I set about learning all these different branches with the greatest assiduity. Next to these came the most elegant art of enameling, in which I never heard of more than one that excelled, and this was a Florentine, named Amerigo, with whom I was not acquainted. His performances were indeed admirable, and such as were never equaled in any part of the globe; nor could I, or any other man, ever boast of having seen a piece of workmanship of the kind that made even a faint approach to their excellence. The art of enameling is extremely difficult on account of the fire, the last thing used in works of that nature, which often spoils them. Nevertheless, I attached myself likewise to it with the greatest ardor; and, though I found it very hard to be acquired, such was the pleasure I took in learning it that its greatest difficulties appeared delightful to me.

About this time, while I was still a young man of three-and-twenty, so dreadful an epidemic disease prevailed in Rome that several thousands died every day. Somewhat terrified at this calamity, I began to indulge in certain recreations, as the fancy took me. On holidays I amused myself with visiting the antiquities of the city, and sometimes took their figures in wax; at other times I made drawings of them. As these antiquities are all ruinous edifices, where pigeons build their nests, I had a mind to divert myself among them with my fowling-piece; but being greatly afraid of the plague, I avoided all commerce with the inhabitants, and made

Paulino carry my gun. Thus we went together to the
ruins, whence I often returned home laden with the
largest pigeons. But I never chose to put more than
a single ball into my piece; and, in this manner, being a
good marksman, I procured a considerable quantity of
game. The fowling-piece was, both inside and outside,
as bright as a looking-glass. I likewise made the powder as fine as the minutest dust; and, in the use of it, I
discovered some of the most admirable secrets that ever
were known till this time. When I had charged my
piece with a quantity of powder equal in weight to the
fifth part of the ball, it carried two hundred paces point
blank. In a word, so great was the delight I took in
shooting, that it often diverted me from the business of
my shop.

By means of this recreation also, I contracted an acquaintance with certain persons that were accustomed to
watch for the peasants of Lombardy, who, at a particular
season, came to work in the vineyards about Rome.
These peasants, in digging the ground, frequently discovered ancient medals, agates, carnelians, emeralds, and
cameos. They likewise found precious stones, such as
sapphires, diamonds, and rubies. Those that went in
quest of the peasants often bought such things of them
for a trifle; and I, dealing with the former, have frequently given them gold crowns for curiosities that had
cost them only so many pence. This traffic, besides the
great profit I derived from it, which was ten-fold at
least, procured me the friendship of most of the Roman
cardinals. One of these rarities was a dolphin's head,
about the size of a large bean. Though art was eminently conspicuous in this head, it was surpassed by
nature; for this emerald was of so fine a color that the
person who purchased it of me for ten crowns caused it
to be curiously set in a gold ring and sold it for a hundred. I had likewise one of the finest topazes that ever

were beheld. Art and nature appeared to rival each other in embellishing this stone, of the size of a large nut; and upon it was carved a remarkably fine head, intended to represent Minerva. I had also another stone, of a different sort from the latter; this was a cameo, upon which was engraved a Hercules binding a Cerberus. This was a piece of such extraordinary beauty, and such admirable workmanship, that our great Michelangelo declared he never had beheld anything that surpassed it.

As I said before, the plague had prevailed for some time in Rome, when an eminent surgeon, named Signor Giacomo da Carpi, arrived in that city. This extraordinary man, among other cures for which he was famous, undertook the most desperate cases in a certain disease. He also understood the art of design extremely well. Happening one day to pass by my shop, he cast his eye upon some drawings, among which were several sketches of little fanciful vases, which I had drawn by way of amusement. These vases being, in form, very different from any that had ever been seen before, Signor Giacomo desired me to make him some of silver, according to the same model; and this I readily agreed to do, because they were of my own invention.

I had no sooner finished these pieces than my new employer showed them to the Pope, and the day following he left Rome. He was a man of great learning, and talked admirably on medical subjects. The Pope was desirous of having him in his service, but he declared he did not care to confine himself to any service whatever, and that whoever had occasion for his assistance should send for him. He was a person of great sagacity, and did very wisely to leave Rome; for, not many months after, all his patients relapsed, so that he would have been murdered if he had stayed. He showed my little vases to the Duke of Ferrara and to several other

princes; and told them they were presents from a great
nobleman at Rome, of whom he had demanded them
upon undertaking to cure him of a disorder; that the
nobleman had told him they were antiques, and begged
he would rather ask anything else, which he could freely
part with, and leave him those; but he refused to cure
him on any other terms, and thus got them into his possession.

This I was told by Signor Alberto Bendidio, at Ferrara, who, with great ceremony, showed me certain figures, at which I laughed without making any remark.
Signor Alberto, who was a proud, haughty man, said to
me in a passion, "You may laugh as much as you please,
but I must tell you that there has not been a man these
thousand years able to make such figures." I, that I
might not seem to detract from their reputation, stood
apparently admiring them. I was afterward told in
Rome, by many noblemen, that these works appeared
to them very extraordinary, and of genuine antiquity.
Encouraged by this declaration, I confessed that they
were my performances. They not giving credit to what
I said, I formed a resolution to make new designs, in
order to prove my veracity, because the above-mentioned
Signor Giacomo had carried off the others.

By this work I made considerable gain. The epidemic
disease continuing to rage for many months, I took to
a freer course of life, because many of my acquaintance
had died of it, while I had remained in perfect health.
It happened one evening, that a companion of mine
brought to his house a courtesan, a Bolognese lady of
extreme beauty. Her name was Faustina. She was
about thirty years of age, and had with her a young
servant-girl, thirteen or fourteen years old. As I knew
she was engaged by my friend, no temptation in the
world would have induced me to act dishonorably. Still
it was evident that she was not ill affected toward me;

4

but finding me resolute in consulting my honor, she soon withdrew with her first lover, leaving, however, her pretty young attendant, as if to console me—a far more agreeable arrangement than if I had been favored with the attentions of the mistress herself. Woe to us, however, had she divined the truth!

The ensuing day, about dinner time, I was seized with a severe headache, and with extreme pain in my left arm, while a tremendous carbuncle broke out on the palm of my left hand. Terrified at the sight, my friend, the great lady, and the little lady all disappeared together. Left alone, except with one of my work-boys, who never would leave me, I felt as if I should be suffocated, and believed myself to be a dead man. The father of this boy happening to pass by the house, and being a medical man, physician to the Cardinal Jacoacci, the youth ran and stopped him: "Come, father, and see Benvenuto, who has been taken rather poorly, and is in bed." Knowing nothing respecting the nature of the attack, the doctor came close to me, and having felt my pulse, saw more than he would have desired. Turning suddenly upon the boy, he exclaimed, "O thou treacherous child, thou hast ruined me for ever! How can I now go before the Cardinal?" To this the son hardly replied, "Why, father, my master, Benvenuto, is worth more than all the cardinals in Rome." Regardless of such consolation, the doctor, turning toward me, said, "Since I am here, I will endeavor to save you. But in most cases such an attack is mortal; it is well yours is not one of the worst kind, and that relief was near."

When he had left, my friend Giovanni Rigogli made his appearance, and taking compassion on my sufferings and loneliness, exclaimed, "Be of good heart, Benvenuto, I will stay with you till you recover." I, on my side, told him not to come near me; that I had no hope; but begged him to take some crowns out of a little box

close to my bed, and, after my death, give them to my
poor father. But he was unwilling to obey me, declaring that he knew what was due to friendship; and, come
what would, he would attend upon me. His care, with
the help of God, and the medicine I took, had a wonderful effect; and I survived that terrific attack. While
my wound was still open, with the lint in it, covered with
a plaster, I used to ride out on a little wild pony I had,
with a long rough coat, about the size of a great bear,
and resembling one in every respect.

In this state I went to visit Rosso, the painter, who
lived beyond the walls, on the road to Civita Vecchia,
at a spot belonging to Count Anguillara, called Cerve-
terra, who seemed rejoiced to see me. "I am come," I
said, "to do as you did to me, many months ago." He
began to laugh, and giving me a hearty welcome, besought me, from regard to the Count, not to flurry myself. The latter, too, treated me with the utmost friendship, setting the greatest dainties before me, and invited
me to remain and enjoy the country air. This I did
more than a month, taking pleasure-rides along the
shores on my little steed; and there I made quite a collection of rare stones, shells, and other aquatic curiosities.

The plague had by this time almost spent its fury,
insomuch that those who had survived it congratulated
one another, and expressed great joy at having escaped
the scourge. At this time there was established in Rome
a society of painters, statuaries, and goldsmiths, the best
had ever had been known in that capital. The founder
of this society was a statuary named Michelagnolo, a
native of Siena, possessed of such extraordinary abilities,
that he might justly vie with any artist belonging to
the profession; but still more eminently distinguished
for being the most complaisant and obliging man in the
universe. He was the oldest member of this society, but

might be considered the youngest, on account of his vigorous constitution. We were together at least twice in the week. I must not omit that to this society also belonged Giulio Romano, a painter, and Giovanni Francesco, both pupils of the great Raffaello da Urbino.

After we had been several times in company together, our worthy president invited us to sup at his house one Sunday, directing that every man should bring with him his *chère amie* (whom he called *cornacchia,* "a crow") ; and he who brought no lady should be obliged to treat the company with a supper. Such members of the society as had no acquaintance among the courtesans were obliged to procure ladies with great trouble and expense, for fear of exposing themselves at this agreeable entertainment. I had thought myself vastly well provided in a fine girl named Pantasilea, who had a fondness for me; but I was obliged to resign her to one of my most intimate friends, named Bacchiaca, who was deeply in love with her. The girl, on this occasion, was somewhat piqued, perceiving that I gave her up to Bacchiaca at the first word, which induced her to imagine that I slighted her, and made a bad return for the affection she bore me. Her resentment afterward involved me in a perplexing affair.

As the time drew near that we were to go to the assembly above mentioned, and I happened to be without a female companion, I thought myself guilty of a great oversight in not having provided one; but not choosing to be disgraced by bringing any low, despicable creature among so many brilliant beauties, I thought of a frolic to increase the mirth of the company. Having formed my plan, I sent for a boy of about sixteen, named Diego, who lived next door to me, and was son of a Spanish coppersmith. This lad was learning Latin at the grammar-school, to which he applied with great diligence. He had a very genteel person, with a fine complexion;

the contour of his face surpassed that of the ancient
statue of Antinous, and I had often drawn his likeness,
by which I acquired great reputation. The boy had no
acquaintance in town, nor was he known to any of the
society; and he neglected his dress, his attention being
engrossed by study. Having sent for him to my house,
I begged that he would dress himself in female attire,
which I had provided. He was easily prevailed on to
comply, and I, by means of a variety of ornaments,
added a considerable luster to the beauty of his countenance I put rings in his ears, in which were beautiful
pearls; the rings, being divided in the middle, fastened
upon his ears, which appeared to be bored. I then
dressed his neck with gold necklaces and costly jewels.
In the same manner I adorned his fingers with rings,
and taking him gently by the ear, placed him before a
looking-glass. The boy, seeing himself in the glass, exclaimed with an exulting tone, "Heavens! Is that
Diego?"

"Yes," I replied, "that is Diego, of whom I never before asked any favor; but now, for the first time, I will
ask him to oblige me in one harmless request; and that
is, to go with me in his present dress to the agreeable
society that I have mentioned so often."

The lad, who was virtuous and discreet, modestly cast
his eyes upon the ground, and deliberated for a few
moments, then suddenly looking up, made answer, "I
will go with you, Benvenuto; let us set out directly."

I put on his head a large handkerchief, which is called
at Rome a summer-cloth. When we came to the place,
the whole company rose to salute me: Michelagnolo
was between Giulio Romano and Giovanni Francesco.
As soon as I had taken the handkerchief from the head
of my beautiful companion, Michelagnolo, who, as I have
already observed, was one of the most facetious and di-
verting men in the world, with one hand taking hold of

Giulio, and with the other of Giovanni Francesco, with his utmost might drew them toward Diego, and obliged them to kneel; at the same time falling upon his knees himself, and calling to the company he exclaimed aloud, "See in what form angels descend from the clouds! Though celestial beings are represented as males, behold there are female spirits in heaven likewise! O beautiful angel! O angel worthy of all praise, vouchsafe to save —vouschsafe to direct me!" At these words the facetious creature lifted his right hand, and gave him a papal benediction. Michelagnolo rising, said, that it was customary to kiss the Pope's feet, but that angels were to be kissed on the cheeks; he then gave him a salute, at which the youth colored deeply, which greatly added to his beauty.

This scene being over, every man produced a sonnet, upon some subject or other; and we gave them to Michelagnolo for his perusal. He at once read them aloud, in a manner that infinitely increased the effect of their excellence. The company fell into discourse, and many fine things were said. One expression I recollect to have heard from that famous painter Giulio. This great man, having looked upon all present with affection, but more attentively upon the ladies, turned about to Michelagnolo, and spoke to him thus: "My dear Michelagnolo, the name of *crow*, which you have given to our ladies, suits them pretty well, though they even seem a little inferior in beauty to crows, when compared with one of the finest peacocks that ever were beheld."

Dinner was now ready, when Giulio begged to be the person that should place us in proper order. His request being granted, he took the ladies by the hand, and made them sit at the upper end of the table, with mine in the midst of them; the men he placed next, and me in the middle, telling me that I was deserving of all manner of honor and distinction. Behind us were rows of flower-pots, with beautiful jessamines, which seemed to heighten the charms of the young ladies, and especially of my Diego, beyond expression. Thus we all began to regale ourselves, with great cheerfulness, at that elegant supper.

After our repast was over, we were entertained with music, both vocal and instrumental; and as the performers sang and played with books before them, my angelic companion desired that he might be allowed to sing his part. He acquitted himself better than any of the rest, and Giulio and Michelagnolo, instead of expressing themselves in the same facetious terms as they had before, appeared to be struck with astonishment, and grew wild and extravagant in their praises. The music being over, one Aurelio Ascolano, a most wonderful *improvisatore*, sang some admirable verses in praise of the ladies. While this person was singing, the two girls who had my beauty between them, never ceased prating and chattering. One of them explained in what manner she had fallen into that sort of life; another asked my companion how it came to be her fate, who were her friends, and how long she had been at Rome, with several other questions of the same kind.

The discourse of the two courtesans began at last to displease my counterfeit lady, who had taken the name of Pomona. As she wished to disengage herself from them, and get rid of their loose conversation, she sometimes turned to one side, sometimes to the other. The lady that Giulio brought with him asked whether she was not ill; and the counterfeit Pomona answered in the affirmative, whispering that she believed herself to be some months advanced in pregnancy, and felt at that very moment far from well. Upon which the two ladies who had her between them, taking compassion on Pomona, begged her to retire; which, in spite of Diego's reluctance, led to a revelation, and the exasperated women loaded him with abusive language. An outcry being constantly set up, accompanied with great laughter and expressions of surprise, the grave Michelagnolo desired permission of all present to inflict upon me a penance at his own discretion. The company gave their assent to this with loud acclamations, and he put me out of pain by thrice repeating "Long live Benvenuto!"

CHAPTER VI

PULCI'S TRAGIC END

I EXERTED myself with the utmost diligence and care to acquire perfection in the variety of arts above enumerated; and therefore with unceasing perseverance worked at them all. Michelagnolo of Siena was at this time employed in erecting a monument to the late Pope Adrian. Giulio Romano the painter had gone into the service of the Marquis of Mantua. The other members had retired to different quarters, as their business happened to lead them, so that our ingenious society was almost entirely dispersed.

Soon afterward I found some little Turkish daggers, the handles of which were of iron as well as the blade, and even the scabbard was of that metal. On these were engraved fine foliages in Turkish style, most beautifully filled up with gold. I found I had a strong inclination to cultivate this branch likewise, which was so different from the rest; and finding that I had great success in it, I produced several pieces in this way. My performances, indeed, were much finer and more durable than the Turkish, for several reasons: one was, that I made a much deeper incision in the steel than is usually

made in Turkish works; the other, that their foliages
are nothing but chiccory leaves, with some few flowers
of echites. In Italy there is a variety of tastes, and we
cut foliage in many different forms. The Lombards
make the most beautiful wreaths, representing ivy and
vine leaves, and others of the same sort, with agreeable
twinings highly pleasing to the eye. The Romans and
the Tuscans have a much better notion in this respect,
for they represent acanthus leaves, with all their festoons
and flowers, winding in a variety of forms; and amongst
these leaves they insert birds and animals of several
sorts with great ingenuity and elegance in the arrangement. They likewise have recourse occasionally to wild
flowers, such as those called lions' mouths, from their
peculiar shape, accompanied by other fine inventions,
which are termed grotesques by the ignorant. These
foliages have received that name from the moderns, because they are found in certain caverns in Rome, which
in ancient days were chambers, baths, studies, halls,
and similar places. The curious happened to discover
them in these subterraneous caverns, whose low situation is owing to the raising of the surface of the ground
in a series of ages; and as these caverns in Rome are
commonly called grottos, they thence acquired the name
of grotesque.

It happened about this time that certain vases were
discovered, which appeared to be antique urns filled with
ashes. Among these were iron rings inlaid with gold,
in each of which was set a diminutive shell. Learned
antiquaries, on investigating the nature of these rings,
declared their opinion that they were worn as charms by
those who desired to behave with steadiness and resolution either in prosperous or in adverse fortune.

I likewise took things of this nature in hand at the
request of some gentlemen who were my particular
friends, and wrought some of these little rings; but I

made them of steel, and then cut and inlaid with gold, so that they were very beautiful to behold. Sometimes for a single ring of this sort I was paid more than forty crowns. At that time small medals were in fashion, upon which it was customary for noblemen and gentlemen to cause to be engraved certain devices and fancies of their own, and they wore them commonly upon their caps. I made several things of this sort, but found such works very difficult. The celebrated artist named Caradosso would not take less than a hundred crowns for one of them, because they contained a variety of figures. I was therefore employed, not so much on account of the greatness of his price, as his slowness in working, by some gentlemen, for whom I made one medal, among others, in emulation of this renowned artist, on which were four figures with which I took uncommon pains. It happened on this occasion that the gentlemen, comparing my work with that of the famous Caradosso, declared mine to be by much the more elegant and masterly, and bade me ask whatever I thought proper for my trouble. To this I answered, that the best recompense I could receive for my labor, and that which I desired most, was the happiness of making an approach to the excellence of so great a master; and if I appeared to gentlemen of their taste to have attained that honor, I thought myself sufficiently rewarded. On my leaving them at these words, they immediately sent me a generous present, with which I was perfectly satisfied; and my ardor to gain the approbation of my employers increased to such a degree that it gave rise to the adventures I am about to relate.

I have already given an account of the ingenious society of artists, and of the adventure of Pantasilea the courtesan, who had so deceitful and dangerous a passion for me, and had been so greatly irritated on account of the frolic of introducing Diego, the Spanish boy, at

supper. I shall now conclude that whimsical adventure.
As she thought herself injured in the most outrageous
manner imaginable, and had vowed revenge, an opportunity soon offered to carry her wicked purpose into
execution.

About this time a young gentleman named Luigi
Pulci, son of one of the Pulci family who had been
beheaded for violating his own daughter, arrived in
Rome. This young gentleman had an uncommon genius for poetry, and was well versed in Latin, and also
wrote with great elegance; he was likewise extremely
handsome and genteel. He had just quitted the service
of some bishop, and was in a very bad state of health.
When he was at Florence, there were meetings in the
open streets during summer, where he sang extempore,
and distinguished himself amongst those who had the
greatest talent that way. This singing was so well
worth hearing, that the divine Michelangelo Buonarroti,
whenever he heard that Pulci was to perform, went
to listen to him with the utmost eagerness, and on these
occasions was usually accompanied by one Piloto,
a goldsmith, and me. This was the beginning of my intimacy with Luigi Pulci. After some years had elapsed,
he discovered to me the distressed condition he was in
at Rome, and begged that I would procure him some
relief. I was moved to pity on account of his excellent
qualities, and further excited by the love of my country
as well as a compassionate disposition. I therefore
took him into my house and had him treated with such
care that, with the assistance of youth and a vigorous
constitution, his health was quickly restored. While
the young man was in this manner endeavoring to recover, he constantly amused himself with reading, and I
procured him as many books as I could. Sensible of the
obligations I laid him under, he often thanked me with
tears in his eyes, assuring me that if God ever prospered

him, or in any way put it in his power, he would endeav-
or to give me convincing marks of his gratitude. I told
him I had not served him as well as I could have wished,
but had done my best, and it was the duty of human
beings to assist one another; only admonishing him to
show the same kindness to others that might happen to
stand in need of his assistance, as he had of mine, and
desiring that he would look upon me as his friend, and
always love me.

In the mean time Luigi Pulci, being cured, every day
took an airing upon his black horse, which he managed
with great skill. One day, after a drizzling rain, having made his horse prance and curvet before Pantasilea's
door, he happened to slip, and the horse fell upon him.
By this accident his right leg was broken, and a few
days later he died in the house of Pantasilea; the curse
which he had solemnly invoked against himself in the
presence of God being thus accomplished.

CHAPTER VII

THE SIEGE OF ROME

ALL Italy was now up in arms, when Pope Clement sent to Signor Giovanni de' Medici for
troops, which accordingly marched to his assistance. These auxiliaries did so much mischief in Rome that tradesmen were not in safety in their
shops, which made me retire to a small house, behind
the place called Banchi, where I worked for my particular friends. I then took great delight in music, and
similar amusements. Pope Clement having, by the ad-

vice of Signor Giacopo Salviati, dismissed the five companies that had been sent to him by Signor Giovanni,
lately deceased in Lombardy, the Constable Bourbon,
finding that there were no troops in Rome, eagerly advanced with his army toward that capital. At the news
of his approach all the inhabitants took up arms. I
happened to be intimately acquainted with Alessandro,
the son of Pietro del Bene, who, at the time that the
Colonnas came to Rome, had requested me to guard his
house. On this more important occasion he asked that
I would raise a company of fifty men to guard the same
house, and undertake to be their commander, as I had
done at the time of the Colonnas. I accordingly engaged
fifty brave young men, and we took up our quarters in
his house, where we were well paid and kindly treated.

The army of the Duke of Bourbon having already
appeared before the walls of Rome, Alessandro del Bene
requested me to go with him to oppose the enemy. I
complied, and, taking one of the stoutest youths with
us, we were joined on our way by a young man named
Cecchino della Casa. We came up to the walls of Campo Santo, and there descried that great army, which was
making every effort to enter the town at that part of
the wall to which we had approached. Many young men
were slain without the walls, where they fought with
the utmost fury. There was a remarkably thick mist.
I turned to Alessandro, and spoke to him thus: "Let us
return home with speed, since it is impossible for us
here to make any stand. Behold, the enemy scales the
walls, and our countrymen fly before them, overpowered
by numbers." Alessandro, much alarmed, answered,
"Would to God we had never come hither." So saying,
he turned with precipitation, in order to depart. I thereupon reproved him, saying, "Since you have brought me
hither, I am determined to perform some manly action,"
and, levelling my arquebuse where I saw the thickest

crowd of the enemy, I discharged it with a deliberate aim at a person who seemed to be lifted above the rest; but the mist prevented me from distinguishing whether he was on horseback or on foot. Then, turning suddenly to Alessandro and Cecchino, I bade them fire their pieces, and showed them how to escape every shot of the besiegers. Having fired twice for the enemy's once, I cautiously approached the walls, and perceived that there was an extraordinary confusion among the assailants, occasioned by our having shot the Duke of Bourbon. He was, as I understood afterward, that chief personage whom I saw raised above the rest.

Quitting our post, we now passed through Campo Santo, and entered by the quarter of St. Peter; thence we passed behind the church of St. Angelo, and reached the gate of the Castle of St. Angelo with the greatest difficulty imaginable; for Signor Rienzo da Ceri and Signor Orazio Baglioni were wounding or killing everybody that deserted the walls. When we arrived at the gate above mentioned, part of the enemy had already entered Rome, and were at our heels. The castellan had thought proper to let down the portcullis; but there was just room enough for us four to enter. No sooner had we entered than the captain, Pallone de' Medici, pressed me into the service, because I belonged to the Pope's household, and forced me to leave Alessandro, much against my will. At this juncture, as I mounted the ramparts, Pope Clement had entered the Castle of St. Angelo, by the long gallery from St. Peter's; for he did not choose to quit the Vatican sooner, never once dreaming that the enemy would storm the city. As soon as I found myself within the castle walls, I went up to some pieces of artillery, which a bombardier, named Giuliano, a Florentine, had under his direction. This Giuliano, standing upon one of the battlements, saw his house pillaged and his wife and children cruelly treated.

Fearing to shoot any of his friends, he did not venture
to fire the guns, but, throwing the match upon the
ground, made a piteous lamentation, tearing his hair,
and uttering the most doleful cries. His example was
followed by several other gunners, which vexed me to
such a degree that I took one of the matches, and, getting some people to assist me who had not the same
passions to disturb them, I directed the fire of the
artillery and falcons, where I saw occasions, and
killed a considerable number of the enemy.

Pope Clement having appointed a Roman nobleman,
Antonio Santa Croce, to be chief engineer, this nobleman came to me in the evening, while the enemy's army
was entering Rome, by the quarter of Trastevere, and
posted me with five great guns in the highest part of
the castle called "dall' Angiolo," which goes quite round
the fortress, and looks both toward the meadows and
toward Rome. He appointed several persons to serve
under me and assist me in managing the artillery; and
then, causing me to be paid beforehand, he gave me a
portion of bread and wine, and asked that I would continue to behave as I had begun. I, who was at times
more inclined to arms than to my own profession,
obeyed my orders with such alacrity that I had better
success than if I had been following my own business.

Night being come, and the enemy having entered
Rome, we who were in the castle, and I, more than any
of the rest, who always took delight in beholding new
and extraordinary sights, stood contemplating this
strange novelty and the fire, which those who were in
any other part of the city could neither see nor conceive.

Pope Clement had sent to ask assistance of the Duke
of Urbino, who was with the Venetian army, and directed his ambassador to tell his Excellency that, so long
as the castle should continue every night to make three
fires on its top, at the same time firing three guns thrice

over, these should be considered as signals that the fort
had not surrendered. I was employed to make these
signals, and to fire the guns; and as the besiegers continued to annoy us greatly, I pointed the artillery in such
a manner as might be likely to injure them most and re-
tard their operations. The Pope on this account conceived a great liking for me, seeing that I acquitted myself with all the prudence and sagacity requisite on such
occasions. The Duke of Urbino never sent the succors
stipulated.

While I continued to be employed in my destructive
business of an engineer, several cardinals came frequently to see me, but above all the Cardinals of Ravenna
and Gaddi, whom I often warned not to come near me,
as their scarlet hats could be seen at a distance, which exposed both them and me to great danger from the neighboring palaces. But persuasion had no effect, and I at
last got them debarred, by which I incurred their enmity and ill-will. Signor Orazio Baglioni, my very good
friend, likewise frequently came where I was. Happening to be one day in conversation with me, he observed some appearances at a certain inn, which stood
without the castle gate, at a place called Baccanello.
The sign of this inn was the Sun, painted between two
red windows, which were shut. Orazio, thinking that
opposite to this sign between the two windows was a
table surrounded by soldiers carousing, said to me:
"Benvenuto, if you were to fire your middle cannon
near yonder sun, I believe you would do execution; for
I hear a great noise, and fancy there must be persons of
consequence in that quarter." "Sir," said I, "what I myself see is sufficient to induce me to make a discharge
at yon sun; but I am afraid of that barrel full of
stones, which stands hard by the mouth of the gun;
for the force of the discharge, and the very wind of the
cannon, will certainly throw it down." Orazio replied,

"For God's sake, Benvenuto, lose no time. In the first place, it is impossible, considering how the barrel stands, that the wind of the cannon should throw it down; but even if it should fall, and the Pope himself be under it, the harm would not be so great as you imagine; so fire! fire!" I, without thinking more of the matter, made a discharge at the sun as I had promised. The barrel that was filled with stones fell to the ground, as I thought it would, exactly between Cardinal Farnese and Signor Jacopo Salviati, both of whom it was near destroying. What saved them was Cardinal Farnese's reproaching Signor Jacopo with being the cause of the sack of Rome; and as they abused and railed at each other, their movements on the occasion prevented the barrel of stones from dashing them to pieces. Orazio having heard the noise, went down as fast as possible; and I, going toward the place where the barrel had fallen, heard some persons say, "Those gunners should be killed." This induced me to turn two falconets toward the steps leading to the battery, with a firm resolution to fire one of them at the first that should presume to ascend. The servants of Cardinal Farnese being sent by their master to attack me, I advanced in order to fire. As I knew some of them, I said, "Villains, if you do not instantly quit the place, or if any of you attempt to mount these stairs, I have two falconets ready charged, with which I will blow you into dust. Go, tell the cardinal from me, that I have done nothing but by the command of my superiors. I have been acting in defence of the clergy, and not to hurt them."

The servants having retired, Orazio came running up stairs; but I ordered him to stand back, declaring that, if he did not, I would kill him on the spot. He stopped a little, not without fear, and cried out, "Benvenuto, I am your friend." I answered, "Sir, only come by yourself, and you may come as often as you think proper."

5

He then made a pause, for he was exceedingly proud, and said peevishly, "I have a mind to come up no more, but to act quite the reverse of what I had intended toward you." I told him that, as I had received my post to defend others, I was likewise able to defend myself. He declared he was alone; and when he came up, he appeared to be so much altered in countenance that I kept my hand upon my sword and looked sternly at him as an enemy. Upon this he began to laugh, and, his color returning, he said to me with all the good humor imaginable, "My dear Benvenuto, no man can be more your friend than I am, and when an apportunity offers I will endeavor to prove it; would to God you had killed those two scoundrels! one of whom has already done so much mischief, and the other is likely to do more."

One day amongst others the Pope happened to walk upon the round rampart, when he saw in the public walks a Spanish colonel, whom he knew by certain tokens; and understanding that he had formerly been in his service, he said something concerning him, all the while observing him attentively. I, who was above at the battery, and knew nothing of the matter, but saw a man employed in getting the trenches repaired, who stood with a spear in his hand, dressed in rose-color, began to deliberate how I should lay him flat. I took my swivel, which was almost equal to a demi-culverin, turned it around, and charging it with a good quantity of fine and coarse powder mixed, aimed it at him exactly, though he was at so great a distance that it could not be expected any effort of art should make such pieces carry so far. I fired off the gun, and hit the man exactly in the middle. He had arrogantly placed his sword before him in a sort of Spanish bravado; but the ball of my piece struck his sword, and the man was seen severed into two pieces. The Pope, who did not dream of any

such thing, was highly delighted and surprised at what
he saw, as well because he thought it impossible that
such a piece could carry so far, as that he could not conceive how the man could be cut into two pieces. Upon
this he sent for me, and made an inquiry into the whole
affair. I told him the art I had used to fire in that manner; but as for the man's being split into two pieces,
neither he nor I was able to account for it. So, falling
upon my knees, I entreated his Holiness to absolve me
from the guilt of homicide, as likewise from other crimes
which I had committed in that Castle in the service of
the Church. The Pope, lifting his hands, and making
the sign of the cross over me, said that he blessed me,
and gave me his absolution for all the homicides I had
ever committed, or ever should commit, in the service
of the Apostolic Church.

On quitting him I again went up to the battery, and,
keeping up a constant fire, I hardly once missed. My
drawing, my elegant studies, and my taste for music, all
vanished before this butchering business; and if I were
to give a particular account of all the exploits I performed in this infernal employment, I should astonish
the world; but I pass them by for the safe of brevity. I
shall touch only upon some of the most remarkable.
As I was incessantly meditating how to employ myself
in defence of the Church, I considered that the enemy
every night changed their guard, and passed through
the great gate of San Spirito, which was indeed a reasonable distance for the artillery to carry; but because I
shot crosswise I did not do so much execution as I
wished. And yet every day a considerable number were
slain, so that the enemy, seeing the pass become dangerous, one night heaped more than a hundred gabions
on the top of a house, which obstructed my prospect.
Having now reflected more maturely upon the matter,
I leveled my whole five pieces of artillery against those

gabions, and waited till dusk for the relieving of the guard. As they imagined themselves in perfect security, they came slower and in greater numbers than usual. I then fired my pieces, and not only threw the gabions to the ground, but with the same shot killed more than thirty men. Upon my repeating this feat two or three times, the soldiers were put into such disorder, that among those who had loaded themselves with plunder at the sacking of Rome, some of them, desirous of enjoying the fruits of their military toil, were disposed to mutiny and march off; but being appeased by a valiant captain, whose name was Gian d'Urbino, they were with great difficulty prevailed on to turn through another pass in order to relieve the guard. This obliged them to fetch a compass of about three miles; whereas at first they had but half a mile to march. This affair being over, all the nobility in the Castle conferred extraordinary favors on me.

I must here anticipate a little in point of time, and inform the reader how Pope Clement, in order to preserve his regalia, together with all the jewels of the Apostolic Chamber, sent for me, and shut himself up with the master of the horse and me in an apartment. This master of the horse had formerly been equerry to Filippo Strozzi, and was a Frenchman. Pope Clement had enriched him considerably. He was a person of mean birth, yet the Pope put as much confidence in him as if he had been his own brother. Thus, while we were shut up together, they placed before me the regalia, with the vast quantity of jewels belonging to the Apostolic Chamber, and his Holiness ordered me to take off the gold in which they were set. I did as I was directed, and wrapping up each of them in a little piece of paper, we sewed them in the skirts of the Pope's clothes, and those of the master of the horse. They then gave me all the gold, which amounted to about one hundred pounds weight, and ordered me to melt it with the utmost secrecy. I went to the Angelo battery, where was my apartment, which I could shut to avoid being seen or interrupted; and having there made a little furnace with bricks, and fastened to the bottom of the furnace a little pot about the size of a dish, I threw the gold upon the coals, and it fell by degrees into the pot.

While this furnace was going, I constantly watched my opportunity to annoy the enemy, and soon did them a great deal of damage in their trenches with certain antique missiles, which I found in the armory. Having taken a swivel and a falconet, both somewhat broken at the mouth, I filled them with those weapons, and then fired off the missiles, which flew down like wild-fire, doing a great deal of damage to the trenches. Thus I kept my pieces constantly in order while I was melt-ing the gold. Toward evening I saw a person mounted upon a little mule, who came upon the border of the trench; the mule went at a great rate, and the person spoke to the men in the trenches. I thought it most ad-visable to fire off my artillery before he came quite op-posite to me; so having taken aim exactly, I fired and wounded him in the face with one of the missiles; the others hit the mule, which instantly fell dead. Hearing a loud noise in the trenches, I discharged the other piece, which did great execution. The person above mentioned was the Prince of Orange, who was carried through the trenches to a neighboring inn, whither all the nobility of the army quickly repaired.

As soon as I had melted the gold, I carried it to the Pope, who returned me thanks, and ordered the master of the horse to give me five-and-twenty crowns, at the same time making an apology because he had it not in his power to recompense me more amply.

CHAPTER VIII

FRIENDSHIP WITH MICHELANGELO

A FEW days later an agreement was concluded with the imperialists, when I set out with Signor Orazio Baglioni and three hundred soldiers toward Perugia. This gentleman wished me to accept the command of those men; but I declined his offer, telling him I chose to see my father first, and settle the affair of my banishment from Florence. He then informed me that I had already been made a captain by the Florentines. Signor Pier Maria di Lotto was also there, on a mission from Florence, to whom Signor Baglioni highly recommended me as a follower of his own. So I went to Florence, in company with several comrades.

The plague had made terrible havoc in that city; but I found my worthy father alive, who thought that I must either have been killed at the sack of Rome, or that I should return to him quite naked and destitute. It proved quite the reverse: I was alive, with my pockets well lined, and had a servant and a horse. So overjoyed was my aged father at the sight of his son that I thought while he was kissing and embracing me he would die of transport. I soon related to him the horrors of the sack of Rome, and presented him with a considerable number of crowns, which I had gained by the war. Our first caresses and demonstrations of joy being over, we visited the magistrates to compromise the affair of my banishment. I told my father that Signor Orazio had appointed me captain in the Florentines' service, and it was proper I should begin to think of raising my company. My poor father, quite

stunned at these words, begged and entreated me not to
think of any such thing, though he was very sensible
that I was equal to that, and even to any undertaking
of the greatest importance; adding that he had already
one son in the army, and that I ought to attach myself
totally to the admirable art that I had followed so many
years with unwearied application.

Though I promised to obey him, he judged, like a man
of sense, that in case Signor Orazio should come to
Florence I should not fail, either through a regard to my
promise or some other motive, to embrace the military
profession. He therefore devised a very good expedient
to prevent it, which was, to persuade me to remove from
Florence; and said, "My dear son, a most dreadful pestilence rages in this city, and you are come home just at
the time of its greatest fury. I remember when I was
very young I went to Mantua, where I met with a kind
reception, and I made a stay of several years. I request
you, and even command you, for my sake to repair
thither, and to do it directly, and not so much as defer it
till to-morrow."

As I was always glad of an opportunity of seeing the
world, and never had been at Mantua, I readily complied
with his request.

As all Italy was at that time ravaged by war and
pestilence, I with great difficulty traveled as far as
Mantua, where I endeavored to get into business, and
was immediately employed by one Signor Niccolo, a
Milanese, who was goldsmith to the Duke. As soon
as I had obtained employment, I went to pay a visit to
Giulio Romano, a most excellent painter and my particular friend. He gave me the kindest reception imaginable, and seemed to take it ill that I had not, on my arrival, come directly to his door. This painter lived like
a nobleman, and was employed in a work for the Duke,
without the gate of Mantua, at a place called the Te?

This work was magnificent, as it appears to this day. Giulio immediately recommended me in the most honorable terms to the Duke, who gave me an order to make a little shrine for the relic of the blood of Christ, which the Mantuans boast of possessing, saying it was brought thither by Longinus. He then turned to Signor Giulio, and asked him to draw a model of the shrine. Giulio made answer, "Please your Excellency, Benvenuto is a man that has no occasion for the design of another artist; and this you will readily acknowledge when you see his performance." Having undertaken this task, I sketched out a design for the shrine, in which the vial of blood could easily be contained. I also made a little model of wax representing Christ sitting, who, in his left hand, which was raised aloft, held his cross, in a reclining attitude, and with his right hand seemed to be about to tear open the wound in his side. When I had finished this model, the Duke was so highly pleased with it that he grew lavish of his favors to me, giving me to understand that I should continue in his service and he would amply provide for me.

At this time I paid my respects to the Cardinal, his brother, who requested the Duke to give me permission to make his pontifical seal, which I immediately took in hand. While I was employed about this work, a quartan fever attacked me, and I grew delirious; then began to curse Mantua, and its sovereign, and all that chose it for their place of residence. These words were reported to the Duke by his Milanese goldsmith, who saw plainly that his Excellency had a desire to retain me in his service. The Duke was incensed against me to the highest degree, and as I was equally dissatisfied with Mantua, our disgust was reciprocal. I finished the seal in about four months, with several other little works that I executed for the Duke in the name of the Cardinal, and was well paid by the latter, who entreated me to return to Rome, to that excellent country where we had become acquainted.

I left Mantua with a good purse, and arrived at Governo, where the brave Signor Giovanni de' Medici was slain. I was attacked in this place by a slight fever, which did not in the least interrupt my journey; there it left me, never to trouble me afterward. On my arrival at Florence, thinking to find my dear father alive, I knocked at the door; when a hump-backed old woman, in a violent rage, looked out of the window, and bidding me, with the most abusive language, be gone, told me I had infected her. I made answer to the hag, "Old beldame, is there no other face to be seen in this house but you, with your unlucky ill-boding voice?" "No! begone, and bad luck to you!" she retorted. I rebuked her sharply; and it was more than two hours before our dispute brought a woman in the neighborhood to her window, who told me that my father and all belonging to my family were dead of the plague; and as I had guessed this to be the case, my grief was the less violent. The good woman told me also that the only one of my relatives left alive was my younger sister, whose name was Liperata; and that a religious lady, Mona Andrea de Bellacci, had taken care of her. I then set out for my inn, and accidentally meeting a friend of mine, Giovanni Rigogli, I alighted at his house, and we went together to the grand square, where I received information that my brother was still living, of whom I went in quest to the house of a friend of his, Bertino Aldobrandi.

When I found my brother, we embraced each other with the utmost ardor of affection, and what rendered our demonstrations of joy the more rapturous was, that we had each received news of the other's death. My brother afterward bursting into a loud fit of laughter, and at the same time expressing the utmost surprise, took me by the hand, and said: "Come, brother, I will conduct you to a place you would never think of. The case is this: I have procured our sister Liperata, who has no doubt of your death, a second husband." While we were going to her house, we related to each other the many extraordinary events that had befallen us; and when we reached the place, our sister was so astonished at the unexpected sight that she fell into my arms in a swoon.

My brother and sister prevailed upon me to remain at Florence, though my own inclination led me to return to Rome. Besides that, my dear friend, by whom I had been assisted in my distress—I mean Piero, the son of Giovanni Landi—joined with them in persuading me to reside some time in Florence, as the Medici family had been driven out of that city—viz., Signor Ippolito and Signor Alessandro (one of whom was afterward cardinal, and the other Duke of Florence). I therefore began to work in the New Market, and set a great number of jewels.

About this time arrived at Florence a native of Siena, a man of lively genius, whose name was Girolamo Mazetti, and who had resided a long time in Turkey. He employed me to make him a golden medal, to be worn upon a hat. He instructed me to represent upon the medal the figure of Hercules tearing asunder the jaws of the lion. I set about the work at once, and while I was employed upon it Michelangelo Buonarroti came to see it. I had taken great pains with this piece; the attitude and strength of the animal were better represented than in any previous performance of the kind. My manner of working was entirely new to the divine Michelangelo, and he praised me to such a degree that I conceived the strongest inclination imaginable to perform something extraordinary. But as I had no other employ than setting jewels, though I could not earn more money in any other branch, I was not yet satisfied, but wished to be concerned in business of more consequence.

It happened about this time that one Federigo Ginori, a young man of sublime genius (who had resided several years at Naples, and, having a very attractive person, had an intrigue with a princess in that city), conceived a fancy for a medal representing Atlas with a world upon his shoulders. He therefore requested the divine Michelangelo to draw him a design. The latter said to him, "Go to a young jeweler whose name is Benvenuto; he will serve you as well as you could wish. But, that you may not think I shun so slight a trouble, I will, with all the pleasure imaginable, sketch you out a design. At the same time speak to Benvenuto to draw you another, and take the better of the two for your model."

Federigo Ginori came to me accordingly, and told me what he wanted, letting me know withal how highly the divine Michelangelo had commended me; that that great man had promised him a design; and that I was also to make a little waxen model. I accordingly set about it with the utmost ardor of application. When I had finished it, a painter, who was an intimate friend of Michelangelo, and whose name was Giuliani Bugiardini, brought me his design of the Atlas. At the same time I showed this Giuliani my little model of wax, which was very different from the drawing made by Michelangelo. Federigo and Bugiardini determined that I should follow my own model. I then began my work, and the divine Michelangelo bestowed the highest praises imaginable, both on me and on my performance. This work was a figure engraved on a thin plate, supporting on its shoulders the heavens, represented by a ball of crystal, on which was cut the zodiac, with a field of lapis lazuli. The effect was exceedingly fine. Under it was this motto, *Summam tulisse juvat*. Federigo, being satisfied with my performance, paid me generously.

Signor Luigi Alamanni, an intimate friend of Federigo, happening to be at this time in Florence, the latter brought him several times to my house, and we became intimately acquainted.

Pope Clement having declared war against Florence, that city prepared to make a defence; orders were therefore given that the militia should muster in every quarter, and I was commanded to take arms myself. I got ready in the best manner I could, and exercised with the first nobility in Florence, who seemed all very well disposed to exert their utmost efforts in defence of their country. The prayers customary on such occasions were made in every quarter of the city. The young men were oftener assembled than usual, and nothing else was talked of but how to repel the enemy. It happened one day, about noon, that several gallant youths, of the first quality in the city, were assembled in my shop, when a letter was brought me from a certain person at Rome, who was called Jacopino della Barca. His true name was Jacopo della Sciorina, but in Rome he had the appellation of "della Barca," because he was master of a ferry over the river Tiber, between the Ponte Sisto and the Ponte St. Angelo. This Jacopo was very ingenious, highly entertaining and agreeable in company. He had formerly been a manufacturer of cloth in Florence, and was now in high favor with Pope Clement, who took great delight in his conversation. As they happened, at a particular time, to be conversing on various topics, the sack of Rome was mentioned, with the affair of the castle. In the course of this conversation, the Pope, recollecting my services, spoke of my conduct on that occasion in the most favorable terms imaginable; adding, that if he knew where I was he should be glad to have me again in his service. Master Jacopo thereupon told him that I resided at Florence, and the Pope requested him to invite me to return. The purport of this invitation was, that I should enter into the service of Pope Clement, which would be considerably to my advantage The young gentlemen present were very earnest to know the contents of the letter, which I endeavored to conceal from them; and I wrote to Signor Jacopo, requesting him to send me no more letters, on any account.

Jacopo, however, growing still more officious and obstinate, wrote me a second epistle, couched in such terms that, if it had been discovered, I might have been involved in great difficulty. The substance of it was, that I should go directly to Rome, where the Pope wished to employ me in affairs of the greatest importance; and that the best course for me to take was to drop all other projects, and not join with a pack of senseless rebels in acting against his Holiness.

When I had perused this letter, I was so much alarmed that I immediately went in quest of my dear friend Pier Landi, who, upon seeing me, asked what had happened, that I appeared to be in such disorder. I answered that I could by no means disclose what occasioned my uneasiness; I only begged of him to take my keys, which I put into his hands, and deliver the jewels, with the gold he should find, to the persons whose names were set down in my memorandum-book; and then pack up the furniture of my house, and keep an account of it, with his usual fidelity and friendship; adding that in a few days, I should let him know what had become of me. Pier Landi, guessing pretty nearly how the matter stood, made answer: "Brother, go your way without loss of time, and write to me afterward. Make yourself quite easy about your affairs, and do not give yourself the least concern on that account." I took his advice. This was the most faithful, the most prudent, virtuous, and loving friend that I ever had in my whole life.

CHAPTER IX

ENGRAVER TO THE MINT

AFTER I had retired from Florence, I went to Rome. There was an old goldsmith in that city, named Raffaello del Moro, who had a high reputation in his profession, and was moreover an honest man. He requested me to go to work in his shop, because he had some business of consequence upon his hands, which could not fail to be of good account. I readily accepted the offer. Ten days elapsed before I saw Jacopo della Barca, who, meeting me by chance, accosted me in the most affectionate manner imaginable. When he asked me how long I had been there I answered, about a fortnight. At this he was highly offended, telling me that I showed very little respect to a Pope who had written for me thrice in terms the most pressing. I was not at all pleased with his freedom, yet made no reply, suppressing my indignation as well as I could. This person, who was exceedingly loquacious, began to run on at a strange rate; and when at last I perceived that he was tired, I merely said that he might conduct me to his Holiness whenever he thought proper.

As soon as his Holiness saw me, he was overjoyed. I approached him in the most humble manner, kissed his feet, and endeavored to show by my gestures that I had something of the last importance to communicate. The Pope thereupon made a sign with his hand, and Signor Jacopo Salviati and the archbishop retired to a considerable distance. I thereupon addressed his Holiness in these terms: "Holy Father, ever since this city was sacked, I have been unable to confess and receive the sacrament, because nobody will give me absolution. The case is this: when I melted down the gold in the tower, after laboring so hard to take off the jewels, your Holiness charged the master of the horse to give me some little recompense for my trouble; but I received nothing from him. On the contrary, he loaded me with abusive language. Thus provoked, I went up to the place where I had melted the gold, and removing the ashes, took out about a pound and a half of that metal, in a number of grains, small like millet; and not having sufficient money to bear my charges in my journey home, I thought to apply them to my private use, and afterward make restitution when I should have an opportunity. I am now here at the feet of your Holiness, who are possessed of the full power of absolving, and request you would be so good as to give me permission to confess and communicate, that I may with your favor be restored to the divine grace."

The Pope, with a faint sigh, perhaps occasioned by the remembrance of his sorrows, uttered these words: "Benvenuto, I have not the least doubt of the truth of what you say; I have it in my power, and am even willing, to absolve you from any guilt you may have incurred. Therefore freely and with confidence confess the whole; for if you had taken the value of one of those triple crowns, I am ready and willing to pardon you." I then said: "Holy Father, I took nothing but what I have mentioned, and its value was not more than one hundred and fifty ducats; for that was the sum I received for the gold at the mint of Perugia, and I went with it to assist my aged father." The Pope replied: "Your father was as virtuous, good, and worthy a man as ever was born, and you do not in the least degenerate from him. I am very much concerned that you got so little money, but I make you a present of it, whatever it was, and absolve you of any crime you may have committed. Declare this to the confessor, if that be all you require; when you have confessed and communicated, let me see you again; it will be for your interest."

I then went to execute all that I had agreed for with the Pope; and when the two festivals were over, I paid him another visit. His Holiness received me still more graciously than before, and told me that if I had come a little sooner to Rome I should have been employed in resetting the jewels that I had taken out of the two crowns at the castle. As that was not a work in which I could gain great reputation, he was resolved, he said, to employ me in an undertaking of the last importance, in which I should have an opportunity of displaying my abilities. "The work," added he, "I mean, is the button for the pontifical cope, which is made round, and in the form of a large trencher, and sometimes like a small one, half or one third of a cubit wide. In this I would have God the Father represented in half rilievo, and in the midst of it I would have the fine edge of the large diamond set, with many other jewels of the greatest value. Caradosso began one some time ago, but never finished it. This I would have completed with all speed, for I should be glad to have the pleasure of wearing it a little while myself. Go and draw a fine design for it."

During the siege of Florence, Federigo Ginori, for whom I made the medal of Atlas, died of consumption, and it fell into the hands of Signor Luigi Alamanni, who soon made a present of it to King Francis I, together with some of his admirable writings. His Majesty being highly pleased with the medal, the worthy Luigi Alamanni spoke of me in such favorable terms to that monarch, that he intimated a desire to know me. Being now employed on this little model, I proceeded with the utmost expedition, making it about the same size as that intended for the work itself. Meanwhile several persons of my profession, who thought themselves equal

to such a task, began to stir upon the occasion, and
among the rest one Micheletto, who had not been long
in Rome, a person noted for his skill in cutting carnelians, and an excellent jeweler. This man was advanced in years, and, having acquired a high reputation,
was employed in adjusting the Pope's triple diadem.
Finding that I was engaged in designing this model, he
expressed great surprise that I had not informed him
of the affair, as he was an intelligent man, and in great
favor with the Pope. At last, perceiving that I did not
go near him, he came to my house, and asked me what
I was about. I answered that I was busy with a work
that was put into my hands by the Pope himself. He
replied that he had received orders to examine the several works then in hand for his Holiness. I told him
I would first inquire of the Pope, and then I should know
what answer to return him. Upon which he said that
he would make me repent.

In a few days I had completed my model, and carried
it one morning to the Pope. Signor Trajano made me
wait a long while, and in the mean time sent for Micheletto and Pompeo in all haste, desiring them to bring
their models with them. As soon as they came, we were
all admitted. Micheletto and Pompeo began to show
their plans, and the Pope to examine them; and because
designers unacquainted with the jeweling business do
not understand the placing of precious stones, unless
those that are practised in the art have taught them the
secret (for when a figure is to be set off with jewels,
the jeweler must know how to design, otherwise he can
produce nothing good), it happened that all those who
had drawn those designs had laid the fine, large, and
beautiful diamond in the middle of the breast of God the
Father. The Pope, who was a person of uncommon
genius, having taken notice of this blunder, was highly
delighted with his own discovery. After he had in-

6

spected about ten, he threw the rest upon the ground, and said, "Let us now see what Benvenuto has," desiring me to give him my model, that he might ascertain whether I had committed the same mistake. Thereupon I came forward, and opened a little round box, when instantly there seemed to flash from it a luster that dazzled the Pope himself, and he cried out, "Benvenuto, had you been my very self, you could not have designed this otherwise than you have. Your rivals have done everything they could to disgrace themselves." Several nobles approaching, the Pope showed them the difference between the models; and when he had bestowed sufficient praises upon it, and my enemies appeared ready to burst with wounded pride and vexation, he turned to me and said, "I discover here an inconvenience which is of the utmost consequence. My friend Benvenuto, it is easy to work in wax, the grand difficulty is to execute it in gold." To which I answered boldly, "Most holy Father, I will make it my bargain with you, that if I do not execute the work itself in a manner ten times superior to this model I am to have nothing for my trouble." When I uttered these words there was a general outcry, the noblemen affirming that I promised too much. But one of them, who was a great philosopher, said, "From the admirable symmetry of shape and happy physiognomy of this young man, I venture to engage that he will perform all he promises, and more." The Pope replied, "I am of the same opinion;" then calling to Trajano, his gentleman of the bedchamber, he ordered him to bring five hundred ducats.

While they were bringing the money, he examined more minutely the ingenious artifice by which I had placed that fine diamond, and God the Father, in a proper position. I had laid the diamond exactly in the middle of the work, and over it I had represented God the Father sitting in a sort of free, easy attitude, which suited admirably well with the rest of the piece, and did not in the least crowd the diamond; his right hand was lifted, giving his blessing. Under the diamond I had drawn three little boys, who supported it with their arms raised aloft. One of these boys, who stood in the middle, was in full rilievo, the other two in half. Round it were several figures of boys placed amongst other glittering jewels. The remainder of God the Father was covered with a mantle, which waved in the wind, whence issued several figures of boys, with other striking ornaments, most beautiful to behold. This work was made of a white stucco upon a black stone. When the officer brought the money, the Pope gave it to me with his own hand, and in the most obliging manner requested me to endeavor to please him by my execution, promising that I should find my account in it.

Having taken leave of his Holiness, I went home with the money and the model, and was in the utmost impatience to begin the work. I set about it with the greatest assiduity, and in a week the Pope sent one of his gentlemen of the bedchamber, a native of Bologna, of great distinction, to ask if I would come to him directly, and bring my work with me. By the way, the gentleman of the bedchamber, who was one of the politest persons at court, told me that the Pope not only wanted to see how far I had advanced in that undertaking, but likewise intended to employ me in another business of great importance, which was the stamping of the coins in the Roman Mint, desiring me at the same time to be in readiness to answer his Holiness, for he had given me previous notice, that I might not be unprepared. I waited upon his Holiness, and showed him the golden plate, upon which was engraved God the Father alone; which figure, even in this sketch, discovered a degree of perfection greatly superior to the model of wax. The Pope exclaimed with astonishment, "From this time I will believe whatever you say." After several other declarations in my favor, he added, "I propose employing you in another work, which you will be as much pleased with as this, or rather more, if you have but the spirit to undertake it." Then, telling me that he would be glad to have his coins struck, he wished to know whether I had ever done anything in that way, and had the courage to engage in such a work. I answered that I was very ready to accept it, and that I had seen how it was done, though I never had been employed in that business.

There was present at this conversation, Signor Tommaso da Prato, datary to his Holiness. This man, being attached to my enemies, said, upon the occasion, "Holy Father, the favors you lavish upon this young man, and his own presumption, would make him promise you a new creation; but as you have put a work of vast importance into his hands, and now are giving him another of still greater, the consequence must be that one will interfere with the other." The Pope turned about to him in an indignant mood, and bade him mind his own business. He then ordered me to make him a model of a broad piece of gold, upon which he wished to have engraved a naked Christ with his hands tied behind him, and the words *Ecce Homo*, as a legend; with a reverse on which should be represented a pope and an emperor together, fixing up a cross, which should appear to be falling, with these words inscribed, *Unus spiritus et una fides erat in eis*. The Pope having employed me to stamp this fine medal, Bandinello, the sculptor, who was not yet made a knight, came forward, and with his usual presumption and ignorance said, before all present, "These goldsmiths must have some person to draw the designs of these fine pieces for them." I immediately turned about and told him that I did not want his assistance in my business; and that I hoped by my skill and designs in a short time to give him some uneasiness with respect to his own professional reputation. The Pope said, "Go, my dear Benvenuto, exert your utmost efforts to serve me, and never mind these blockheads." So, having taken my leave, I, with great expedition, made two dies; and having stamped a piece of gold, I carried both the money and the dies to the Pope one Sunday after dinner. He then said his surprise was equal to his satisfaction; and though the execution pleased him highly, he was still more amazed at my expedition.

In order to increase his satisfaction and surprise, I had brought with me all the old coins that had formerly been struck by those able artists, who had been in the service of Pope Julius and Pope Leo; and seeing that mine gained much higher approbation, I took a petition out of my bosom, requesting to be made stamp-master to the mint, the salary annexed to which place was six gold crowns a month. Besides that, the dies were afterward paid for by the superintendent of the mint, who for three gave a ducat. The Pope, having approved of my request, charged the datary to make out my commission; but the latter said, "Holy Father, do not so precipitate matters; things of this nature require mature deliberation." The Pontiff replied, "I know what you would be at; give me that petition directly." Having taken it, he instantly signed it, and putting it into the hand of the datary, said, "Now you have no further objections to make, draw up the commission at once, for such is my pleasure; the very shoes of Benvenuto are more precious than the eyes of all those blunderers."

CHAPTER X

A DISAPPOINTMENT IN LOVE

I CONTINUED still to work in the shop of Raffaello del Moro. This worthy man had a handsome young daughter, respecting whom he formed a design on me; and I, having partly discovered his views, felt well disposed to second them. I did not, however, make the least discovery of the affair, but was so discreet and circumspect that her father was highly pleased with my behavior. This girl was attacked by a disorder in her right hand, which corroded the two bones belonging to the little finger and the one next to it. Through the inadvertency of her father, she had fallen into the hands of an ignorant quack, who declared it as his opinion that she would lose her right arm, if no worse were to befall her. Seeing her father terribly frightened, I told him not to mind what was said by that ignorant pretender. He said he had no acquaintance with either physicians or surgeons, and requested me to recommend him a skilful person, if I knew any such: I then sent for one Signor Jacopo of Perugia, an eminent surgeon. As soon as he had seen the girl, and been informed what the quack had said, he affirmed that she was in no danger, but that she would have the full use of her right hand, though two fingers might remain somewhat weak. As he had undertaken the cure, and was preparing to cut off part of the diseased flesh about the two little bones, her father called me, and asked that I be a spectator of the operation.

Having observed that Signor Jacopo was making use of some clumsy instruments, with which he hurt the girl very much, and did her no manner of good, I bade him wait for about a quarter of an hour. I then ran to my shop, and made a little instrument of the finest steel, which I delivered to the surgeon, who continued his operation with so gentle a hand that the patient did not feel the least pain, and the affair was soon over. Upon this and many other accounts the worthy man conceived so warm a friendship for me that he seemed to love me better than his two sons, who were grown young men, and applied his own attention to the recovery of his fair daughter.

I attached myself with unremitting application to my work, which I was in haste to finish, and likewise attended to my business at the Mint, when the Pope set me to make a piece equal in value to two carlins, upon which was his Holiness's head, on the reverse, Christ walking on the sea and stretching out his hands to St. Peter, with this inscription round it, *Quare dubitasti?* This piece gave such high satisfaction that a certain secretary to the Pope, a man of great worth, named Sanga, said on the occasion, "Your Holiness may boast of having a coin superior to that of the Roman emperors, amidst all their pomp and magnificence." The Pope made answer, "Benvenuto may also boast of serving a prince like me, who knows his merit." I continued my grand work in gold, frequently showing it to the Pope, who was very earnest to see it and every day expressed new admiration at the performance.

A brother of mine was at this time in Rome, in the service of Duke Alessandro, for whom the Pope had procured the duchy of Penna; in the same service were also a considerable number of gallant men, trained in the school of that great prince, Giovanni de' Medici; and my brother was esteemed by the Duke, as one of the bravest of the whole corps. Happening one day, after dinner, to be in the part of the town called Banchi, at the shop of Baccino della Croce, to which all those brave fellows resorted, he had lain down on a bench, and was overcome with sleep. At this time a company of city guards passed by, having in their custody one Captain Cisti, a Lombard, who had been bred likewise in the school of the same great Signor Giovanni, but was not then in the service of the duke. Captain Cattivanza degli Strozzi happening to be in the shop of Baccino della Croce, Captain Cisti saw him, and cried out, "I was bringing you that large sum of money that I owed you. If you want it, come for it, before they carry me to jail." This Cattivanza was very ready to put the courage of others to the proof, but did not care to take any risk himself; and as some gallant youths were present, who were willing to undertake the hazardous enterprise, though hardly strong enough for it, he desired them to advance toward Captain Cisti, in order to get the money from him, and, in case the guards made any resistance, to overpower them if necessary. These four young men were all beardless. The first was Bertino Aldobrandi, the second Anguillotto da Lucca; I cannot recollect the names of the rest. Bertino had been pupil to my brother, who was beyond measure attached to him. These four bold young men came up to the city guards, who numbered more than fifty pikemen, musketeers, and two-handed swordsmen. After a few words they drew their swords, and the four youths pressed the guards so hard that if Captain Cattivanza had only just shown himself a little, even without drawing his sword, they would inevitably have put their adversaries to flight; but as the latter made a stand for a while, Bertino received some dangerous wounds, which brought him to the ground. Anguillotto too, at the same time, was wounded in his right arm, and being so far disabled that he could not hold his sword, he retreated; whereupon the others followed his example. Bertino was taken up in a dangerous condition.

During this transaction we were all at table, having dined about an hour later than usual. On hearing of the disturbance, the eldest of the young men rose from table, to go and see the encounter: his name was Giovanni. I said to him, "For God's sake, do not go hence, for in such affairs as this the loss is always certain, and there is nothing to be gained." His father spoke to him to the same effect, begging he would not leave the room. The youth, without minding a word that was said to him, instantly ran downstairs. Being come to the place where the grand confusion was, and seeing Bertino raised from the ground, he began to turn back, when he met with my brother Cecchino, who asked him the cause of this quarrel. Giovanni, though warned by some persons not to tell the affair to Cecchino, cried out, foolishly and indiscreetly, that Bertino Aldobrandi had been murdered by the city guards. At this my brother set up a loud howl, and said to Giovanni, "Alas! unhappy wretch that I am—can you tell me which of them it was that killed him?" Giovanni made answer that it was one who wore a large two-handed sword, with a blue feather in his hat. My poor brother having followed the guards, and knowing the person by the mark he had been told of, fell upon the murderer with great agility and bravery, and in spite of all resistance ran his sword through his body, pushing him with the hilt of it to the ground. He then assailed the rest with such intrepidity that he alone and unassisted would have put all the guards to flight. But unluckily, when he turned about to attack a musketeer, the latter, finding himself obliged to fire in his own defence, hit the valiant but unfortunate youth just above the right knee, which brought him to the ground; whereupon the guards made haste to retreat, lest some other formidable champion should fly to his assistance.

Finding the tumult continue, I likewise rose from table, and, putting on my sword, as swords were then worn by everybody, I went to the bridge of St. Angelo, where I saw a great concourse. I advanced up to the crowd, and as I was known to some of them, room was made for me, when they showed me what I by no means was pleased to see, though I had discovered a great curiosity to inquire into the matter. At my first coming up, I did not know my brother, for he was dressed in different clothes from those I had seen him in a short time before; but he knew me at once, and said, "Dear brother, do not be afflicted at my misfortune; it is what I, from my condition of life, foresaw and expected. Get me quickly removed from this place, for I have but few hours to live." After he had related to me the accident that had befallen him, with all the brevity that such cases require, I answered him, "Brother, this is the greatest misfortune that could happen to me in this world; but have a good heart, for before you die you shall see me revenge your much-lamented fate."

The city guard was about fifty paces distant from us. Maffio their captain had caused part of them to return, in order to carry off the corporal whom my brother had slain. I walked up to them with the utmost speed, muffled up in my cloak; and as I had forced my way through the crowd, and reached Maffio, I should certainly have put him to death; but when I had drawn my sword half out of the scabbard, behind me came Berlinghieri, a gallant youth, my particular friend, and with him four brave young men, who said to Maffio, "Fly instantly, for this man will kill you!" Maffio having asked them who I was, they answered, "He is the brother of him you see lying there." Not choosing to hear anything further, he retired with the utmost precipitation to the tower of Nona. The others then said to me, "Benvenuto, the hindrance we have been to you, however disagreeable, was intended for a good end. Let us now go to the assistance of the dying man." So we went to my brother, whom I ordered to be removed to a neighboring house.

A consultation of surgeons being immediately called in, they dressed his wound; but he would not hear of having his leg cut off, though it would have been the likeliest way to save his life. As soon as they had done, Duke Alessandro made his appearance, and spoke to my brother with great tenderness. The latter, being still in his right mind, said to his Excellency, "My dear lord, there is nothing I am grieved at but that you are going to lose a servant, who may be surpassed by others in courage and abilities, but will never be equaled for his fidelity and attachment to your person." The Duke hoped he would endeavor to live, declaring that he knew him to be in all respects a valiant and worthy man. He then turned about to his people, and bade them supply the youth with whatever he wanted.

No sooner was the Duke departed, than the flow of blood, which could not be stanched, affected my brother's brain, insomuch that he became the next night delirious. The only sign of understanding he discovered was, that when they brought the sacrament to him, he said, "You would have done well to make me begin with confessing my sins; it does not become me to receive that divine sacrament with this crazy and disordered frame. Let it be sufficient that my eyes behold it with a profound adoration; it will be received by my immortal soul, and that alone supplicates the Deity for mercy and pardon." When he had made an end of these words, and the sacrament was carried away, his delirium returned again. His ravings consisted of the greatest abominations, the strangest frenzies, and the most horrid words that could possibly come from the mouth of man; and thus he continued during the whole night, and till next day. No sooner had the sun appeared on the horizon, than he turned to me and said, "Brother, I do not choose to stay here any longer, for these people might make me commit some extravagant action, which would cause them to repent having any way molested me;" then disengaging both his legs, which we had put into a box, he made an effort as if he were going to mount on horseback, and turning his face about to me, he said three times, "Adieu, adieu, adieu!" At the last word, his generous soul departed. The hour for the funeral being come, which was about ten o'clock at night, I got him honorably interred in the Church of the Florentines; and afterward caused a fine marble monument to be erected over him, on which were represented certain trophies and standards. I must not omit that one of his friends having asked him who it was that shot him, and whether he should know him again, he answered in the affirmative, and told him all the marks by which he might be distinguished; and though he took the utmost care to conceal this declaration from me, I overheard all that passed, and when the opportunity came I avenged him by killing his murderer.

He was twenty-five years of age; and though in the army he was called Cecchino the musician's son, I chose to give him our family name, with the arms of Cellini. This name I ordered to be carved in the finest antique characters, all of which were represented broken except the first and last. Being asked the reason of this by the person who had written the epitah for me, I told them that the letters were represented broken, because his corporeal frame was destroyed; and those two letters, namely, the first and last, were preserved entire—the first in allusion to that glorious present, which God has made us, of a soul enlightened by his divine rays, subject to no injury; the last on account of the great renown of his brave actions.

Meanwhile I exerted my utmost efforts to finish the

work in gold which I was employed in by Pope Clement:
his Holiness was very earnest to have it completed,
and sent for me two or three times a week to observe
my progress. He was more and more pleased with it
every time, but frequently found fault with my deep sorrow for the loss of my brother. Seeing me one day more
dejected than usual, he said to me, "Benvenuto, I did
not think you were so weak a man; did you never know
that death is unavoidable? You seem to wish to follow
your brother." I took my leave of his Holiness, and
went on with the work he had put into my hands, as
well as the business of the Mint.

More than eight days passed without the Pope's once
sending for me according to his usual custom; at last
he ordered the Bolognese gentleman of his bedchamber
to call upon me, who, with great modesty, said that the
Pope knew all that had happened; that his Holiness was
very much my friend, and desired me to go on with my
business, without giving myself any uneasiness. When
I came into the presence of the Pontiff, he frowned upon
me, and with angry looks seemed to reprimand me; but,
upon viewing my performance, his countenance grew
serene, and he praised me highly, telling me that I had
done a great deal in a short time; then looking attentively at me, he said, "Now that you have recovered your
health, Benvenuto, take care of yourself." I understood
his meaning, and told him that I should not neglect his
advice. I opened a fine shop in the place called Banchi,
opposite to Raffaello, and there I finished the work I
had in hand. The Pope soon afterward having sent me
all the jewels except the diamond, which he had pawned
to certain Genoese bankers, in order to supply some
particular necessities, I took possession of all the rest,
but had only the model of the diamond.

I kept five able journeymen, and besides the Pope's
business did several other jobs, insomuch that the shop

contained different wares in jewels, gold, and silver, to a very considerable amount. I had in the house a fine large shock-dog, which Duke Alessandro had presented to me. It was an admirably good pointer, for it would bring to me all sorts of birds, and other animals, that I shot; and it was an excellent house-dog besides. It happened about this period (as my time of life permitted, I being then only in my twenty-ninth year) that, having taken into my service a young woman equally genteel and beautiful, I made use of her as a model in my art of drawing; and it was not long before our intimacy assumed an amorous character. My chamber was at a considerable distance from that of my workpeople, and also from my shop; and although in general no man's sleep is lighter than mine, on some occasions it is very profound.

It happened one night that a thief, who had been at my house, pretending to be a goldsmith, and had laid a plan to rob me of the above-mentioned jewels, watched his opportunity and broke into my shop, where he found several small wares in gold and silver; but as he was breaking open the caskets in order to come at the jewels, the dog flew at him, and the thief found it a difficult matter to defend himself with a sword. The faithful animal ran several times about the house, entering the journeymen's rooms, which were open, it being then summer-time; but as they did not seem to hear him barking, he drew away the bed-clothes, and pulling the men alternately by the arms, forcibly awakened them; then, barking very loud, he showed the way to the thieves, and went on before; but they would not follow him. The scoundrels being quite provoked with the noise of the dog, began to throw stones and sticks at him (which they found an easy matter, as I had given them orders to keep a light in their room the whole night), and at last locked their door. The dog, having lost all hope of the assistance of these rascals, undertook the task alone, and ran downstairs. He could not find the villain in the shop, but came up with him in the street, and, tearing off his cloak, would certainly have treated him according to his deserts, if the fellow had not called to some tailors in the neighborhood, and begged, for the love of God, they would assist him against a mad dog. The tailors, giving credit to what he said, came to his assistance and with great difficulty drove away the poor animal. Next morning, when my young men went down into the shop, they saw it broken open, and all the caskets rifled; upon which they began to make a loud outcry, and I coming to them quite terrified, they said, "Alas, we are undone; the shop has been plundered by a villain, who has broken all the caskets and carried off everything valuable." Such an effect had these words upon my mind, that I had not the heart to go to the chest, to see whether the Pope's jewels were safe; but being quite shocked at the report, and scarce able to trust my own eyes, I bade them open it, and see whether his Holiness's jewels were missing. When the young men, who were in their shirts, found all the Pope's jewels, as likewise the work in gold, they were overjoyed, and said "There is no harm done, since both the work and the jewels are untouched. The thief, however, has stripped us to our shirts; for, as the heat was excessive last night, we undressed in the shop, and there left our clothes." Hearing this, I perfectly recovered my spirits, and desired them to provide themselves with clothes, as I would pay for whatever damage had been done.

When I had heard the whole affair at my leisure, what gave me most concern, and had thrown me into great confusion at opening the chest, was my apprehension lest I should be thought to have invented this story of the thief, merely with a design to rob the Pope of his jewels. Besides, it had been said to Pope Clement, by one of his greatest confidants, and others, that they were surprised how his Holiness could trust such a quantity of jewels with a wild young man who was more soldier than an artist, and not yet quite thirty. The Pope asked whether they had ever known me guilty of anything that could justly give ground for suspicion. "Most holy Father," answered Francesco del Nero, "I have not, for he never had any such opportunity before." To this the Pope replied, "I take him to be an honest man in every respect, and if I thought him otherwise, I should not trust him." This suddenly recurring to my memory, gave me all the uneasiness I have described before.

As soon as I had ordered my journeymen to go and get themselves new clothes, I took both the work and the jewels, and putting them in their places as well as I could, went directly to the Pope, who had been told something of the adventure of my shop by Francesco del Nero. The Pope thereupon conceiving a sudden suspicion, and giving me a most stern look, said with a harsh tone, "What are you come hither about? What's the matter?" To this I answered, "Holy Father, here are all your jewels and the gold; nothing is missing." His Holiness, with a serene brow, said, in allusion to my name, "Then are you indeed *welcome*." I showed him my work, and while he was examining it, told him the whole affair of the thief, the dilemma I had been in, and what had been the chief cause of my uneasiness. At these words he frequently looked me full in the face, in the presence of Francesco del Nero, seeming to be half sorry that he had not opposed that man's insinuations. At last the Pope turning all he had heard into merriment, said, "Go and continue to show yourself an honest man; I know you deserve that character."

CHAPTER XI

DISCOURAGEMENTS

WHILE I continued to go on with the work, and at the same time did business for the Mint, certain false coins impressed with my dies appeared in Rome, which my enemies carried to the Pope, endeavoring to fill him with new suspicions. The Pope ordered Giacopo Balducci, master of the Mint, to use his utmost endeavors to discover the offender, that my innocence might be manifest to the world. This treacherous man, being my sworn enemy, said, "God send, most holy Father, that it may turn out as you say, and that we may have the good fortune to detect the criminal." The Pope thereupon turned about to the Governor of Rome, and ordered him to exert all his diligence to discover the delinquent. At the same time his Holiness sent for me, and with great art and address entering upon the affair of the false coins, said, "Benvenuto, do you think you could find it in your heart to make counterfeit money?" I answered, that I thought myself much better able to counterfeit coins than the low fellows that were usually guilty of that crime; for, I added, "the men that commit such offences are not persons of any great genius that can gain much by their business. Now, if I with my slender abilities, make such profits that I have always money to spare, (for when I made the dies for the Mint, I every day before dinner gained at least three crowns, so much being always paid me for those instruments; but the stupid master of the Mint hated me, because he fain would have reduced them to a lower price), what I gain with the favor of God and man is enough for me, with-

7

out resorting to the infamous and less profitable trade of
false coining."

When I had at last finished my work, a great inundation overflowed the whole city. As I was waiting
the issue, the day being far spent, the waters began to
increase. The fore part of my house and shop was in
the quarter of Banchi, and the back part jutted out
several cubits toward Monte Giordano. Making the preservation of my life my first care, and my honor the
next, I put all my jewels in my pockets, left my work
in gold under the care of my journeymen, and, taking
off my shoes and stockings, went out at a back window,
and waded through the water as well as I could, till I
reached Monte Cavallo. There I found Signor Giovanni Gaddi, a clerk of the chamber, and Bastiano, the
Venetian painter. Accosting Signor Giovanni, I gave
him all my jewels to take care of, knowing he had as
great a regard for me as if I had been his brother. A
few days later, the waters having subsided, I returned
to my shop, and finished my work with the help of God
and by my own industry so happily, that it was looked
upon as the most exquisite performance of the kind
that ever had been seen in Rome. On carrying it to the
Pope, I thought he never would have been tired of
praising it.

After the Pope had made an end of his rodomontade,
I asked him for a mace-bearer's place, which had just
become vacant. He answered that it was his intention
to give me a much more considerable employ. I again
desired his Holiness to grant me that other trifling post
by way of earnest. He replied, with a laugh, that he
was willing to gratify me, but did not choose I should
serve with the common mace-bearers. He advised me
therefore to make it my agreement with them to be
exempt from attendance; and to get me excused, he
would grant them a favor for which they had applied

to him, viz.: to be allowed to demand their salaries by authority; which accordingly was done. This place brought me more than two hundred crowns a year.

While I continued in the service of the Pope, sometimes employed by him in one way, sometimes in another, he ordered me to draw a fine chalice for him; and I accordingly sketched a design and model of such a cup. This model was of wood and wax. Instead of the boss of the chalice, I had made three little figures representing Faith, Hope, and Charity. On the foot of it I represented the stories relative to those figures on three bosses in basso rilievo—on one was the nativity of Christ, on another the resurrection, on a third St. Peter crucified with his head downward—for in that attitude I was ordered to draw him.

During the progress of this work the Pope several times desired to see it; but finding that his Holiness had quite forgotten to give me any preferment, the place of one of the fraternity del Piombo (the seal-office) being vacant, I one evening asked him for it. The good Pope, no longer recollecting the florid harangue he had made upon my finishing the other work, answered me thus: "The place you ask has a salary of more than eight hundred crowns a year, so that if you were to have it you would think of nothing afterward but indulging yourself and pampering your body; thus you would entirely forget that admirable art of which you are at present so great a master, and I should be condemned as the cause of it." I instantly replied that good cats mouse better to fatten themselves than merely through hunger; and that men of genius exert their abilities always to most purpose when they are in affluent circumstances; insomuch that those princes who are most munificent to such men may be considered as encouraging, and, as it were, watering the plants of genius, which left to themselves wither and die away; it is encouragement alone that makes them spring up and flourish. "I must, however, inform your Holiness," I added, "that I did not petition for this preferment expecting to have it granted me; I looked upon myself as happy in getting the poor place of mace-bearer: it was only a transient thought that just came into my head. You will do well to bestow it upon some man of genius that deserves it, and not upon an ignorant person who will make no other use of it but to pamper his body, as your Holiness expresses it. Take example of Pope Julius, of worthy memory, who gave such a place to Bramante, an ingenious architect." Having spoken thus, I made him a low bow and took my leave.

Bastiano, the Venetian painter, then coming forward, said to him, "Most holy Father, please to give this place to some person that exerts himself in the ingenious arts; and as your Holiness knows me to have dedicated my time to those studies, I humbly request you would think me worthy of that honor." The Pope made answer, "This devil Benvenuto cannot bear a word of rebuke. I did intend to bestow the place upon him; but it is not right to behave so proudly to a Pope; I therefore do not know how I shall dispose of it." The Bishop of Vaison, suddenly coming forward, took Bastiano's part, and said, "Most holy Father, Benvenuto is a young man, the sword becomes him much better than the monk's habit. Please your Holiness to bestow it upon this ingenious man, Bastiano, and you may give Benvenuto some other lucrative place that will suit him better." The Pope then, turning to Signor Bartolomeo Valori, said to him, "How much too hard you are for Benvenuto! Tell him that he himself was the cause of the place he applied for being given to Bastiano, the painter; and that he may depend upon it, he shall have the first lucrative post that becomes vacant. In the mean time, request him to exert himself and finish my business."

The evening following, two hours after sunset, I happened to meet Signor Bartolommeo Valori hard by the Mint, as he was driving on precipitately with two torches before him, being sent for by the Pope. He called out to me, and in the most friendly manner told me all that his Holiness had said. I answered, that I would finish the work I had in hand with greater diligence than I had shown on any other occasion, but without hope of being recompensed by his Holiness. Signor Bartolommeo thereupon reprimanded me, adding that I should not receive the offers of a Pope in that manner. I replied that if I were to depend upon such promises before they took effect, I should be a fool. Signor Bartolommeo doubtless informed the Pope of my bold answer, and in all probability added something to it; for it was two months before his Holiness sent for me, and during all that time I would not go to court on any account.

His Holiness being upon the point of leaving Rome to go to Bologna, when he found that I never thought of going near him, sent of his own accord Signor Ruberto Pucci to request me to bring my work, for he wished to see how far I had proceeded. I took it with me, and showed his Holiness that the most important part of the work was finished, but requested him to advance me five hundred crowns, partly on account, and partly to buy some more gold, which was wanting to complete the chalice. The Pope said, "Make haste and finish it." I answered, in going away, that I would obey him, if he would leave me money.

The Pope set out for Bologna, leaving Cardinal Salviati his legate in Rome, and ordered him to hurry me on with the work, saying, "Benvenuto is a man that sets but little value upon his abilities, and less upon me; so be sure you hurry him on, that the chalice may be finished at my return." This stupid Cardinal sent for me in about eight days, ordering me to bring my work with me; but I went to him without it. As soon as I came into his presence, he said "Where is this fantastical work of yours? Have you finished it?" I answered, "Most reverend sir, I have not finished my fantastical work, as you are pleased to call it, nor can I finish it, unless you give me wherewithal to enable me." Hardly had I uttered these words when the Cardinal, whose physiognomy was more like that of an ass than a human creature, began to look more hideous than before, and said, "I'll confine you on board of a galley, and then you will be glad to finish the work." As I had a brute to deal with, I used the language proper on the occasion, which was as follows: "My Lord, when I shall be guilty of crimes deserving the galleys, then you may send me thither; but for such an offence as mine, I am not afraid. Nay, I will tell you more; on account of this ill treatment, I will not finish the work at all; so send no more for me, for I will not come, unless I am dragged hither by the city guards." The foolish Cardinal then tried by fair means to persuade me to go on with the work in hand, and to bring what I had done, that he might examine it. In answer to all his persuasions, I said, "Tell his Holiness to send me the materials, if he would have me finish this fantastical work;" nor would I give him any other answer, insomuch that, despairing of success, he at last ceased to trouble me with his importunities.

The Pope returned from Bologna, and immediately inquired after me, for the Cardinal had given him by letter the most unfavorable account of me he possibly could. His Holiness, being incensed against me in the highest degree, ordered me to come to him with my work, and I obeyed. While he was at Bologna, I had so severe a defluxion upon my eyes that life became almost insupportable, which was the first cause of my not proceeding with the chalice. So much did I suffer by this disorder that I really thought I should lose my sight; and I had computed how much would be sufficient for my support when I should be blind.

On my way to the palace I meditated within myself an excuse for discontinuing the work, and thought that while the Pope was considering and examining my performance, I might acquaint him with my case; but I was mistaken, for as soon as I appeared in his presence he said to me, with many unbecoming words, "Let me see that work of yours: is it finished?" When I produced it he flew into a more violent passion than before, and said, "As there is truth in God, I assure you, since you value no living soul, that if a regard to decency did not prevent me, I would order both you and your work to be thrown this moment out of the window." Seeing the Pope thus transformed to a savage beast, I was for quitting his presence directly; and, as he continued his bravadoes, I put the chalice under my cloak, muttering these words to myself, "The whole world would prove unable to make a blind man proceed in such an undertaking as this." The Pope then, with a louder voice than before, said, "Come hither. What is that you say?" For a while I hesitated whether I should not run downstairs. At last I plucked up courage, and, falling on my knees, exclaimed as loud as I could (because he continued to bawl), "Is it reasonable that when I am becoming blind with a disorder, you should oblige me to continue to work?" He answered, "You could see well enough to come hither, and I don't believe one word of what you say." Observing that he spoke with a milder tone, I replied, "If your Holiness will ask your physician, you will find that I declare the truth." "I shall inquire into the affair at my leisure," said he.

I now perceived that I had an opportunity to plead my cause, and therefore delivered myself thus: "I am persuaded, most holy Father, that the author of all this mischief is no other than Cardinal Salviati; because he sent for me immediately upon your Holiness's departure, and, when I came to him, called my work a fantastical trifle, and told me he would make me finish it in a galley. These opprobrious words made such an impression on me that, through the great perturbation of mind I was in, I felt my face all on a sudden inflamed, and my eyes were attacked by so violent a heat that I could hardly find my way home. A few days later two cataracts fell upon them which blinded me to such a degree, that I could hardly see the light, and since your Holiness's departure I have not been able to do a stroke of work." Having spoken thus, I withdrew. I was told that the Pope said after I was gone, "When places of trust are given, discretion is not always conveyed with them. I did not bid the Cardinal treat people quite so roughly. If it be true that he has a disorder in his eyes, as I shall know by asking my physician, I should be inclined to look upon him with an eye of compassion."

There happened to be present a person of distinction, who was a great favorite with the Pope, and equally conspicuous for his virtues and extraordinary endowments. Having inquired of the Pontiff who I was, he added, "Holy Father, I ask you this, because you appeared to me, in the same breath, to fall into a most violent passion and to be equally affected and softened into pity, so I desire to know who he is. If he be a person deserving of assistance, I will tell him a secret to cure his disorder." The Pope made answer, "The person you speak of is one of the greatest geniuses, in his way, that the world ever produced. When I see you again I will show you some of his admirable performances, as likewise the man himself; and it will be a great satisfaction to me, if you are able to do him any service."

In a few days the Pope sent for me after dinner, and the above-mentioned person of distinction was present. No sooner was I come than his Holiness sent for the button of his pontifical cope, which has been already described. In the mean time I produced my chalice; upon seeing which, the gentleman declared he never had beheld so extraordinary a piece of work in his life. The button being brought, his surprise was greatly increased. He looked at me attentively and said, "He is but a young man, and therefore the better able to make a fortune." He then asked me my name. I told him it was Benvenuto. He replied, alluding to my name, "Upon this occasion I am *welcome* to you. Take lily-of-the-valley with its stalk, flower, and beard altogether, distil them with a gentle fire, bathe your eyes with the water several times a day, and you will certainly get rid of your complaint; but before you begin the bathing, take physic."

My disorder, which was serious, contracted at the time of the robbery, had remained latent for four months, and then broke out. The only external symptom was little red blisters, about the size of a farthing, all over me. The physicians would never call this malady by its right name, though I told them the causes to which I ascribed it. They continued to treat me in their own way, but I received no benefit from their prescriptions. At last I resolved, contrary to the advice of the most eminent physicians of Rome, to have recourse to lignum vitæ. This I took with all the precautions and abstinence imaginable, and recovering surprisingly, in fifty days was perfectly cured.

CHAPTER XII

TROUBLE OVER THE CHALICE

CARDINAL Salviati happened about this time to be made legate of Parma, when a certain Milanese goldsmith, named Tobbia, was arrested in that city for counterfeiting the current coin. On his being condemned to the flames, a great man spoke in his favor to the legate. The Cardinal caused the execution to be respited, and wrote to Pope Clement, giving him to understand that there had fallen into his hands one of the ablest artists living in the goldsmith and jewelers' business, and that he had been condemned to be burned alive for coining, but that he was a mere simpleton. This appeared by his saying he had asked the opinion of his confessor, who told him he gave him permission, and that he might do it with a safe conscience. He added, "If your Holiness should send for this great artist to Rome, you will have the means of humbling the pride of your favorite Benvenuto, and I make no doubt but the workmanship of Tobbia will please you much more than Benvenuto's."

The Pope sent for this person to Rome, and on his arrival ordered us both into his presence. He then commanded each of us to draw a design for setting a unicorn's horn, the most beautiful that ever was seen, which had cost 17,000 ducats: and as the Pope purposed making a present of it to King Francis, he chose to have it first richly adorned with gold; so he employed us both to draw the designs.

When we had finished them, we carried them to the Pope. Tobbia's design was in the form of a candlestick; the horn was to enter it like a candle, and at the bottom

of the candlestick he represented four little unicorns'
heads—a most simple invention. As soon as I saw it I
could not avoid smiling at the oddity of the conceit.
The Pope, perceiving this, said, "Let me see that design
of yours." It was a single head of a unicorn, fitted to
receive the horn. I had made the most beautiful sort
of head conceivable, for I drew it partly in the form of
a horse's head, and partly in that of a hart's, adorned
with the finest sort of wreaths and other devices; insomuch that no sooner was my design seen than the whole
court gave it the preference. However, as some Milanese gentlemen of great authority were witnesses of this
contest, they said, "Most holy Father, if you purpose
sending this noble present to France, you should take it
into consideration that the French are an undiscerning,
tasteless people, and will not be sensible of the excellence of this masterly piece of Benvenuto's. But they
will be pleased with these grotesque figures of Tobbia's,
which will be sooner executed; and Benvenuto will in
the mean time finish your chalice. Thus will two works
be completed at once, and this poor man will be employed, without having reason to complain that he has
been brought hither for nothing." The Pope, who was
in haste to have his chalice finished, readily acquiesced
in the opinion of these Milanese; so the day following
he gave the unicorn's horn to Tobbia, and sent word by
his wardrobe-keeper that I was to finish his chalice.

I answered that there was nothing I more ardently
desired than to complete the fine piece of work I was
about; adding, that if it were to be made of any other
materials than gold I could easily finish it myself, and
that without assistance; but that his Holiness must now
supply me with more gold. Hardly had I uttered these
words when this man, a low retainer of the court, bade
me take care how I asked money of the Pope; if I did,
I should put him into such passion, that I should re-

pent it. To this I replied, "Then, good sir, please to inform me how bread can be made without flour; just in the same manner can this work be finished without gold." The wardrobe-keeper, who felt the keenness of the ridicule, told me he would inform his Holiness of all I had said, and was as good as his word. The Pope, flying into a most furious passion, said he would see whether I was mad enough to neglect finishing it. He waited, however, two months, during which, though I had declared I would not work a single stroke, I had wrought constantly with the utmost diligence. The Pope, finding I did not bring the chalice, declared that he was resolved to punish me.

There was present, when he uttered these words, a Milanese, his Holiness's jeweler, named Pompeo, a near relative of one Signor Trajano, who of all Pope Clement's servants was most in his master's favor. These two in concert said to the Pope, "If your Holiness were to deprive him of his place in the Mint, perhaps he would think of finishing the chalice." The Pope replied, "That would rather be productive of two misfortunes— one that I should be ill served at the Mint, which is of the greatest consequence to me, the other that I should certainly never see the chalice." But the two Milanese used such persuasions that at last he deprived me of my place in the Mint, and gave it to a young Perugian, who had the surname of Fagiolo. Pompeo came to tell me that his Holiness had removed me from my place in the Mint, and would deprive me of something else, if I did not make haste to finish my work. "Tell his Holiness," I answered, "that he deprives himself and not me of the place in the Mint; that the case would be the same with respect to other matters; and that if his Holiness should be never so desirous to restore my place to me, I would upon no account accept it."

This vile wretch thought it an age till he could see the

Pope again, in order to repeat to him every word I said, to which he took care to add something of his own. About a week later, the Pope sent me word that he no longer desired I should finish the chalice, but wanted to have it exactly in the state to which I had brought it. I answered, "Pompeo, this is not like the place in the Mint, which it was in his power to deprive me of. Five hundred crowns, which I received, are indeed his Holiness's property, and those I will restore to him; as for the work, it is mine, and that I will dispose of as I think proper." Pompeo hastened to repeat this to the Pope, with some severe and sarcastic expressions, which I threw out against himself, and which he well deserved.

Three days later, on a Thursday, two of the Pope's favorite gentlemen of the bedchamber came to me, and addressed me thus: "The Pope sends us, Benvenuto, because you have trifled with him, and would not be prevailed on by fair means: we have orders, in case you do not give us the chalice, to conduct you directly to prison." I looked them in the face boldly, and said, "Gentlemen, were I to give his Holiness my work, I should give him my property, and not his, and I do not intend to part with anything that is mine; for, as I have brought this piece to a high degree of perfection with the sweat of my brow, I do not choose that it should be put into the hands of some ignorant fellow, who would probably spoil it."

The goldsmith Tobbia was present, and was so rash as to require of me the models of my work. The words with which I answered him would not be proper here to insert. As the gentlemen of the bedchamber pressed me to determine what I intended to do, I told them I had already determined; and having taken my cloak, before I went out of the shop, I turned to an image of Christ, and said with the utmost reverence and devotion, holding my cap in my hand, "Merciful and immortal, just and holy Lord, all that thou dost is according to thy justice, which is not to be equaled. Thou knowest that I am arrived at maturity of years, and that I was never before threatened with imprisonment for any action whatever. Since it is now thy pleasure that I should go to jail, I submit, and thank thee with a heart resigned." Then turning to the two gentlemen, I said to them with a smile, "Surely, gentlemen, a man of my consequence well deserved such a guard as you; therefore put me between you, and conduct me wheresoever you think proper."

These two well-bred gentlemen, laughing very heartily, placed me between them, and chatting all the way, carried me before the Governor of Rome, whose name was Magalotti. The procurator of the Exchequer was with him. The gentlemen, laughing all the while, said to the Governor, "We consign this prisoner to you. Be sure to take proper care of him. We are very glad that we have saved your officers some trouble, for Benvenuto told us that, as this was the first time of his being arrested, meaner guards would have been unworthy of him." They then went to the Pope, and gave him an account of all that had passed.

In the mean time the Governor and the procurator partly rated, partly expostulated with me, and partly gave me their advice, telling me that it was but just and reasonable that he who employs another in any work whatever, should take it back when and in what manner he thinks proper. I answered that this was not agreeable to justice, and that a Pope had no right to act in that manner; because his Holiness was not like those petty tyrants who oppress their subjects to the utmost, paying no regard either to law or justice; but he was Christ's Vicar, and therefore was not allowed to pursue the same measures. The Governor, in a tone and manner that might become a bailiff, cried out, "Benvenuto, Ben-

venuto, you will at last oblige me to use you according
to your deserts." "If so," replied I, "you will behave honorably and politely to me; since I deserve no less." He
then said, "Send for the work directly, and don't make
me speak to you a second time." I thereupon rejoined:
"Gentlemen, do me the favor to permit me to say but
four words more in my defence." The procurator of the
Exchequer, who was more humane than the Governor,
turned about to the latter, and said to him: "My Lord,
indulge him in a hundred words; provided he returns the
work, that is sufficient." I then delivered myself in
these terms: "If a man were to build a house or a
palace, he might justly say to the mason employed in
that business, give me my house; I don't choose you
should work any longer at my palace or my habitation,
and, upon paying the mason for his trouble, he would
have a just right to dismiss him. If it were even a nobleman, who gave directions for setting a jewel worth a
thousand crowns, and if he perceived that the jeweler
did not do it to his mind, he might say, give me my
jewel, for I don't approve of your workmanship. But
the present case is quite different; for neither a house
nor a jewel is here in question: nothing more can be
required of me but that I should return five hundred
crowns, which I have received. So, my Lord, do what
you will, you shall have nothing more than the five
hundred crowns, and this you may tell the Pope. Your
menaces do not in the least intimidate me, for I am an
honest man, and fear God only."

The Governor and procurator of the Exchequer said
they were going to his Holiness, and that, when they
had his orders, they would return to my sorrow.

As soon as the Governor returned with the procurator
of the Exchequer, he called to me and said, "Benvenuto, I am sorry to come back from his Holiness with
so severe an order: either quickly produce the chalice,

or beware of the consequences." I answered that as I could never persuade myself that a vicar of Christ was capable of doing injustice, I would not believe it till I saw it; so that he might do whatever he thought proper. The Governor replied, "I have two words more to say to you from his Holiness, after which I shall proceed to execute my orders. It is the Pope's pleasure you shall bring your work hither, that I may get it put into a box, and then I am to carry it to his Holiness, who promises upon his word to keep it sealed up as he receives it, and will quickly return it to you without ever meddling with it; but he requires that this should be complied with, as his honor is concerned in the affair." To these words I answered, smiling, that I would very readily put my work into his hands in the manner he required, because I was desirous to know what dependence there could be upon the faith of a pope.

Accordingly, having sent for my work, I put it into his hands, sealed up in the manner required. The Governor having returned to the Pope with the box sealed up as above, his Holiness, after turning it several times, as I was afterward informed by the Governor, asked the latter whether he had seen my work? He answered that he had, and it had been sealed up in his presence; adding that it appeared to him a very extraordinary performance. Upon which the Pope said, "You may tell Benvenuto that Roman Pontiffs have authority to loose and bind things of much greater importance than this;" and while he uttered these words, he with an angry look opened the box, taking off the cord and the seal. He then examined it attentively, and, by what I could learn, showed it to Tobbia, the goldsmith, who praised it highly. The Pope asked him whether he would undertake to make a piece of work in the same style, and according to the same model. The other answered that he would. The Pope desired him to follow that model ex-

actly; and, turning to the Governor, spoke to him thus:
"See whether Benvenuto is disposed to let us have it in
its present condition. In case he is ready to comply, he
shall be paid for it whatever price it may be valued at
by any intelligent person. If he is willing to finish it,
let him take his own time, and give him whatever assistance he can reasonably require." Hereupon the
Governor answered, "Most holy Father, I am acquainted
with the audacious character of this young man: grant
me authority to deal sharply with him in my own way."
The Pope replied that he gave him full liberty as to
words, though he was sure he would only make the
breach wider; adding that when he found all ineffectual,
he should order me to carry the five hundred crowns
to his jeweler Pompeo.

The Governor sent for me to his apartment, and addressed me thus, with the bluff air of a grenadier:
"Popes have authority to loose and bind the whole
world; and what they do in this manner upon earth, immediately receives the sanction of heaven. Here is your
box, which has been opened and examined by his Holiness." I then exclaimed, "I return thanks to Heaven
that I am now qualified to set a proper value on the
word of God's vicegerent." The Governor thereupon
offered me many gross insults, both in word and deed;
but perceiving that all his brutality had no effect, he
despaired of success in what he had undertaken, namely,
to browbeat me into compliance. He therefore assumed
a milder tone, and said to me, "Benvenuto, I am sorry
you are blind to your own interest; since that is the case,
carry the five hundred crowns to Pompeo when you
think proper."

Having taken back the box, I went directly to Pompeo with the five hundred crowns. The Pope thought
that, either through inability or some other accident, I
would not carry the money quite so soon; but as he had

8

still a great desire to get me again into his service, when
he saw Pompeo come smiling with the money, he began
to rate him soundly, and expressed great concern that
the affair had taken such a turn.   He then said to him,
"Go to Benvenuto's shop, behave with as much complaisance to him as your stupidity and ignorance will
permit, and tell him that if he will finish that piece
of work, to serve as a shrine for carrying the holy sacrament when I walk in procession with it, I will grant
him whatever favor he desires of me."   Pompeo came
and called me out of the shop, and behaving with a great
deal of awkward ceremony and grimace, repeated all the
Pope had said to him.   I immediately answered that the
highest pleasure I could wish for in this world was to
recover the favor of so great a Pontiff, which I had
lost, not by any fault of my own, but by sickness and
misfortune; as also by the ill offices of those envious
persons who take pleasure in injuring their neighbors.
"But, as his Holiness has a great number of servants,"
I continued, "let him no more send you to me, if he
values your life; and be sure you mind your own business.   I shall never cease by day or night to think and
do all I can to serve the Pope; but remember that you
have spoken ill of me to his Holiness, and never inter-
pose any more in what concerns me.   If you do, I will
make you sensible of your error by treating you according to your deserts."   The fellow repeated every word I
had said to the Pope, but misrepresented it in such a
manner as to make me appear in a much worse light
than I otherwise should have done.   Here the affair
rested for a time, and I again attended to my shop and
business.

CHAPTER XIII

LOVE AND NECROMANCY

ABOUT this time I fell in love, as young men are apt to do. The object of my passion was a Sicilian girl, of extraordinary beauty, who seemed to repay my attachment with an equal ardor. Although we concealed our mutual regard from her mother, the old lady perceived it, and was apprehensive of the consequences. I had indeed formed a design to run away with the girl to Florence, and stay there a year with her, unknown to her mother. The latter, being apprised of my intention, quitted Rome one night with her daughter, and, having taken the road to Naples, gave out that she was going to Civita Vecchia, but went to Ostia. I went to Civita Vecchia, and was on the point of losing my senses or dying of grief.

Two months later, the girl wrote to me that she was in Sicily, extremely unhappy. I was then indulging myself in pleasures of all sorts, and had engaged in another amour to cancel the memory of my Sicilian mistress. Through a variety of odd accidents I made acquaintance with a Sicilian priest, who was a man of genius, and well versed in the Latin and Greek authors. Happening one day to have some conversation with him on the art of necromancy, I told him that I had all my life felt a curiosity to be acquainted with the mysteries of this art. The priest answered that the man must be of a resolute and steady temper who enters upon that study. I replied, that I had fortitude and resolution enough, if I could but find an opportunity. The priest then said, "If you think you have the heart to venture, I will give you all the satisfaction you can desire."

One evening he asked me to look out for a companion or two. I invited one Vincenzio Romoli, who was my intimate acquaintance; and he brought with him a native of Pistoia, who cultivated the black art himself. We went to the Coliseum, and the priest, according to the custom of necromancers, began to draw circles upon the ground with the most impressive ceremonies imaginable. He likewise brought thither assafœtida, several precious perfumes, and fire, with some compositions that diffused noisome odors. As soon as he was in readiness, he made an opening in the circle, and having taken us by the hand one by one, he placed us within it. Then, having arranged the other parts and assumed his wand, he ordered the other necromancer, his partner, to throw the perfumes into the fire at a proper time, entrusting the care of the fire and the perfumes to the rest, and began his incantations. This ceremony lasted more than an hour and a half, when several legions of devils appeared, insomuch that the amphitheater was filled with them.

I was busy about the perfumes when the priest, perceiving there was a considerable number of infernal spirits, turned to me and said, "Benvenuto, ask them something." I answered, "Let them bring me into the company of my Sicilian mistress, Angelica." That night we obtained no answer of any sort; but I had received great satisfaction in having my curiosity so far indulged. The necromancer told me it was requisite we should go a second time, assuring me that I should be satisfied in whatever I asked, but that I must bring with me a pure and immaculate boy.

I took with me a youth who was in my service, about twelve years of age, together with the same Vincenzio Romoli, who had been my companion the first time, and one Agnolio Gaddi, an intimate acquaintance, whom I likewise prevailed on to assist at the ceremony. When we came to the place appointed, the priest, having made his preparations as before, with the same and even more striking ceremonies, placed us within the circle, which he had drawn with a more wonderful art and in a more solemn manner than at our former meeting. Thus having committed the care of the perfumes and the fire to my friend Vincenzio, who was assisted by Agnolino Gaddi, he put into my hand a pintaculo or magical chart, and bade me turn it toward the places that he should direct me; and under the pintaculo I held my boy. The necromancer, having begun to make his tremendous invocations, called by their names a multitude of demons, who were the leaders of the several legions, and invoked them by the virtue and power of the eternal uncreated God, who lives for ever, in the Hebrew language, as likewise in Latin and Greek; insomuch, that the amphitheatre was almost in an instant filled with demons a hundred times more numerous than at the former conjuration. Vincenzio Romoli was busied in making a fire with the assistance of Agnolino, and burning a great quantity of precious perfumes. I, by the direction of the necromancer, again desired to be in the company of my Angelica. The former thereupon turning to me said, "Know, they have declared that within a month you shall be in her company."

The priest declared that, though he had often entered magic circles, nothing so extraordinary had ever happened to him. As we went along he would fain have persuaded me to assist with him at consecrating a book, from which he said we should derive immense riches. We should then ask the demons to discover to us the various treasures with which the earth abounds, which would raise us to opulence and power; but that those love affairs were mere follies from which no good could be expected. I answered that I would have accepted his proposal readily, if I had understood Latin. He redoubled his persuasions, assuring me that the knowledge of the Latin language was by no means material, and added that he could have found Latin scholars enough, if he had thought it worth while to look out for them, but that he never could have met with a partner of resolution and intrepidity equal to mine, and that I should by all means follow his advice. While we were engaged in this conversation, we arrived at our respective homes, and all that night dreamed of nothing but devils.

As I saw the priest every day, he did not fail to renew his solicitations to engage me to come into his proposal. I asked him what time it would take to carry his plan into execution, and where this scene was to be acted. He answered that in less than a month we might complete it, and that the place best calculated for our purpose was the mountains of Norcia; though a master of his had performed the ceremony of consecration hard by the mountains of the Abbey of Farfa, but that he had met with some difficulties, which would not occur in those of Norcia. He added that the neighboring peasants were men who might be confided in, and had some knowledge of necromancy, insomuch, that they were likely to give us great assistance. Such an effect had the persuasions of this holy conjurer, that I readily agreed to all he asked, but told him, that I should be glad to finish first the medals I was making for the Pope. This secret I communicated to him, but to nobody else, and begged he would not divulge it. I constantly asked him whether he thought I should, at the time mentioned by the devil, have an interview with Angelica; and finding it approach, I was surprised to hear no tidings of her. The priest always assured me that I should without fail enjoy her company, as the demons never break their promise, when they make it in that solemn manner. He bade me wait patiently, and avoid giving cause for any scandal upon that occasion, but make an effort to bear something against my nature, as he was aware of some great danger

I was to encounter; adding that it would be happy for me if I would go with him to consecrate the book, as it would be the way to obviate the danger, and could not fail to make both him and me happy.

I, who began to be as eager to undertake the enterprise as he, told him there was just come to Rome one Giovanni da Castello, a native of Bologna, an excellent artist; that he was particularly skilful in making such dies of steel as I was employed upon; and I desired nothing more than to emulate this great man, in order to display my genius, hoping by that means, and not by the sword, to subdue my numerous enemies. The priest continued his persuasions notwithstanding, and said to me, "My dear Benvenuto, come along with me, and keep out of the way of a very great danger, which I see impending over you." The end of the month was now approaching, but my mind was so taken up with my medal that I thought no more either of Angelica or of anything else, except my present task.

One day, about the hour of vespers, I went at an unusual hour to my shop (fronting Banchi, while my house was at the back), where I left all the business to the care of my partner, Felice. Having stayed there a short time, and recollecting that I had something to say to Alessandro del Bene, I set out, and being arrived in the quarter of Banchi, accidentally met a friend named Benedetto. He was a notary public, a native of Florence, son of a blind man of Siena, who lived by alms. This Benedetto had resided several years at Naples, whence he went to Rome, where he transacted business for certain merchants of Siena named Figi. My partner had several times requested him to pay for some rings that Benedetto had given him to mend. Meeting him that day in the quarter of Banchi, he asked him again for the money, with some asperity (which was customary with him), when Benedetto was with his employers. These, observing what passed, rebuked Benedetto severely, telling him they would employ another person, to prevent their being any longer disturbed with such uproars. Benedetto made the best defence he could, assuring them that he had paid that goldsmith, and could not prevent madmen from raving. The merchants, not satisfied with this excuse, dismissed him their service. Immediately after this affair, he dressed himself and came to my shop, in a great rage, perhaps in order to abuse Felice. It happened that we met exactly in the middle of the Banchi quarter. As I knew nothing of what had passed, I saluted him with my usual complaisance, but he returned my politeness with a torrent of opprobrious language. I thereupon recollected what the necromancer had told me of an impending danger, and keeping upon my guard in the best manner I could, I said to him, "My dear friend, Benedetto, don't be angry with me, for I have done you no injury, and know nothing of the misfortunes that may have befallen you. If you have anything to do with Felice, go and settle it with him; he is very able to give you an answer. As I am entirely ignorant of the affair in question, you are in the wrong to give me such language, especially as you know that I am not a man to put up with an affront." He answered that I was thoroughly acquainted with the whole transaction; that it should not end so; and that Felice and I were both great scoundrels.

By this time a crowd had gathered about us to hear the dispute. Provoked by his abusive language, I stooped, and taking up a lump of mud (for it had just been raining), I aimed it at him, intending to throw it full in his face, but he bowed a little, and it hit exactly in the middle of his brow. In this dirt was a sharp flint, which cut him severely, so that he fell upon the ground insensible, and like a dead person. From this circumstance, and from the great quantity of blood that flowed from his wound, all the bystanders thought he must have been killed.

While he lay stretched out on the ground, and some porters who were in the crowd expected to be employed to carry off the corpse, Pompeo, the jeweler, whom the Pope had sent for, happening to pass by, and seeing the man in so dismal a plight, asked who had used him in that manner. He was told that Benvenuto was the man, but that it had been all the fool's own seeking. Pompeo ran in all haste to the Pope, and said to him, "Most holy Father, Benvenuto has just murdered Tobbia; I saw it with my own eyes." The Pope flew into a violent passion, and ordered the Governor, who happened to be present, to seize and hang me directly upon the very spot where the murder was committed. He enjoined him to use the utmost diligence in taking me.

As soon as I beheld the unfortunate man in the situation I have described, I began to think of taking measures for my safety. I therefore retired to the house of Signor Gaddi, clerk of the chamber, intending to get myself in readiness with all possible expedition, and go where Providence should direct me; though Signor Gaddi advised me not to be in such a hurry, as the danger might be much less than I imagined. Having sent for Signor Annibale Caro, he desired him to inquire into the affair. While we were talking of this matter, there came to us a Roman gentleman, who lived with the Cardinal de' Medici and had been sent to us by that prince. This gentleman, taking Signor Gaddi and me aside, told us that the Cardinal had repeated to him the words above-mentioned, which he had heard uttered by the Pope; he added that it was impossible to save me, advising me to fly that first ebullition of anger, and not venture, on any account, to remain in Rome. As soon as the gentleman was gone, Signor Gaddi, looking at me attentively, seemed to shed tears, and said, "Alas! how unfortunate

am I, that I have it not in my power to assist you." I
answered, "With the help of God I shall extricate myself
out of all difficulties; all I ask of you is, that you will be
so good as to lend me a horse." Instantly a brown
Turkish horse, one of the handsomest and best in Rome,
was got ready for me; I mounted it, and placed a wheel
musket at the pummel of the saddle.

When I arrived at Sixtus's bridge I found the whole
body of city guards, horse and foot, drawn up there; so,
making a virtue of necessity, I boldly clapped spurs to
my horse and, by God's mercy, passed free and unob-
served. Thus I went with the utmost speed to Palom-
bara, the residence of Signor Giambattista Savelli; and
thence I sent back the horse. Signor Giambattista, after
treating me in the most generous manner two whole
days, advised me to bend my course towards Naples, till
the first gust of the Pope's fury should be over. Having
procured me company, he put me in the road to Naples.

CHAPTER XIV

FLIGHT TO NAPLES

SOLOSMEO having reviewed his work at Monte
Casini, we traveled together toward Naples.
Within half a mile of that capital we were accosted by an innkeeper, who invited us to put
up at his house, and told us that he had lived several
years in Florence with Cardinal Ginori. We told the
man several times that we did not choose to stop at his
house, yet he continued to ride on with us; and frequently turning back, repeated that he should be very
glad of our company at his inn. Tired at last of his im-

portunity, I asked him whether he could direct me to a
Sicilian lady named Beatrice, who had a daughter Angelica, and who were both courtesans. The innkeeper,
thinking I was in jest, made answer, "Curse on all such,
and all that take pleasure in their company;" then clapping spurs to his horse, he galloped off.

I began to applaud the address with which I had got
rid of this impertinent devil; though I still was never the
nearer, for when I recollected my passion for Angelica,
I fetched a deep sigh, and began to talk of her to Solosmeo. As we were thus engaged in chat, the innkeeper
rode up again at full speed, and as soon as he joined us,
said, "Two or three days ago, a lady and her daughter
came to lodge next door to me, of the very name you
mention; but whether they are Sicilians or not I cannot
justly say." I replied, "The name of Angelica has such
charms for me that I am resolved by all means to take up
my quarters at your inn." Thus we rode into Naples in
company with the innkeeper, and dismounted at his
house.

I thought it an age before I had put everything belonging to me into proper order; and then went to the
house adjoining the inn, where I found my dear Angelica,
who received me with the greatest demonstrations of affection.

I happened to have in my purse a diamond, which was
particularly noticed by the goldsmiths; and though but
a young man, I was generally known in Naples for a
person of some consequence, and was greatly courted by
the citizens. Among others a very worthy man, a jeweler named Signor Dominico Fontana, was lavish of his
civilities to me, and discontinued the business of his shop
during three days that I passed at Naples. He showed
me the most interesting remains of art both in and beyond the city, and moreover introduced me to the viceroy, who had intimated a desire to see me. As soon as

I came into the presence of his Excellency, he showed me a thousand civilities, during which my diamond dazzled his eye. When at his particular desire I had shown it to him, he told me that if I were disposed to part with it he hoped I would not forget him. On his returning the diamond to me, I again put it into his Excellency's hand, telling him that both the jewel and its owner were very much at his service. He declared that he set a high value upon the diamond, but should be better pleased if I would reside at his court; adding that he would take care I should be satisfied with my treatment. Many civilities thereupon passed between us; but the conversation afterward turned on the value of the diamond, and his Excellency commanded me to set a price upon it. I told him it was worth exactly two hundred crowns. To this he answered, that I appeared not to be unreasonable; but that he ascribed the extraordinary beauty of the stone to its being set by me, who was one of the first men living in the jeweling business; and if it were set by another hand it would not seem to be of half the value. I told him it was not I that had set the diamond, for the work was but indifferent, and that he who did it had considered only its intrinsic value; but, if I were to set it myself it would appear to much greater advantage and shine with redoubled lustre. Thereupon I put my thumb-nail to the ligatures of the diamond, and drew it out of the ring. Then, rubbing it a little, I handed it to the viceroy. His Excellency's surprise was equal to his satisfaction, and he wrote me an order that the two hundred crowns I demanded should be paid at sight.

On returning to my lodgings I found a letter from the Cardinal de' Medici, by which I was requested to go back to Rome without loss of time; and, immediately upon my arrival, to dismount at his palace.

On my arrival at Rome I alighted at the palace of the Cardinal de' Medici, to whom I paid my respects, with thanks for his favors. I at the same time requested him to secure me from danger of imprisonment, or even from a fine, if it were possible. The Cardinal appeared overjoyed to see me, and told me to fear nothing. He then turned to one of his gentlemen, whose name was Pierantonio Pecci of Siena, and bade him, in his name, command the city guards not to meddle with me. He asked him next in what condition the person was, whom I had wounded in the head with a stone. Pierantonio answered that he was very ill, but would soon be worse; for, having heard that I was at Rome, he declared he should willingly die to do me mischief. The Cardinal answered laughing, "The man could not have taken a surer way to convince us that he was born in Siena." Addressing himself next to me he said, "For my sake and yours, avoid being seen in the quarter of Banchi for four or five days; after that you may go where you please, and let fools die when they will."

I went to my own house, and set about finishing the medal I had begun, which was a head of Pope Clement; on the reverse was a figure representing Peace. This was a little woman, dressed in a thin garment, with a torch in her hand, a heap of arms tied together like a trophy, near to which was part of a temple, with a figure of Discord bound by many chains, and round it these words as a motto: *Clauduntur belli portœ.*

A few days later, having finished my medal, I stamped it in gold, silver, and copper, and showed it to Signor Piero, who immediately introduced me to the Pope. I was admitted into the presence of his Holiness one day just after dinner; it was April, and the weather very fine, when he was at Belvedere. On entering the apartment I delivered to him the medals, with the steel dies. Observing the great ingenuity with which they were made, he looked at Signor Piero and said, "Were the ancients ever as successful in striking medals as we?" While they were examining, now the dies, now the medals themselves, I addressed the Pope in the most modest terms I could think of. "If the influence of my adverse stars had not been counteracted by a power still greater than theirs, your Holiness would have lost a faithful and zealous servant, without its being either your fault or mine. For it must be admitted to be right and well-judged in cases of the utmost emergency, to do according to the proverbial expression of the vulgar, namely, to look before you leap; since the lying tongue of one of my malicious adversaries had so irritated your Holiness against me, that you commanded the Governor to seize and hang me at once. I do not doubt, however, that your Holiness on reflecting on your loss, and the prejudice you had done to your own interest, in depriving yourself of such a servant as you acknowledge me to be, would have felt some remorse. Neither parents nor masters, possessed of prudence or good-nature, will ever proceed to sudden severities against their children or their servants, since to repent afterward of what they have done in a passion can avail them nothing. But as the Divine Providence has defeated this malignant influence of the stars, and preserved me for your Holiness's service, I must entreat that for the future you would not so easily suffer yourself to be incensed against me."

The Pope was listening to me with attention. As several noblemen of the first rank were present, he colored a little, and appeared to be in some confusion. Not knowing how to palliate what he had done, he declared that he did not remember to have ever given any such order. I then turned the conversation to other topics, in order to amuse him and dissipate his confusion. His Holiness, again entering upon the subject of the medals, asked me by what means I had contrived to stamp them so well, for he never had seen any antique medals of the same size. We talked of this for a while, and his Holiness being apprehensive that I might say something still more severe than I had said already, told me that the medals were very fine, that he was highly pleased with them, and should be glad to have another reverse made to them, agreeable to his fancy, if medals of that sort could be stamped with two reverses. I declared they could. Upon this he ordered me to represent that part of the history of Moses where he strikes the rock and water issues from it, with a Latin inscription to this effect, *Ut bibat populus*. I exerted myself to the utmost, and lost no time till I had finished the reverse, with the figure of Moses upon it.

CHAPTER XV

CELLINI KILLS POMPEO

IN the mean time, the Pope was taken ill, and as his physicians were of opinion that he was in great danger, my adversary, who was still afraid of me, hired certain Neapolitan bravoes to treat me in the manner he was apprehensive I should treat him; so that I found it a very difficult matter to defend my life from his attacks. However, I finished my work, and waited on the Pope, whom I found very ill. He gave me the kindest reception, and, expressing a desire to see both the medals and the dies, ordered his spectacles and a light to be brought, but could discern nothing of the workmanship. He therefore began to examine them by the touch, fetched a deep sigh, and told some of his courtiers that if it pleased God to restore his health, he would settle matters to my satisfaction. Three days later he died, and I had my labor for my pains.

Totally forgetting the injuries I had received from Pompeo, I put on my sword and went to St. Peter's, where I kissed the feet of the deceased Pontiff, and could not refrain from tears. I then returned to Banchi, to reflect undisturbed on the confusion that happens on such occasions. While I was sitting here in the company of several of my friends, Pompeo happened to pass by in the midst of ten armed men, and when he came opposite to the place where I sat, he stopped a while, as if he intended to begin a quarrel. The brave young men, my friends, were for having me draw directly; but I instantly reflected that if I complied with their desire, I could not avoid hurting innocent persons, and I thought it most advisable to expose none but myself to danger. Pompeo having stopped before my door, while you might say two *Ave Marias,* began to laugh in my face; and when he went off his comrades fell a-laughing likewise, shook their heads, and made many gestures in derision and defiance of me. My companions were for interposing in the quarrel, but I told them that I was man enough to manage all my feuds by myself, so that every one might mind his own business. Mortified at this answer, my friends went away muttering to themselves. Among these was the dearest friend I had in the world, Albertaccio del Bene, brother to Alessandro and Albizzo. He was one of the most surprising young men I ever knew, as intrepid as Cæsar, and loved me as he loved himself. He was well aware that my forbearance was not an effect of pusillanimity, but of the most daring bravery. In answer, therefore, to what I said, he begged of me as a favor that I would indulge him so far as to take him for my companion in whatever enterprise I might meditate. To this I replied, "My dearest friend, Albertaccio, a time will soon come when I shall need your assistance; but on the present occasion, if you love me, do not give yourself any concern about me; only mind

your own affairs, and quit the place directly, as the rest
have done, for we must not trifle away time."

In the mean time my enemies of the Banchi quarter
had walked slowly toward a place called Chiavica, and
reached a place where several streets meet; but that in
which stood the house of my adversary, Pompeo, led directly to the Campo di Fiore. Pompeo entered an
apothecary's shop at the corner of the Chiavica, and remained there some time. I was told that he had boasted
of having bullied me; but it turned out a fatal adventure
to him. Just as I arrived at that quarter he was coming
out of the shop, and his bravoes, having made an opening,
formed a circle around him. I thereupon clapped my
hand to a sharp dagger, and having forced my way
through the file of ruffians, laid hold of him by the throat
so quickly, and with such presence of mind, that not one
of his friends could defend him. I pulled him toward
me, to give him a blow in front, but he turned his face
about through excess of terror, so that I wounded him
exactly under the ear, and when I repeated my blow, he
fell dead. It had not been my intention to kill him, but
blows are not always under command. Having withdrawn the dagger with my left hand, and drawn my
sword with the right, in order to defend myself, when
I found that all the heroes of his faction ran to the dead
body, and none of them seemed disposed to encounter
me, I retreated down the street Julia, considering whither
I could make my escape.

When I had walked about three hundred paces, Piloto, the goldsmith, my intimate friend, came up to me,
and said, "Brother, since the mischief is done, we must
think of preserving you from danger." I answered him,
"Let us go to Albertaccio del Bene, whom I told awhile
ago that I should shortly have occasion for his assistance." As soon as we reached Albertaccio's dwelling
infinite caresses were lavished on me, and all the young

persons of condition, of the different nations in the quarter of Banchi, except those of Milan, made their appearance, offering to risk their lives to preserve mine. Signor Luigi Rucellai also sent to make me a tender of all the service in his power, as did likewise several of the nobility besides him. They were glad that I had despatched Pompeo, from an opinion that he had insulted me past all enduring, and they expressed great surprise that I had so long been patient under accumulated injuries.

In the mean time, the affair coming to the knowledge of Cardinal Cornaro, he sent thirty soldiers, and as many spear-men, pike-men, and musketeers who were charged to conduct me to his house. I went with them, accompanied by more than an equal number of the brave young fellows mentioned above. Signor Trajano, Pompeo's relative, first gentleman of the bedchamber, being informed of the affair, sent a person of quality, of Milan, to Cardinal de' Medici, to acquaint him with the heinous crime I had committed, and excite him to bring me to condign punishment. The Cardinal answered, "Benvenuto would have done very wrong not to prefer the lesser to the greater evil. I thank Signor Trajano for having informed me of what I was ignorant of." Then, in the presence of the person of quality above mentioned, he turned to the Bishop of Forli, his intimate acquaintance, and said, "Make diligent inquiry after my friend Benvenuto, and conduct him hither, because I intend to befriend and assist him, and shall look upon his enemies as mine." Hearing this, the Milanese gentleman colored, and left the place, while the Bishop of Forli came in search of me to Cardinal Cornaro's palace. He told him that the Cardinal de' Medici had sent for Benvenuto, and purposed taking him under his protection. Cornaro, one of the most erratic men, flew into a violent passion, and told the bishop that he was as proper a person to take care of

me as the Cardinal de' Medici. The bishop replied, that
he begged it as a favor that he might be allowed to
speak a word to me about some other business of the
Cardinal's. Cornaro answered that he should not see me
that day. The night following, without Cornaro's
knowledge, I went, well guarded, to visit the Cardinal,
and begged that he would permit me to stay with Cornaro, telling him of the great politeness with which the
latter had treated me. Otherwise his reverence might
dispose of me as he judged proper. He answered that I
might act as I thought fit.

A few days later, Cardinal Farnese was elected Pope.
As soon as this new Pontiff had settled other affairs
of great importance, he inquired after me, and declared
that he would employ nobody else to stamp his coins.
When he spoke thus, a gentleman, Signor Latino Gio-
vinale, said I was obliged to abscond for having killed
one Pompeo, a Milanese, in a fray, and then gave an
account of the whole affair, putting it in the most favorable light for me that was possible. The Pope said: "I
never heard of the death of Pompeo, but I have often
heard of Benvenuto's provocation; so let a safe-conduct
be instantly made out, and that will secure him from all
manner of danger."

About this time, Signor Latino Giovenale gave me an
order to work for the Mint at once. Thereupon all my
enemies used their utmost endeavors to prevent me from
being employed in that department. I began to make
the dies for crown-pieces, on which I represented the bust
of St. Paul with this legend, *Vas Electionis*. This piece
proved far more agreeable to his Holiness than those of
the other artists, who worked in competition with me;
insomuch, that he declared that I alone should have the
stamping of his coins. I therefore exerted all diligence
in my art, and Latino Giovenale introduced me occasionally to the Pope, who had made choice of him for that

purpose. I applied again for the place of engraver to the Mint; but the Pope, having asked advice upon this point, told me that I must first receive pardon for the manslaughter, which I should have by the festival of the Virgin Mary in August, by order of the Caporioni. Every year, at that solemn festival, twelve persons under sentence of banishment are pardoned at the request of those magistrates. He directed that, during this interval, another safe-conduct should be taken out in my behalf,

My enemies, finding they could by no means exclude me from the Mint, had recourse to another expedient. Pompeo, whom I sent to the other world, having left a portion of three thousand ducats to a bastard daughter of his, they prevailed upon a favorite of Signor Pier Luigi, bastard son of the Pope, to marry her; and this was brought about by means of that lord. This favorite was a country fellow in narrow circumstances. It was said that he received but very little of the money, for Pier Luigi laid hands on it. But as this favorite had several times, through complaisance to his wife, requested Pier Luigi to get me taken into custody, the latter promised to bring it about, as soon as the high favor in which I was with the Pope had somewhat subsided.

A few days later I was told by an intimate friend that Signor Pier Luigi had given express orders for taking me that evening. This I heard at eight o'clock. I thereupon spoke to some of my friends, who advised me to make my escape without loss of time; and as the order was to be carried into execution at one in the morning, I took post at eleven for Florence.

CHAPTER XVI

A TRIP TO VENICE

ON my arrival at Florence I visited Duke Alessandro, who gave me the most gracious reception, and pressed me to stay with him. There happened to be in Florence at that time a statuary named Tribolo, to one of whose children I had stood godfather. In some conversations between us, he informed me that Giacopo del Sansovino, his first master, had sent for him to Venice; and as he never had seen that city, and expected to gain considerable there, he was glad of an opportunity of making the trip. He asked me whether I had ever seen Venice? I answered in the negative, whereupon he pressed me to bear him company. I accepted his proposal, and told Duke Alessandro that on my return I should be at his service. I got myself in readiness the next day, and went to take my leave of the Duke, whom I found at the palace of Pazzi, where the wife and daughter of Signor Lorenzo Cibo were also lodged. I having given his Excellency to understand that I was just setting out for Venice, an answer was brought me by Signor Cosmo de' Medici, the present Duke of Florence, that I should go to Niccolo di Monte Acuto, to receive fifty crowns, of which his Excellency made me a present, and that after I had taken my pleasure at Venice, he expected I would return to his service.

My friend Tribolo, who was ready for his journey, asked me whether I had bound up my sword. I told him that a man who has just mounted for a journey had no occasion for any such precaution. He replied that it was the custom in Florence; for there was in that city a certain Signor Maurizio, who for the least offence used to plague and persecute everybody, so that travelers were obliged to keep their swords bound up till they had passed the gate. I laughed at this; so we set out with the procaccio or postman of Venice, named Lamentone, and traveled in his company.

Having passed the other towns without stopping at any of them, we at last arrived at Ferrara, and took up our quarters at the inn in the great square.

As soon as we had supped, the master of a bark came to carry us to Venice. I asked him whether he would let us have the bark to ourselves, to which he agreed. In the morning we took horse betimes, to ride to the port, which is but a few miles from Ferrara. When we got there we met with the brother of Niccolo Benintendi, and three of his companions, who waited my coming; they had two pikes, and I had purchased a fine spear at Ferrara. Being thus well armed, I was not in the least terrified, as Tribolo was, who exclaimed, "God help us! these men have waylaid us and will murder us." Lamentone said to me, "The best course you can take is to turn directly to Ferrara, for I see there is great danger. My dear Benvenuto, avoid the fury of these savage beasts." "Let us go on boldly," said I; "God assists those who are in the right, and you shall see how I assist myself. Is not this bark hired for us?" "It is," answered Lamentone. I then rejoined, "We will make our passage without them, or I will die for it." I spurred my horse forward, and when I was within ten paces of them, dismounted, and boldly advanced, with my spear in my hand. Tribolo stayed behind, and had so contracted himself upon his horse, that he seemed to be frozen. Lamentone, the procaccio, who always puffed and blew in such a manner that he might have passed for Boreas, now puffed more than ever.

When I reached the bark, the master told me that a considerable number of gentlemen from Florence wished to sail in the vessel, if it were agreeable to me. "The boat," said I, "is hired for us, and for nobody else; and I am very sorry that I cannot have the pleasure of their company." To this a stout young fellow, named Magalotti, answered, "Benvenuto, we will contrive matters so as to put it in your power." I replied, "If God and the justice of my cause, together with my own arm, have any efficacy or influence, you will never be able to fulfil your promise." Having uttered these words, I leaped into the bark, and turning the point of my weapon toward them, said, "By this I will prove to you that I cannot comply with your request." In order to show that he was in earnest, Magalotti clapped his hand to his sword, and made toward me; when instantly I jumped upon the side of the bark, and gave him so violent a thrust, that, if he had not instantly fallen flat, I should have run him through the body. His companions, instead of assisting him, retreated; and I, seeing that it was in my power to kill him, would not repeat my blow, but said, "Arise, brother, take your arms, and go about your business. I have sufficiently shown you that I can do nothing contrary to my own will; and that which I am able to do, I have not wished to do." I then called to Tribolo, the master of the bark, and Lamentone, and we set out for Venice together.

After we had sailed ten miles upon the Po, the young fellows above mentioned, having embarked in a skiff, came up with us, and when they were opposite to our boat, that fool Piero Benintendi said, "Benvenuto, this is not the time to decide our difference; but you are to be seen again at Venice." "Take care of yourself," said I, "for I am going thither, and shall frequent all places of public resort."

In due time we arrived at Venice, where I applied to a brother of Cardinal Cornaro's for permission to wear a sword. He told me I was at liberty to do so, and the worst that could befall me was, that I might lose my sword. Thus having received permission to carry arms, we went to visit Giacopo del Sansovino the statuary, who had sent for Tribolo: he caressed me greatly, and invited both of us to dinner. In his conversation with Tribolo, he told him he had no business for him, but that he might call another time. Hearing him speak thus, I burst out a-laughing, and said jestingly to Sansovino, "His house is at too great a distance from yours for him to call again." Poor Tribolo, quite shocked at the man's behavior, said, "I have your letter in my pocket, inviting me to come and see you at Venice." Sansovino replied that such men as himself, of abilities and unexceptionable character, might do that and greater things. Tribolo shrugged his shoulders, muttering *Patience* several times. On this occasion I took my friend Tribolo's part, who was certainly in the right; and as Sansovino had never ceased to boast at table of his own performances, whilst he made very free with Michelangelo and all other artists, however eminent, I was so disgusted at his behavior that I did not eat one morsel with appetite. I expressed my sentiments thus: "O Signor Giacopo, men of worth act as such; and men of genius, who distinguish themselves by their works, are much better known by the commendations of others than by vainly sounding their own praises."

A few days later we set out on our return to Florence. On my arrival at that city, I went directly to Duke Alessandro, and returned him a great many thanks for the fifty crowns, telling his Excellency that I was ready to undertake anything to serve him. He answered that he wanted me to be engraver to his Mint. I accepted the offer; and the first coin I stamped was a piece of forty pence, with the Duke's head on one side, and on the other a San Coscino and a San Damiano. He declared that these silver coins were the finest in Christendom; and all Florence said the same. I then desired to be put into possession of the offices, with a provision, to which the Duke replied that it should be done, that I must devote myself to his service, that I should receive more than I required, and that he had given orders to Carlo Acceainolo, the master of the Mint, to supply me with everything I should want. After that I made a stamp for the half giulios, on which I represented a head of St. John, in profile, with a book in his hand, and the ducal arms upon the reverse. This was the first piece of the kind that ever had been made of so thin a plate of silver. The difficulty of such a piece of work is known only to masters of the business. I then made stamps for the gold crowns, on which a cross was represented on one side, with certain figures of little cherubim, and on the other were the Duke's arms. When I had finished this job, that is, when I had stamped these four sorts of pieces, I again requested his Excellency that he would provide apartments for me according to his promise, if he was satisfied with my services. He answered in the most obliging terms, that he was perfectly satisfied, and would give the proper orders.

Two days later I waited upon him with some little sketches I had received orders from his Excellency to draw, for works in gold; these he had given me directions to begin directly, proposing to send them as presents to his consort, who was then at Naples. I again pressed him to provide for me in the manner he had promised. He thereupon told me I should make the mould for a fine portrait of him, as I had done for Pope Clement. I began this portrait in wax, and his Excellency gave orders, that at whatever hour I came to take his likeness I should be admitted. Perceiving that the affair hung a long time upon my hands, I sent for one Pietro Paolo of Monte-ritondo, the son of him at Rome, whom I had known from a child; and finding that he was then in the

service of one Bernardaccio, a goldsmith, who did not
use him well, I took him from his master, and taught
him the art of coining. In the mean time I drew the
Duke's lineness, and often found him taking a nap after
dinner, with his kinsman Lorenzo de' Medici, who afterward murdered him, but with nobody else. I was very
much surprised that so great a prince should have so
little regard to the security of his person. It came to
pass that Ottaviano de' Medici, who seemed to have the
general direction of affairs, showed a desire, contrary to
the Duke's inclination, to faver the old master of the
Mint, named Bactiano Connini. This man, who adhered
to the ancient taste, and knew little of the business, had
caused his ill-contrived dies to be used promicuously
with mine in stamping the crowns. This I complained
of to the Duke, who, finding that I spoke the truth, grew
very angry, and said to me, "Go tell Ottaviano of this,
and let him see the pieces." I went at once, and showed
him the injury that was done to my fine coins. He told
me bluntly that it was his pleasure to have matters conducted in that manner. I answered that it was a very
improper manner, and extremely disagreeable to me. He
replied, "But suppose it should be agreeable to the
Duke?" "Even so I should disapprove of it," said I, "for
the thing is neither just nor reasonable." He then bade
me begone, telling me I must swallow the pill were I
even to burst. On my return to the Duke, I related the
whole contest, requesting his Excellency not to suffer the
fine pieces I had stamped for him to be brought into disgrace; and at the same time I desired my discharge. He
then said, "Ottaviano presumes too much; you shall
have what you require of me, for the insult upon this
occasion is offered to myself."

That very day, which was Thursday, I received from
Rome an ample safe-conduct of the Pope's, directing me
to repair forthwith to that city, at the celebration of the

feast of the Virgin Mary in August, that I might clear
myself from the charge of murder. When I waited on the
Duke I found him in bed. I finished in a little more than
two hours what remained for me to do of his waxen medal,
and he was highly pleased with it. I then showed his
Excellency the safe-conduct, telling him at the same time,
that his Holiness was for employing me in some works,
which would give me an opportunity of seeing once more
the beautiful city of Rome, and in the mean time I would
finish his Excellency's medal. The Duke answered, half
angrily, "Benvenuto, do as I desire of you, I will provide for you and assign you apartments in the Mint, with
much greater advantages than you could expect from me,
since what you ask is but just and reasonable. Who
else do you think is able to stamp my coins like you, if
you should leave me?" I replied, "My Lord, I have
taken care to obviate all inconveniences: I have a pupil
of mine here, a young Roman, whom I have trained to
my business, and who will serve your Excellency to your
satisfaction, till I finish the medal, and at my return I
will devote myself for ever to your service. As I have
a shop open in Rome, with workmen and some business,
as soon as I have received my pardon at the capital, I
intend to leave all my affairs at Rome under the care of
a pupil of mine, who resides in that city, and then, with
your Excellency's permission, I will come back to serve
you." On this occasion there was present Lorenzo de'
Medici, to whom the Duke made several signs for him to
join in persuading me to stay; but Lorenzo never said
more than, "Benvenuto, your best way would be to remain where you are." I answered that I was resolved
by all means to see Rome again. Lorenzo did not add
another word; but continued to eye the Duke with malicious glances. Having finished the medal, and shut it up
in a little box, I said to his Excellency: "My Lord, you
shall have reason to be satisfied, for I will make you a

much finer medal than that of Pope Clement. It is natural that I should succeed better in this than in the other,
as that was my first essay; and Signor Lorenzo, being a
person of learning and genius, will furnish me with a device for a fine reverse." Lorenzo instantly replied, "That
is the very thing I was just thinking of, to give you the
hint of a reverse worthy of his Excellency." The Duke
smiled, and looking upon Lorenzo, said,"You shall give
him the subject of the reverse, and he will stay with us."
Lorenzo thereupon answered without hesitation, "I will
think of it as soon as I possibly can: my intention is to
produce something to surprise the world." The Duke,
who sometimes was inclined to think him a little foolish,
and sometimes to look upon him as a coward, turned
about in bed, and laughed at his boasts.

CHAPTER XVII.

AT THE POINT OF DEATH

IN my journey to Rome I carried with me a fine
gun that had been given to me by Duke Alessandro, and with great pleasure made use of
it several times by the way. I had a little
house in the street Julia at Rome; but as it was
not in order on my arrival in that capital, I went
to dismount at the house of Signor Giovanni Gaddi, a clerk of the chamber, to whose care I had at
my departure committed some choice arms, and many
other things upon which I set a high value. I did not,
therefore, choose to alight at my own shop; but sent for
my partner Felice, and asked him to set my little house
in order. The day following I went to lie there, intend-

ing the next morning to pay my respects to the Pope, and thank him for all favors. I had two servant boys, and a laundress, who cooked for me incomparably.

Having in the evening entertained several of my friends at supper, and passed the time very agreeably, I went quietly to bed; but hardly had the morning dawned, when I heard a violent knocking at the door. I thereupon called to the eldest of my boys, named Cencio (the very same whom I carried with me into the necromancer's circle), and bade him go and see what fool knocked at such a strange rate at that unseasonable hour. While Cencio was gone, I lighted another candle (for I always kept one burning by night), and immediately put over my shirt an excellent coat of mail, and over that again some clothes that accidently came to hand. Cencio returning, said, "Alas! master, it is the captain of the city guards, with all his followers; and he declares that if you make him wait, he will pull the door off the hinges; they have lighted torches and a thousand implements with them." "Go tell them," I answered, "that as soon as I have huddled on my clothes I will come down." Thinking that it might be an attempt to assassinate me, like that already made by Signor Pier Luigi, I took an excellent hanger in my right hand, and in my left the Pope's safe-conduct, and ran directly to the back window, which looked into certain gardens, where I saw more than thirty of the city guards, which convinced me that it would be impossible to make my escape on that side. Having placed my two boys before me, I directed them to be ready to open the door when I should bid them; then holding the hanger in my right hand, and my safe-conduct in my left, in a posture of defence, I ordered the boys to open the door and fear nothing.

That instant Vittorio, captain of the city guards, rushed in with two of his myrmidons, thinking they should find it an easy matter to seize me; but when they saw me prepared for them, they fell back, and said one to another, "This affair is no jest." I threw them the safe-conduct, and said, "Read that: you have no authority to arrest me, and I am resolved you shall not so much as touch my person." The captain of the guard ordered some of his followers to seize me, adding that he would examine the safe-conduct at his leisure. Upon this I was animated with new courage, and brandishing my sword, I exclaimed, "You shall not take me alive!" The place we were in was very narrow: they seemed determined to have recourse to violence, and I was resolved to defend myself. The captain perceived that there was no probability of getting me alive into their power. The clerk being called, while he was reading the safe-conduct, the captain made signs two or three times to his men to lay hands on me, but they were intimidated at seeing me continue in the same posture of defence. At last, giving up the enterprise, they threw the safe-conduct upon the ground, and went away without me.

I went to bed again, but found myself extremely fatigued, and could not sleep a wink. Though I formed a resolution to be bled as soon as it should be day, I asked the advice of Signor Giovanni Gaddi, who consulted his physician: the latter desired to know whether I had been frightened. Here was a pretty physician to ask such a question, after I had related an event so replete with terror. He was one of those vain triflers that are always laughing, the least thing being sufficient to put him into a merry mood; so in his usual jocular strain he had me drink a glass of good Greek wine, be cheerful, keep up my spirits, and fear nothing.

In the mean time the festival of the Virgin Mary drew near; and as it was customary for those who had received such a pardon as mine to surrender themselves prisoners, I went again to the Pope, and told his Holiness I did not choose to be confined, but begged that he would dispense with my going to prison. The Pope answered that it was an established custom, and I must conform to it. I fell upon my knees again, and returned thanks for the safe-conduct his Holiness had granted me; adding, that I should return with it to serve my patron the Duke of Florence, who waited for me with so much eagerness and ardent affection. On this, his Holiness turned about to one of his confidants, and said, "Let the pardon be granted to Benvenuto without his complying with the condition of imprisonment; and let his patent be properly made out." On the day appointed for that purpose I walked honorably in procession, between two gentlemen, and received a full pardon.

About four days later I was attacked by a violent fever, which began with a terrible shivering. I was confined to my bed, and supposed the disease to be mortal. I sent, however, for the most eminent physicians of Rome, among whom was Signor Francesco da Norcia, an old physician, of the highest reputation. I told the physicians what I apprehended to be the cause of my disorder, and that I had desired to be bled. Signor Francesco answered that bleeding could then be of no service, though it might have been so at first; for if I had opened a vein in time I should have had no illness, but now it would be necessary to have recourse to a different method of cure. In a week the physicians gave me up, and directed that whatever I desired should be given me. Signor Francesco said, "As long as there is breath in his body send for me at all hours, for it is impossible to conceive how great the power of nature is in such a young man: but even if it should quite fail him, apply these five medicines one after another, and send for me. I will come at any hour of the night, and should be better pleased to save his life than that of any cardinal in Rome."

Signor Giovanni Gaddi came to see me two or three

times a-day, and was continually handling my fine fowl-
ing-pieces, my coat of mail, and my swords, saying, "This
is very fine; this again is much finer." So also of my
little models, and other knick-knacks, insomuch that he
tired my patience. With him came one Mattio Franzesi,
who seemed quite impatient for me to die; not because
he was to inherit anything of mine, but he wished for
what Signor Giovanni appeared to have so much at heart.
I had with me my partner Felice, who gave me the greatest assistance that ever one man afforded another. Nature was in me debilitated to such a degree that I was
hardly able to fetch my breath; but my understanding
was as unimpaired as when I enjoyed perfect health.
Nevertheless, I imagined that an old man, of a hideous
figure, came to my bedside to haul me violently into a
large bark: I thereupon called to my friend Felice, and
asked him to drive away the old villain. Felice ran toward the bedside in tears, and cried out, "Get thee gone,
old traitor, who attemptest to bereave me of all that is
dear to me in life." Signor Gaddi, who was present,
said, "The poor man raves, and has but a few hours to
live." Mattio observed that I had read Dante, and in
the violence of my disorder was raving from passages in
that author; so he continued to say laughing, "Get hence,
old villain, and do not disturb the repose of our friend
Benvenuto." Perceiving that I was derided, I turned to
Signor Gaddi, and said, "My dear sir, do not think I
rave: what I tell you of the old man who persecutes
me so cruelly is strictly true. You would do well to
turn out that cursed Mattio, who laughs at my sufferings; and since you do me the honor to visit me, you
should come in the company of Signor Antonio Allegretti, and Signor Annibale Caro, with the other men of
genius of your acquaintance, who are very different in
sentiment and understanding from that blockhead."
Thereupon Signor Gaddi, in a jesting way, bade Mattio

quit his presence for ever. Though the fellow laughed, the jest became earnest, for Gaddi would never see him more, but sent for Signor Antonio Allegretti, Signor Lodovico, and Signor Caro.

No sooner had those worthy persons appeared, than I began to take comfort, and conversed with them awhile in my right senses. As I, notwithstanding, from time to time urged Felice to drive away the old man, Signor Lodovico asked me what I thought I saw, and what appearance the old man had. While I was giving him a description of this figure, the old man pulled me by the arm, and dragged me by main force toward his horrid bark. When I had uttered the last word, I was seized with a terrible fit, and thought that the old man threw me into the vessel.

Those that were present, imagining that the agonies of death were coming upon me, gave me over and went to their respective homes. Mattio heard the news, and immediately wrote to Florence, to Benedetto Varchi, my most intimate friend, that I had expired at such an hour of the night. That great genius, upon this false intelligence, wrote an admirable sonnet. It was three hours before I came to myself, and all the remedies prescribed by Signor Francesco having been administered without effect, my good friend Felice flew to the doctor's house, and with tears in his eyes entreated him to come and see me, as he was afraid I had just expired. Signor Francesco, who was one of the most passionate men living, answered, "To what purpose should I go? If he is dead, I am more sorry for him than yourself. Do you think, even if I should go, that I am possesed of any nostrum to restore him to life?" Perceiving that the poor young man was going away in tears, he called him back and gave him an oil to anoint the several pulses of my body, directing my little fingers and toes to be pressed hard, and said they might send for him again in

10

case I was to come to myself. Felice did all that he was ordered by Signor Francesco, and in vain continued to do so until daylight. They all believed the case to be hopeless, and were just going to lay me out. In a moment, however, I came to myself, and called to Felice to drive away the old man that tormented me. Felice was for sending for Signor Francesco, but I told him he need not send for anybody, that he had nothing more to do but to come close to me himself, for the old man was afraid of him, and would immediately quit me upon his approach.

One day Felice happened to be out, and there were left to take care of me an apprentice and a girl named Beatrice. I asked the apprentice what had become of my boy, Cencio, and why I had never seen him there to attend me? The lad told me that Cencio had been afflicted with a more severe disorder than mine, and was then at the point of death; adding that Felice had strictly enjoined them to conceal it from me. Shortly afterward I called Beatrice and begged of her to bring me a large crystal wine-cooler, which stood hard by full of cold water. The girl ran directly and brought it. I told her to hold it up to my mouth, and that if she would let me drink a good draught, I would make her a present of a new gown. Beatrice, who had stolen some things of value from me, and was apprehensive that the theft might be discovered, wished very much for my death; she therefore let me, at two draughts, take as much water as I could swallow. I then covered myself up with the bed-clothes, began to sweat, and fell asleep.

Felice, returned after I had slept about an hour, and asked the boy how I was? He answered, "I cannot tell, Beatrice has taken the wine-cooler full of water, and he has drunk it nearly all. I do not know now whether he is dead or alive." They say the poor young man was so affected at this intelligence, that he was almost ready to drop; but seizing a stick he soundly cudgeled the girl, exclaiming, "Ah! traitress, that you should be the cause of his death." Beatrice ran into my chamber, bawling so loud that I awoke and said, "Let the girl alone. With a design, perhaps, to hurt me, she has done me more good than you, with all your kind attentions: now lend me a helping hand, for I have just had a sweat." Finding myself much better, I began to have hopes of recovery. Signor Francesco soon made his appearance, and seeing me so much better, the girl crying, the apprentice running backward and forward, and Felice laughing, concluded from this hurry, that something extraordinary had happened, which was the cause of so great a change. Immediately after came in Bernardino, who had disapproved bleeding me in the beginning. Signor Francesco, who was a man of sagacity, could not help exclaiming, "O wonderful power of Nature! She knows her own wants; physicians know nothing!" The fool Bernardino thereupon said that if I had drunk another flask, I had been immediately cured. Signor Francesco da Norcia said, "The devil give you good of such a notion!" and turning to me, asked me whether I could have drunk any more? I answered that I could not, as I had completely quenched my thirst. Then addressing himself to Bernardino, "Do not you see," said he, "that nature took just what she had need of, and neither more nor less. In like manner she required what was necessary for her relief when the poor young man begged of you to bleed him. If you knew that drinking two flasks of water would save his life, why did you not say so before? you would then have had something to boast of." At these words the little doctor took himself off crestfallen, and never made his appearance again. Signor Francesco directed that I should be removed out of that apartment, to a lodging upon one of the hills of Rome.

CHAPTER XVIII

CELLINI INTERPRETS A PORTENT

HAVING waited a week, I found myself so little better that my patience was almost tired out. I resolved to delay no longer, and in an open carriage Felice and I set out directly for Florence. I went to my sister's, who welcomed me with tears and smiles. The same day many friends came to see me, and among them Pier Landi, one of the best and dearest I ever had.

A day or two later came one Niccolo da Monte Acuto, who was likewise my particular acquaintance. He said, "Alas! my dear Benvenuto, what brought you hither? Did you not know that you had given offence to the Duke? I have heard him swear that you had fallen into a snare." I answered, "Signor Niccolo, I beg you will put his Excellency in mind that Pope Clement was going to treat me in the same manner, and with as little reason. Let him but suffer me to recover my health thoroughly, and I shall convince him that I am the most faithful servant he ever had in his life, and that some of my enemies have prejudiced him against me."

The person that had thus brought me in disgrace with his Excellency was Giorgetto Vasellai, of Arezzo, the painter, in return for the many favors I had conferred on him. I had maintained him at Rome, and borne his charges, though he had turned my house topsy-turvy; for he was troubled with a sort of dry leprosy, which made him contract a habit of scratching himself continually: hence, as he lay with a journeyman of mine, named Manno, while he thought he was scratching himself, he tore the skin off one of Manno's legs, with his great

claws—for he never pared his nails. Manno thereupon
left me, and would have put him to death; but I found
means to reconcile them. I afterward got Giorgio into
the service of the Cardinal de' Medici, and was always a
friend to the man. In return for all these favors and
acts of friendship, he told Duke Alessandro that I had
spoken ill of his Excellency, and had made it my boast
that I should be one of the first to scale the walls of
Florence and assist his enemies against him. These
words, as I understood afterward, he dropped at the instigation of Ottaviano de' Medici, whose aim was to be
revenged for the trouble the Duke gave him on occasion
of my coins, and my departure from Florence. As I
knew myself entirely innocent I was not under any sort
of apprehension.

In the mean time I despatched my trusty partner Felice
to Rome, to look into the state of my affairs in that city.
As soon as I could raise my head from the pillow, which
was at the end of a fortnight, being still unable to walk,
I asked to be carried into the palace of the Medici, to the
little terrace, and there to be left seated till the Duke
should pass by. A great number gathered about me, and
they all seemed to consider my being there a sort of
miracle, not so much from their having heard that I was
dead, as that I should make my appearance there in such
a state. I said to the gentlemen that some malicious villain had told the Duke I had boasted I should be one of
the first to scale his Excellency's walls, and that I had
spoken disrespectfully of him; therefore I could neither
live nor die contented till I had cleared myself of the
infamous aspersions cast upon me, and discovered the villain who invented so black a calumny. When I spoke
thus, there was about me a crowd of courtiers, all of
whom seemed deeply to compassionate my case, and expressed their sentiments variously concerning it. As for
me, I declared my resolution never to quit the place till

I had discovered my accuser. When I had uttered these words, Signor Agostino, the Duke's tailor, came up to me and said, "If that is all you are so solicitous to know, you shall soon be satisfied." Just at that instant, Giorgetto the painter passed that way, and Agostino said, "There goes your accuser. Whether what he says be true or false, you know best." Though I could not stir, I boldly asked Giorgetto whether it was true that he had accused me in that manner? Giorgetto answered that he never had said any such thing. Agostino then replied, "Abandoned wretch, don't you know that I speak upon a certainty?" Giorgetto instantly left the place, declaring it was false. Soon afterward the Duke himself appeared. I caused myself to be supported in his Excellency's presence, and he stopped. I then said, that I was come there for no other motive but to justify my conduct. The Duke looked at me attentively, and expressing great surprise that I was still alive, bade me endeavor to show myself an honest man, and take care of my health. As soon as I had got home, Niccolo da Monte Acuto came to me, and told me that I was in the most dreadful jeopardy conceivable, such as he never should have believed; that I was a marked man; that it was most advisable therefore for me to endeavor to recover my health with all convenient speed, for danger impended over my head from a man that was to be feared. He then added, "Consider with yourself, how have you offended that good-for-nothing Ottaviano de' Medici?" I answered that I never had offended him, but that he had wronged me; so I related to him the whole affair of the Mint. His reply was, "Go your way, in God's name, with all the expedition possible, and make yourself quite easy, for you will have the pleasure of being revenged sooner than you desire." I made a short stay to recover my health, gave Pietro Paolo my directions with regard to stamping the coins, and then set out upon my return to Rome, without saying a word to anybody.

On my arrival in that capital, I began the Duke's medal, and in a few days had engraved the head on steel. It was the finest work of the sort that ever came from my hands.

I then sent to Florence to let Lorenzo know that it was time for him to send me the reverse of the medal. Niccolo da Monte Acuto, to whom I wrote on this occasion, returned for answer that he had applied to that melancholy simpleton Lorenzo, who assured him that he thought of nothing else day and night, and that he would finish it as soon as he could. He at the same time advised me not to depend upon that reverse, but devise one of my own imagination, and as soon as it was finished carry it to Duke Alessandro. Having made a design of what appeared to me a proper reverse, I began to work upon it with all expedition. But as I had not yet thoroughly got the better of my late dreadful disorder, I often took recreation in fowling. On one of these occasions I was accompanied by Felice. It was nightfall when we arrived at a small eminence; and happening to look toward Florence, we both exclaimed in the utmost astonishment, "Great God! what wonderful phenomenon is that which appears yonder over Florence!" In figure it resembled a beam of fire, which shone with extraordinary luster. I said, "We shall certainly hear that some great event has occurred at Florence." By the time we arrived at Rome it was exceedingly dark; and when we were come near the Banchi quarter, not far from our own house, I going at a brisk canter, there chanced to be a heap of rubbish and broken tiles in the middle of the street, which neither my horse nor I perceived. He ascended it with precipitation; and then descending, stumbled and fell with his head between his legs; but by God's providence I escaped unhurt. I found some of my friends at home, to whom I gave an account of my achievements in fowling, and of the strange phenomenon we had seen. They inquired what could be the meaning of such an appearance. "Doubtless," answered I, "some revolution must have happened at Florence." Thus we supped together cheerfully, and late the day following news was received at Rome of the death of Duke Alessandro.

Beginning now to attend to the business of my shop, I set about some jobs that were not of great importance; for I made the recovery of my health my chief care, and did not think myself entirely secure from a relapse. About this time the Emperor returned victorious from his enterprise against Tunis, when the Pope sent for me and asked what sort of present he should make that prince. I answered that the most proper present was a golden crucifix, for which I had devised a sort of ornament that would be extremely suitable, and do both his Holiness and me great honor; having already made three small figures in gold, round, and about a span high. These were the same figures that I had begun for the chalice of Pope Clement, and were intended to represent Faith, Hope, and Charity. Having therefore added, in wax, what was wanting at the foot of the cross, I carried it to the Pope with the figure of Christ in wax, and several other elegant ornaments, with which he was highly pleased, and before I left him we agreed upon everything that was to be done, and calculated the expense of the work.

This was a little after sunset, and the Pope had given orders to Signor Latino Giovenale to supply me with money the next morning. Latino, who had a great dash of the fool in his composition, wished to furnish the Pope with a new invention, which should come entirely from himself, so that he counteracted all that his Holiness and I had settled. In the morning, when I went for the money, he said, in that coarse tone of presumption

so peculiar to him: "It is our part to invent, yours to
execute: before I left the Pope last evening, we designed
something much better." When he had uttered these
words, I did not suffer him to proceed, but said, "Neither
you nor the Pope can ever think of a better device than
this, in which Christ is represented with his cross, so
now you may continue your courtier-like impertinence."

His Holiness sent for me, and told me that I had given
very good advice, but that they intended to make use of
an office of the Virgin Mary, with admirable illumina-
tions, which had cost the Cardinal de' Medici more than
two thousand crowns, and that this would be a very
proper present for the Empress; that the Emperor should
afterward receive what I had proposed, which would be
indeed a present worthy of his Majesty; but now there
was no time to lose, that prince being expected in about
six weeks. For this book, the Pope wished to have a
cover made of massy gold, richly chased, and adorned
with a considerable number of jewels, worth about six
thousand crowns: so I set about the work, and, as I used
all possible expedition, it appeared in a few days to be of
such admirable beauty, that the Pontiff conferred extraordinary favors upon me.

CHAPTER XIX

CONFERENCE WITH CHARLES V

WHEN I had almost finished the work above
mentioned, the Emperor arrived at Rome, and
a great number of grand triumphal arches
were erected for his reception. Immediately
on his arrival he made the Pope a present of a diamond,

which had cost him twelve thousand crowns. The Pope
sent for me, and putting the diamond into my hands,
ordered me to set it in a ring for his finger. But first to
bring him the book, unfinished as it was. When I carried it to his Holiness, he was highly pleased with it, and
consulted me respecting the excuse to be made to the
Emperor for the non-completion of the work. I said,
"The most plausible apology was my being indisposed,
which his Imperial Majesty would be very ready to believe, on seeing me so pale and emaciated." The Pope answered that he highly approved of the excuse; but
wished me to add in his name, that in presenting his
Majesty with the book, I at the same time made him a
present of myself.

His Holiness at the same time ordered out two Turkish horses, which had formerly belonged to Pope Clement, and were the finest that ever had been brought into
Christendom. These he committed to the care of Signor
Durante, his chamberlain, to conduct them to the porch
of the palace, and there present them to the Emperor,
at the same time directing him what to say on the occasion. We went together, and when we were admitted
into the presence of that great prince, the two horses
entered the palace with so much grandeur and spirit,
that the Emperor and the bystanders were astonished.
Thereupon Signor Durante advanced in the most awkward and ungracious manner, and delivered himself in a
sort of Brescian jargon, with such hesitation, and so disa-
greeably, that the Emperor could not help smiling. In the
mean time I had already uncovered my work, and perceiving that his Majesty looked at me very graciously,
I stepped forward and expressed myself thus: "Sire,
our holy Father, Pope Paul, sends this office of our Lady
as a present to your Majesty. It was written, and the
figures of it were drawn, by the ablest man that the
world ever produced. He presents you likewise with this

rich cover of gold and jewels, which as yet remains unfinished in consequence of my indisposition.   On this account his Holiness, together with the book, presents me also, desiring that I should come to finish the work near your sacred person, and also serve your Majesty in whatever you may require of me, so long as I live." To this the Emperor answered: "The book is highly agreeable to me, and you are so likewise; but I wish you to finish the work for me at Rome, and when it is completed, and you are thoroughly recovered, I shall be glad to see you at my court."

I exerted myself with the utmost assiduity to finish the ring for the diamond, on which account four of the most eminent jewelers in Rome were ordered to consult with me. The Pope had been informed that the diamond had been set at Venice by the first artist in the world, whose name was Miliano Targhetta; and as the stone was somewhat sharp, it was thought too difficult an attempt to set it without advice and assistance. I made the four jewelers highly welcome; among whom was a native of Milan, named Gajo—one of the most arrogant blockheads breathing, who pretended to great skill in what he was altogether ignorant of. The rest were men of singular modesty and merit. Gajo took the lead, and said, "Endeavor to preserve the tint of Miliano; to that, Benvenuto, you must show due respect; for as the tinting of diamonds is the nicest and most difficult article in the jeweler's business, so Miliano is the greatest jeweler the world ever produced, and this is the hardest diamond that ever was worked upon." I answered, that it should be so much the more glorious for me to vie with so renowned an artist. Then addressing myself to the other jewelers, I added, "You shall see now that I will preserve the tint of Miliano, and try whether I can in so doing improve it. In case I should fail of success, I will restore its former tint."

I must acknowledge that this diamond gave me the most trouble of any that ever, before or since, fell into my hands, and Miliano's tint appeared to be a masterpiece of art; however, I was not discouraged. My genius being upon this occasion in a particular manner sharpened and elevated, I not only equaled but surpassed it. Perceiving that I had conquered Miliano, I endeavored to excel even myself, and by new methods made a tint much superior to my former. I then sent for the jewelers, and having given to the diamond Miliano's tint, I afterward tinted it again with my own. I showed it to the artists, and one of the cleverest amongst them, whose name was Raffaello del Moro, took the stone in his hand, and said to Giovanni, "Benvenuto has surpassed Miliano's tint." Gajo, who could not believe what he heard, upon taking the jewel into his hand, cried out, "Benvenuto, this diamond is worth two thousand ducats more than it was with Miliano's tint." I replied, "Since I have surpassed Miliano, let me see whether I cannot outdo myself." Having requested them to have patience a few moments, I went into a little closet, and unseen by them gave a new tint to my diamond. When I showed it again, Gajo exclaimed, "This is the most extraordinary case I ever knew in my life; the diamond is now worth above 18,000 crowns, and we hardly valued it at 12,000." The other artists, turning to Gajo, said, "Benvenuto is an honor to our profession: it is but just that we should bow to the superiority of his genius and the excellence of his tints." Gajo answered, "I will go and inform the Pope in what manner he has acquitted himself; and contrive so that he shall receive a thousand crowns for setting this diamond." Accordingly he waited on his Holiness and told him all he had seen. The Pontiff thereupon sent three times that day to inquire whether the ring was finished.

Toward evening I carried it to him; and as I had free

access, and was not obliged to observe any ceremony, I
softly lifted a curtain, and saw his Holiness with the
Marquess of Guasto, who would fain persuade him to
something he did not approve of. I heard the Pope say
to the Marquess, "I tell you no, for it is proper that I
should be neutral in the affair." As I immediately drew
back, the Pope himself called to me; upon which I advanced, and put the fine diamond into his hand. His
Holiness then took me aside, and the Marquess retired to
some distance. The Pope, while he was examining the
diamond, said to me, "Benvenuto, pretend to talk to me
of some subject of importance, and never once leave off
while the Marquess stays in this apartment." So choosing the subject that was most interesting to myself, I
began to discourse of my method in tinting the diamond.
The Marquess stood leaning on one side against a tapes-
try-hanging; sometimes he turned round on one foot,
sometimes on the other. The subject of this conversation of ours was of such consequence that we could have
talked upon it three hours. The Pope took such delight
in it that it counterbalanced the disagreeable impression
the conference with the Marquess had made upon his
mind. As I mixed with our conversation that part of
natural philosophy which is connected with the jeweler's art, our chat was protracted almost to an hour, and
the Marquess's patience was so worn out that he went
away half angry. The Pope then showed me great kindness, and concluded with these words, "My dear Benvenuto, be diligent in your business, and I will reward your
merit with something more considerable than the thousand crowns which Gajo told me you deserved for your
trouble."

I took my leave, and his Holiness praised me afterward
in the presence of his domestic officers, among whom
was Latino Giovenale, who, being now my enemy, endeavored to do me all the ill offices in his power. Per-

ceiving that the Pope spoke of me so advantageously, he said, "Benvenuto indeed is acknowledged to be a person of extraordinary talents; but though it is natural for every man to be partial to his own countrymen, and give them the preference, still the manner of speaking to so great a personage as a Pope deserves a proper degree of attention. He has had the boldness to declare that Pope Clement was the handsomest prince that ever existed, and that his virtues and abilities were worthy of his majestic person, though he had adverse fortune to struggle with. This man at the same time affirms that your Holiness is quite the reverse, that your triple crown does not sit well on your head, and that you appear to be nothing more than a figure of straw dressed up, though you have always had prosperous fortune." These words were pronounced in so emphatic a manner that the Pope believed him. I had neither uttered such words, nor had it ever come into my head to make any such comparison. If the Pope had had it in his power to do it without hurting his character, he would certainly have done me some great injury, but being a man of understanding, he pretended to turn the thing into a jest: yet he bore me an inconceivable grudge in his heart, and I soon began to perceive it; for I now found it exceedingly difficult to be admitted into his presence.

I worked at my little book with the utmost assiduity, and when I had finished it I carried it to the Pope, who extolled it to the skies. I thereupon reminded him of his promise of sending me with it to the Emperor. He answered that he would do what was proper, and that I had done my part. He then gave orders that I should be well paid for my trouble. Yet for the different works upon which I had been employed two months, I was paid five hundred crowns, and no more. All the great promises that had been made me were totally forgotten. I received for the diamond a hundred and fifty crowns only; the remainder I had for the little book, for which I deserved more than a thousand crowns, as the work was rich in figures, foliages, enamel, and jewels. I took what I could get, and formed a resolution to quit Rome directly. His Holiness sent the book to the Emperor by a nephew of his, Signor Sforza, and that great prince bestowed excessive praises on it, and immediately inquired after me. Signor Sforza, having received proper instructions, answered that an indisposition had prevented my waiting upon his Imperial Majesty.

CHAPTER XX

THE JOURNEY TO PARIS

J HAD formed a resolution to set out for France, as well because I perceived that the Pope's favor was withdrawn from me, as for fear that those of my enemies who had most influence might still do me some greater injury. I was desirous to remove to some other country, and see whether fortune would there prove more favorable to me. Having determined to set out the next morning, I bade my faithful Felice enjoy all I had as his own till my return; and in case I should never come back, my intention was that the whole should fall to him. Happening at this time to have a Perugian journeyman, who assisted me in the last-mentioned work for the Pope, I paid him off and dismissed him. The poor man entreated me to let him go with me, offering to bear his own expenses. He said, moreover, that if I should happen to be employed for any length of time by the King of France, it was proper I should have Italians in my service, especially such as

I knew and were most likely to be of use to me. I agreed to carry him with me upon his own terms. Ascanio, happening to be present at this conversation, said to me, with tears in his eyes, "When you took me again into your service I intended it should be for life, and now I am resolved it shall." I answered, that it should not be so upon any account. The poor lad was then preparing to follow me on foot. When I perceived that he had formed such a resolution, I hired a horse for him.

I bent my course to Florence, whence I traveled on to Bologna, Venice, and Padua. On my arrival at the last city, my friend, Albertaccio del Bene, took me to his own house from the inn where I had put up. The day following I went to pay my respects to Signor Pietro Bembo, who had not then been made a cardinal. He gave me the kindest reception I had ever met with, and said to Albertaccio, "I am resolved that Benvenuto shall stay here with all his company, if they were a hundred; so make up your mind to stay here with him, for I will not restore him to you upon any account." He had caused an apartment to be prepared for me, which would have been too magnificent even for a cardinal, and insisted upon my sitting constantly next to him at table. He then intimated, in the most modest terms he could think of, that it would be highly agreeable to him if I were to model his likeness. There was nothing that I desired more; so, having put some pieces of the whitest alabaster into a little box, I began the work. I made so fine a sketch of the head that my illustrious friend was astonished at it; for though he was a person of immense learning, and had an uncommon genius for poetry, he had not the least knowledge of my business; for which reason he thought I had finished the figure when I had hardly begun it; insomuch, that I could not make him sensible that it required a considerable time to bring it to perfection. At last I formed a resolution to take my own time about it, and finish it in the completest manner I could; but as he wore a short beard, according to the Venetian fashion, I found it a very difficult matter to make a head to please myself. I, however, finished it at last, and it appeared to me to be one of the most complete pieces I had ever produced. He seemed to be in the utmost astonishment; for he took it for granted, that as I had made it of wax in two hours, I could make it of steel in ten; but when he saw that it was not possible for me to do it in two hundred, and that I was upon the point of taking my leave of him, in order to set out for France, he was greatly concerned, and begged I would make him a reverse for his medal, and that the device should be the horse Pegasus, in a garland of myrtle. This I did in about three hours, and it was finished in admirable taste. He said, "Such a horse as this appears to be a work ten times more considerable than that little head, upon which you bestowed so much pains: I cannot possibly account for this." He then asked me to make it for him in steel, and said, "I hope you will oblige me; you can do it very soon if you will." I promised him that, though it did not suit me to make it there, I would do it for him without fail at the first place at which I should happen to fix my residence.

I took the road through the Grisons, for it was unsafe to travel any other way, on account of the war. We passed the two great mountains of Alba and Merlina (it was then the eighth of May, yet they were covered with snow), at the utmost hazard of our lives. When we had traveled over them, we stopped at a little town, which, as nearly as I can remember, is called Valdistà.

Setting out betimes in the morning, we arrived at a place between Valdistà and Vessa, where there is a lake, upon which we were to sail to Vessa. When I saw the boats, I was terribly frightened, because they are made of deal boards, neither well nailed together,

11

nor even pitched; and if I had not seen four German
gentlemen, with their horses, in one of them, I never
should have ventured on board. I thought, seeing the
stupid security of these gentlemen, that the waters of the
German lakes did not drown the passengers like those of
Italy. My two young fellow-travelers said, "Benvenuto,
it is a dangerous thing to enter one of these boats with
four horses." My answer was, "Don't you see, you poor
cowards, that those four gentlemen have entered one before you, and that they sail away merrily? If it were a
lake of wine, I should fancy that they were rejoiced at
the thoughts of being plunged into it; but as it is a lake
of water only, I take it for granted they have no more
inclination to be drowned in it than ourselves." This
lake was fifteen miles long, and about three broad: the
country, on one side, was a lofty mountain, full of
caverns, on the other it was level, and covered with
grass.

When we had advanced about four miles, it began to
grow stormy, insomuch that the watermen called out to
us for help, begging that we would assist them in row-
ing; and so we did for a time. I signified to them that
their best way was to make the opposite shore; but they
said it was impossible, because there was not a sufficient
depth of water, so that the bark would be soon beaten
to pieces in the shallows. As I perceived them in such
terror and jeopardy, having a horse on board, I put on its
bridle, and held it in my left hand. The horse, by a kind
of instinct and intelligence common to these animals,
seemed to perceive my intention; for by turning his face
toward the fresh grass, I wanted him to swim to the opposite shore, and carry me over. At the very same instant there poured in from that side a wave so large
that it almost overwhelmed the vessel. Ascanio then
crying out, "Mercy! help me, dear father!" was going
to throw himself upon me; but I clapped my hand to my

dagger, and bade the rest follow the example I had set them, since by means of their horses they might save their lives, as I hoped to save mine; adding, that I would kill the first who should offer to throw himself upon me.

In this manner we proceeded several miles in the most imminent danger of our lives. When we had advanced about half-way, we saw a piece of level ground under the foot of a mountain, where we might get ashore and refresh ourselves. Here the four German gentlemen landed. But upon our expressing a desire to go on shore, the watermen would not consent to it on any account. I then said to my young men, "Now is the time, my boys, to show your spirit; clap your hands to your swords, and compel them to land us." We effected our purpose with great difficulty, as they made a long resistance; however, even after we had landed, we were obliged to climb a steep mountain for two miles, which was more difficult than going up a ladder of equal height. I wore a coat of mail, had heavy boots, with a fowling-piece in my hand, and it rained as hard as it could pour. Those devils of Germans ascended at a surprising rate with their horses, while ours were unequal to the task.

The four German gentlemen who had reached the summit of the craggy precipice before us, sent some peasants to our assistance. At last we arrived at the miserable inn, wet, tired, and hungry. We were received in the kindest manner by the people of the house, and met with most comfortable refreshment.

Having risen very early next morning, we proceeded on our journey, and went to dine at a very agreeable place called Lacca. We then took guides to conduct us to a town called Zurich. The guide who attended me passed over a dyke which was overflowed, so that the stupid creature slipped, and both the horse and he tumbled into the water. I, who was behind, having that instant stopped my horse, stayed awhile to see him rise, and behold, the fellow, as if nothing at all had happened, fell a-singing again, and made signs to me to go on. I thereupon turned to the right, and breaking through certain hedges, served as a guide to Burbacca and my young men. The guide began scolding, telling me in the German language that if the country-people saw me they would put me to death.

Our next stage was Zurich, a fine city, which may be compared to a jewel for luster, and there we stayed a day to rest ourselves. We left it early in the morning, and arrived at another handsome town called Solothurn. Thence we proceeded to Lausanne, Geneva, and Lyons. We stopped four days at this last city, having traveled thither very merrily, singing and laughing all the way. I enjoyed myself highly in the company of some of my friends; was reimbursed the expenses I had been at; and at the expiration of four days set out for Paris.

CHAPTER XXI

CELLINI MEETS FRANCIS

I WENT in search of Rosso the painter, who was then in the service of King Francis. I took it for granted that this man was one of the best friends I had in the world, because in Rome I had behaved to him in as obliging a manner as it is possible for one person to behave to another.

When he was at Rome he endeavored to depreciate the works of Raffaello da Urbino, at which his pupils were provoked to such a degree that they were bent on killing him. This danger I preserved him from, watching over

him day and night with the greatest fatigue imaginable.
On another occasion he had spoken ill of Signor Antonio
da San Gallo, an excellent architect; in consequence of
which the latter soon had him turned out of an employment he had procured for him from Signor Agnolo da
Cesi, and from that time became so much his enemy that
he would have starved if I had not often lent him ten
crowns. As he never had discharged this trifling debt,
I went to pay him a visit, being informed that he was
in the King's service, and thought he would not only return me my money but do all that lay in his power in
recommending me to the service of the great monarch.
But the fellow no sooner saw me than he appeared to
be in a terrible confusion, and said, "My friend Benvenuto, you have put yourself to too great an expense to
come so long a journey, especially at such a time as this.
when the court is entirely taken up with the approaching
war, and can give no attention to our trifling performances." I answered that I had brought with me
money enough to bear my expenses back to Rome, in the
same manner that I had traveled to Paris; adding, that
he made me a very indifferent return for all I had suffered on his account, and that I began to believe what
Signor Antonio da San Gallo had told me concerning
him. On his turning what I said into a jest, I saw
through his low malice, and showed him a bill of ex-
change for 500 crowns addressed to Ricardo del Bene.
The wretch was greatly ashamed, and would have detained me in a manner by force, but I laughed at him,
and went away in the company of a painter that happened to be present.

I afterward solicited an interview with the King, to
his treasurer, who carried me with him to Fontainebleau,
his treasurer, who carried me with him to Fontainebleu,
and introduced me into the presence of the monarch, of
whom I had a most favorable audience a whole hour.

The King was preparing for a journey to Lyons, which made him desire Signor Giuliano to take me with him, adding that we should discourse by the way of some fine works his Majesty intended to have executed. So I traveled in the retinue of the court, and cultivated the friendship of the Cardinal of Ferrara, who had not as yet received the scarlet hat. I had every evening a long conversation with this great personage, who told me that I should stay at Lyons at an abbey of his, and there enjoy myself till the King returned from the campaign.

On our arrival at that city I was taken ill, and Ascanio found himself attacked by a quartan ague; I now began to dislike the French and their court, and to be impatient to return to Rome. The Cardinal, seeing me resolved to go back, gave me a sum of money to make him a basin and a cup of silver. Then my young man and I set out for Rome.

As we crossed the mountains of the Simplon, I happened to fall into the company of some Frenchmen, with whom we traveled part of the way. Ascanio had his quartan ague, and I a slow fever, which I thought would never leave me. My stomach was so much out of order that for four months I hardly ate a roll a week, and was very eager to get to Italy, choosing rather to die in my own country than in France. When we had passed the mountains of the Simplon, we came to a river hard by a place called Isdevedro. This river was very broad and deep, and had a long, narrow bridge over it without rails. A shower had fallen in the morning, so that when I came to the bridge, some time before the rest, I perceived it to be very dangerous. I therefore ordered my young men to dismount, and lead their horses. Thus I safely got over, and rode on, talking to one of the Frenchmen, who was a person of condition. The other, who was a scrivener, stayed behind us, and laughed at the French gentleman and me for being so fearful about nothing as to

take the trouble of walking. I turned about, and seeing
him at the middle of the bridge, begged of him to come
on cautiously, as the place was exceedingly dangerous.
He, keeping up to the national character of his country,
told me in French that I was a poor, timid creature, and
there was no danger at all.   While he uttered these
words, he spurred his horse a little, which, instantly
stumbling, fell close by the side of a great rock; but as
God is very merciful to fools, the stupid rider and his
horse both tumbled into a great hole.

I ran as fast as I could, and with great difficulty got
upon the rock; from this I reached down, and catching
at the border of the scrivener's cloak, pulled him up,
while the water still ran from his nostrils. I congratulated him on his escape, and expressed my joy at having
saved his life. He answered that I had done nothing
at all, and the point of most importance was his having
lost a bundle of papers, to the value of many score
crowns; and this he seemed to say in anger. I turned
about to our guides, and asked them to help the fool,
telling them I would pay them for their trouble. One
of the men fished up his papers, so that the scrivener
lost nothing, while the other would put himself to no
trouble to assist him or save his bundle.

When we arrived at the place above mentioned, we
had made up a purse, which was to be at my disposal.
After dinner I gave several pieces out of the purse to
the guide that had helped the scrivener. The latter said
that I might be liberal of my own, for he did not intend
to give the man anything more than was in our agreement for conducting us. This provoked me to give the
sordid wretch much opprobrious language. The other
guide, who had taken no trouble, came up, and insisted
on sharing the reward. When I told him that he who
had borne the cross deserved the recompense, he answered that he would soon show me a cross, at which I

should bewail my folly. I told him I would light a candle at that cross, by means of which I hoped he should be the first that would have cause to weep.

As we were then upon the confines of the Italian and German territories, the fellow ran to alarm the neighborhood, and returned with a hunting-pole, followed by a crowd. I being still on horseback, cocked my piece, and turning to my fellow-travelers, said, "I will begin with shooting that man, and do you endeavor to do your duty. These fellows are cut-throats and common assassins, who catch at this opportunity to rob and murder us." The innkeeper, at whose house we had dined, then called to one of the ringleaders of the band, a man advanced in years, and begged he would endeavor to prevent mischief, telling him that they had a young man of great spirit to deal with; that even if they were to cut me to pieces, I should be sure to kill a number of them; and that after all I might very probably escape out of their hands, and even kill the guide. Thereupon the old ruffian said to me, "Go your ways; you would have enough to do to cope with us, even if you had a hundred men to back you." I shook my head and answered that I should have done my best and endeavored to show myself a man. Soon afterward I arrived at Ferrara, accompanied only by my two fellow-travelers.

I had no sooner dismounted than I went to pay my respects to the Duke, that I might set out next morning for our Lady of Loreto. After I had waited till it was dark, the Duke made his appearance. I kissed his hand, and he received me with all possible demonstrations of kindness, asking me to stay to supper. I answered, "Most excellent sir, for these four months past I have eaten so little that it is almost a wonder I should be alive. As I am, therefore, sensible that I can eat nothing that is served on your table, I will pass the time you are at supper in chat, which will prove more agreeable to us both than if I were to sup with your Excellency."

In the morning I repaired to our Lady of Loreto, and after paying my devotions at that place, I continued my journey to Rome, where I found my faithful friend Felice, to whom I resigned my shop, with all my furniture and ornaments, and opened another next door to Sugarello, the perfumer, which was much more spacious and handsome than that which I had quitted. I took it for granted that the great French monarch would forget me, and therefore I engaged in several works for noblemen. Amongst others I began the cup and basin that I had promised to make for the Cardinal of Ferrara. I had a number of hands at work, and several things to be done both in gold and silver. I had made an agreement with my Perugian journeyman, who had kept an exact account of all the money that had been laid out for him in clothes and other articles (which, with his traveling expenses, amounted to about seventy crowns), that three crowns a months should be set aside to clear them off, as he earned more than eight crowns a month in my service. In about two months the rogue left my shop, while I had a great deal of business upon my hands, declaring that I should have no further satisfaction. I was advised to have recourse to the law, for I had formed a resolution to cut off one of his arms; and should certainly have done it, if my friends had not advised me to take care how I attempted any such thing, as it might be the cause of my being banished for a second time from Rome.

While I was thus going on with my business, I received a letter from the Cardinal of Ferrara, the purport of which was as follows:

"My dear friend Benvenuto: A few days ago his Most Christian Majesty mentioned your name, and said he would be glad to have you in his service. I told him you had made me promise that, whenever I should send

for you upon his Majesty's account, you would come directly. His Majesty replied, 'I desire he may be supplied
with money, to enable him to perform the journey in a
manner becoming so eminent an artist.' On saying this,
he instantly spoke to his admiral to order me to be paid
a thousand gold crowns out of the treasury. Cardinal
Gaddi, who happened to be present at this conversation,
thereupon told his Majesty it was unnecessary for him
to give such an order, as he had himself remitted to
you a proper supply of money, and you were already on
the road. If you have neither received the money, nor
are set out upon the journey, nor have heard anything
of the matter, but it should be a mere finesse of the Cardinal, to show that he patronizes men of genius favored
by the King, or to make an ostentatious parade of having befriended you (as I am inclined to think it is nothing more), immediately upon receiving this letter send
me your answer. In consequence thereof I will, at my
next interview with the great monarch, contrive, in the
presence of the crafty Cardinal, to make the conversation
turn upon you, and I will tell him you never received
the money that Cardinal Gaddi pretends to have remitted
to you, nor ever set out upon the journey, but are still at
Rome: and I intend to make it evident that Cardinal
Gaddi said this merely through vanity, and shall contrive matters so that his Majesty shall again speak to his
admiral to order the charges of your journey to be de-
frayed by the treasury."

Let the whole world learn from this the great power
of malignant stars and adverse fortune over us poor
mortals. I never had spoken twice to this foolish little
Cardinal Gaddi, and he played this trick merely through
folly and senseless ostentation, that he might be thought
to patronize men of genius whom the King was desirous
to have in his service, and to concern himself in their
affairs in the same manner as the Cardinal of Ferrara.

He was guilty of another folly in not apprising me of it afterward; for rather than expose him to shame, I should, for the sake of my country, have thought of some excuse to palliate the absurdity of his conduct. I had no sooner received the letter from the Cardinal of Ferrara than I wrote to him that I had heard nothing at all from Cardinal Gaddi, and that even if he had made me any proposal I never should have quitted Italy without the knowledge of my friend the Cardinal of Ferrara; especially as I then had in Rome more business than I ever had before; but that at the first intimation of his most Christian Majesty's pleasure, signified to me by so great a personage as his reverence, I should instantly lay aside all other business and set out for France.

When I had sent my letters, my treacherous Perugian journeyman thought of playing me a trick, in which he was but too successful, through the avarice of Pope Paul Farnese, and still more through that of his bastard son, who then had the title of Duke of Castro. This journeyman gave one of the secretaries of Signor Pier Luigi to understand that, having worked in my shop several years, he had discovered that I was worth not less than eighty thousand ducats; that the greatest part of this wealth consisted in jewels that belonged to the Church; that they were part of the booty I had obtained in the Castle of St. Angelo, at the time of the sack of Rome: and that I ought without delay to be examined.

I had one morning worked more than three hours at the jewels of the above-mentioned married lady; and while my shop was opening, and my servants were sweeping it, I put on my cloak in order to take a turn or two. Bending my course through the Julia street, I entered the quarter called Chiavica, where Crispino, captain of the city guard, met me with his whole band of followers, and told me roughly that I was the Pope's prisoner. I answered him, "Crispino, you mistake your man." "By no means," said Crispino. "You are the ingenious artist Benvenuto. I know you very well, and have orders to conduct you to the Castle of St. Angelo, where noblemen and men of genius like yourself are confined." As four of his soldiers were about to fall upon me, and deprive me forcibly of a dagger I had by my side, and of the rings on my fingers, Crispino ordered them not to offer to touch me. It was sufficient, he said, for them to do their office and prevent me from making my escape. Then coming up to me, he very politely demanded my arms. While I was giving them up, I recollected that it was in that very place I had killed Pompeo. Thence they conducted me to the Castle, and locked me up in one of the upper apartments of the tower. This was the first time I ever knew the inside of a prison, and I was then in my thirty-seventh year.

CHAPTER XXII

IMPRISONMENT OF CELLINI

PIER LUIGI, the Pope's illegitimate son, considering the great sum of money I was charged with having in my possession, applied to his father to make that money over to him. The Pope readily granted his request; at the same time adding that he would assist him in the recovery of it. After I had been detained prisoner a week, they appointed commissioners to examine me. I was thereupon sent for into a large handsome hall in the castle, where the examiners were assembled. These were, first, the Governor of Rome, Signor Benedetto Conversini, a native of Pistoia, who was afterward Bishop of Jesi; the second, the procurator of the Exchequer, whose name I cannot now recollect; the third, the judge of criminal causes, Signor Benedetto da Galli. They began first to examine me in an amicable way, but afterward broke out into the roughest and most menacing terms imaginable, occasioned, as I apprehend, by this speech of mine: "Gentlemen, you have for more than half an hour been questioning me about an idle story, such nonsense that it may be justly said you are trifling, and there is neither sense nor meaning in what you say; so I beg of you, as a favor, that you would tell me your meaning, and let me hear something like sense and reason from you, and not idle stories and fabulous inventions." At these words the Governor could no longer disguise his brutal nature, but said to me, "You speak with too much confidence, or rather with too much insolence; however, I will humble your pride, and make you as tame as a spaniel, by what I am going to tell you, which you will find to be neither an idle story nor nonsense, but such conclusive reasoning that you will be obliged to submit to it." So he began to deliver his sentiments as follows:

"We know with certainty that you were in Rome at the time of the sacking of this unfortunate city, and in this very Castle of St. Angelo, where you performed the office of gunner. As you are by trade a goldsmith and jeweler, Pope Clement, having a particular knowledge of you, and being unable to meet with others of the business, employed you secretly to take out all the precious stones from his crowns, mitres and rings; and putting entire confidence in you, desired you to sew them up in your clothes. You availed yourself of that confidence to appropriate the full value of eighty thousand crowns, unknown to his Holiness. This information we had from a journeyman of yours, to whom you discovered the whole affair and boasted of the fraud. We now therefore command you to find these jewels, or the value of them, after which we will set you at liberty."

I could not hear these words without bursting out into a loud laugh. When I had sufficiently indulged my mirth, I expressed myself thus: "I return my hearty thanks to God, that, this first time it has pleased his divine Majesty that I should be made a prisoner, I have the happiness not to be confined for any criminal excess of passion, as usually happens to young men. If what you say were true, I am in no danger of suffering corporal punishment, as the laws at that time had lost all their force and authority; for I might excuse myself by affirming that, as a servant to his Holiness, I had kept that treasure as a deposit for the Apostolic See, with an intention to put it into the hands of some good pope, or of those that should claim it of me, as you do now, if the fact were as you represent it."

The tyrannical Governor would not suffer me to proceed any farther, but interrupting me at these words, cried out in a fury, "Give what gloss you please to the affair, Benvenuto, it is enough for us that we have discovered the person who possessed himself of the treasure. Be as expeditious therefore as possible; otherwise, we shall take other methods with you, and not stop at words." As they were then preparing to depart, I said to them, "Gentlemen, you have not finished my examination; hear me out, and then do as you please." They seated themselves again, though they appeared to be much enraged, and unwilling to hear anything I could say for myself; nay, they seemed to be in a manner satisfied with their inquiry, and to think they had discovered all they wanted to know. I therefore addressed them in the following terms: "You are to know, gentlemen, that I have lived in Rome nearly twenty years, and I was never before imprisoned either here or anywhere else." At these words the brute of a Governor interrupted me and said, "Yet you have killed men enough in your time." I replied, "That is your bare assertion, unsupported by any acknowledgment of mine; but if a person were to endeavor to deprive you of life, no doubt you would defend yourself in the best way you could; and if you were to kill him, you would be fully justified in the eye of the law. So let me conclude my defence, as you purpose to lay it before his Holiness, and profess that you mean to pass a just judgment.

"I must repeat it to you, gentlemen, that I have been nearly twenty years an inhabitant of this great metropolis, and have been often employed in works of the greatest importance. I am sensible that this is the seat of Christ, and should, in case any temporal prince had made a wicked attempt against me, immediately have had recourse to this holy tribunal, and to God's Vicegerent, to prevail on him to espouse my cause. But alas! what power shall I have recourse to in my present distress? To what prince shall I fly, to defend me from so wicked an attempt? Should not you, before you ordered me to be arrested, have inquired where I had put the eighty thousand crowns? Should not you likewise have examined the list of those jewels, as they were carefully numbered in the Apostolic Chamber five hundred years ago? In case you had found anything wanting, you should have taken my books and myself, and confronted them with the jewels. I must inform you that the books, in which the Pope's jewels and those of the triple crown have been registered, are all extant; and you will find that Pope Clement was possessed of nothing that was not committed to writing with the utmost exactness. All I have to add is, that when the unfortunate Pope Clement was for making an accommodation with the Imperial freebooters, who had plundered Rome and insulted the Church, there came a person to negotiate the accommodation, whose name was Cæsar Iscatinaro, if my memory does not fail me, who virtually concluded the treaty with that injured Pontiff, and the latter, in order to compliment the negotiator, let a ring drop from his finger, worth about four thousand crowns, and, upon Iscatinaro's stooping to take it up, his Holiness desired him to wear it for his sake. I was present when all this happened, and if the diamond be missing, I have told you what became of it; but I am almost positive that you will find even this registered. You may therefore well be ashamed of having thus attacked a man of my character, who has been employed in so many affairs of importance for the Apostolic See. I must acquaint you, that had it not been for me, the morning that the Imperialists scaled the walls of Rome, they would have entered the castle without meeting with any opposition. I, though unrewarded for my services, exerted myself vigorously in managing the artillery, when all the soldiers had forsaken their posts. I likewise animated for the fight a companion of mine, named Raffaello da Montelupo, a statuary, who had quitted his post like the rest, and hid himself in a corner. When I saw him entirely neglect the defence of the castle, I roused his courage, and he and I, unassisted, slaughtered such numbers of our foes that the soldiers turned their force another way. I was the man that fired at Iscatinaro because I had heard him speak disrespectfully to Pope Clement, like a Lutheran and an impious heretic as he was. Pope Clement, notwithstanding, caused the person who had performed that glorious action to be sought all over the Castle in order to have him hanged. I was the man that shot the Prince of Orange in the head, under the ramparts of this Castle. I have, moreover, made for the use of the Holy Church a vast number of ornaments of silver, gold, and precious stones; as likewise many medals, and the finest and most valuable coins. Is this, then, the priest-like return which is made to a

man that has served you with so much diligence and
zeal? Go now and repeat to the Pope all I have said,
assuring him that he has all his jewels, and that I got
nothing else in the Church's service at the melancholy
sack of this city but wounds and bruises; and reckoned
upon nothing but an inconsiderable recompense that Pope
Paul had promised me. Now I know what to think of
his Holiness, and of you his ministers."

While I uttered these words they stood astonished,
and, looking attentively at one another, departed with
gestures that testified wonder and surprise. They then
went to inform the Pope of what I had said. The latter,
in some confusion, gave orders that a diligent and ac-
curate inquiry should be made into the account of all
the jewels; and on finding that none of them were missing, they left me in the castle, without taking any further
notice of me. Signor Pier Luigi, however, endeavored
to destroy me, in order to conceal his own misconduct in
the affair.

At this time of agitation and trouble, King Francis
had heard a circumstantial account of the Pope's keeping me in confinement so unjustly; and as a nobleman
belonging to his court, Monsieur de Monluc, had been
sent ambassador to his Holiness, he wrote to him to
apply to his Holiness for my release, as a person that belonged to his Majesty. The Pope, though a man of sense
and extraordinary abilities, behaved in this affair of mine
like a person of as little virtue as understanding: the answer he returned the ambassador was, that the King
his master need not give himself any concern about me,
as I was a very turbulent, troublesome fellow; therefore
he advised his Majesty to leave me where I was, because
he kept me in prison for committing murder and other
atrocious crimes. The King of France answered, that
justice was strictly observed in his dominions, and that
as he rewarded and favored good men, so he punished and

12

discountenanced the bad, adding that as his Holiness had suffered me to leave Italy, and had been no longer solicitous about my services, he, upon seeing me in his dominions, had gladly taken me under his patronage, and now claimed me as his subject. Though these were the greatest honors and favors that could possibly be conferred upon a man in my station of life, they were highly prejudicial and dangerous to my cause. The Pope was so tormented with jealous fear, lest I should go to France and reveal his base treatment of me, that he was constantly watching for an opportunity to get me despatched, without hurting his own reputation.

The constable of the Castle of St. Angelo was a Florentine named Signor Giorgio Ugolino. This worthy gentleman behaved to me with the greatest politeness, permitting me to walk freely about the castle on my parole, and for no other reason but because he saw the severity and injustice of my treatment. When I offered to give him security for this indulgence, he declined it, because he heard everybody speak of me as a man of truth and integrity, though he knew the Pope to be greatly exasperated against me. Thus I gave him my word and honor, and he even put me into a way of working a little at my business. As I supposed the Pope's anger would soon subside, on account not only of my innocence, but of the King of France's intercession, I caused my shop to be kept open, and my young man Ascanio came often to the castle, bringing things to employ me, though I could do very little while confined.

Among the soldiers that advised me to make my escape was one, a man of great wit and courage, who reasoned with me thus: "My good friend, Benvenuto, you should consider that a man who is a prisoner neither is nor can be bound to keep his word, nor to anything else. Take my advice, and fly from this villain of a Pope, and from his bastard son, who have sworn your destruc-

tion." But I, being determined rather to lose my life
than break my promise, bore my hard lot as patiently as
I could.

I had for the companion of my confinement a monk
of the Pallavicini family, who was a celebrated preacher.
He was confined for heresy, and had a great deal of wit
and humor in conversation, but was one of the most
profligate fellows in the world. I admired his shining
qualities, but his odious vices I freely censured and held
in abhorrence. This monk was constantly preaching to
me that I was under no obligation to keep the word I
had given to the constable of the castle, because I was
a prisoner. I answered that he spoke like a monk, but
not like a man; for he that is a man and not a monk
thinks himself obliged to keep his word on all occasions,
and in whatever circumstances he happens to be. Therefore, as I was a man and not a monk, I was resolved
never to violate my plighted faith. The monk, perceiving that he could not corrupt me by all the subtle and
sophistical arguments that he urged with so much force,
had recourse to other means to seduce my virtue. For
several days after that, he read to me the sermons of the
monk Jeronimo Savonarola, and made so admirable a
comment upon them that I was more delighted with it
than even with the discourses themselves, though they
had given me such high satisfaction; in fine, I had conceived so high an opinion of him, that I would have done
anything else at his recommendation, except breaking
my word. The monk, seeing me astonished at his great
talents, thought of another expedient: he asked me what
method I should have had recourse to if they had made
me a close prisoner, in order to effect my escape? Desirous of giving the ingenious monk some proof of my
own acuteness, I told him that I could open any lock,
even the most difficult, especially those of that prison,
which I should make no more of forcing than of eating

a bit of cheese. The monk, in order to make me reveal
my secret, began to disparage my ingenuity, observing
that men who have acquired fame by their talents make
many boasts, and that, if they were afterward called
upon to carry their boastings into execution, they would
soon forfeit all the reputation they had acquired; adding, that what I said seemed so far to pass all the bounds
of probability that he apprehended were I to be put to
the trial I should come off with but little honor.

Finding myself pushed hard by this artful monk, I
told him that I usually promised much less than I was
able to perform, and that I had said concerning the locks
was a mere trifle; for I would soon convince him that I
had said nothing but the truth: in a word, I incon-
siderately revealed to him my whole secret, and the
monk, affecting to take little notice of what he saw,
learned the mystery. The worthy constable continued
to permit me to walk up and down the castle, as I
thought proper, and did not even order me to be locked
up at night like the rest of the prisoners; at the same
time, he suffered me to work as much as I pleased in
gold, silver, and wax. I had been employed some weeks
on a basin for the Cardinal of Ferrara, but being weary
of my confinement, I grew tired also of large works, and
only amused myself with now and then making little
figures of wax. The monk stole a piece of this wax,
and by means thereof put in practice all I had incon-
siderately taught him with regard to counterfeiting the
keys of the prison. He had taken for his associate and
assistant a clerk named Luigi, who was a native of
Padua. On their attempting to counterfeit these keys,
the smith detected them.

As the constable sometimes came to see me at my
apartment, and saw me working in this wax, he immediately knew it, and said, "That poor unfortunate Benvenuto has indeed been very hardly used; he should not,

however, have concerned himself in such tricks, since I have done so much to oblige him; for the future I must confine him close prisoner, and show him no indulgence." So he ordered me to be confined closely, and with some circumstances of severity, which I suffered from the reproaches and opprobrious language of his servants, who had been my well-wishers, but now upraided me with the obligations their master had laid me under. As one of them was more bitter and abusive on the occasion than was consistent with decency, I, being conscious of my own innocence, answered boldly that I never had acted the part of a traitor or a faithless man; that I would assert my innocence at the hazard of my life; and that if either he, or any other, ever again offered to give me any such abusive language, I should, without hesitation, give him the lie. Not being able to bear this affront, he ran to the constable's apartment, and brought me the wax, with the model of the key. As soon as I saw the wax I told him that both he and I were in the right; but begged to speak with the constable, that I might let him into the whole affair, which was of much greater importance than they imagined. The constable soon sent for me, and I told him all that had passed. He thereupon put the monk into close confinement, and the latter informed against the clerk, who had nearly been hanged for it. The constable, however, hushed up the affair, which was already come to the ears of the Pope, saved the clerk from the gallows, and restored to me the liberty I had enjoyed before.

But, finding I had been treated with so much rigor in this affair, I began to think seriously, and said within myself, "If this man should again happen to take such a whim, and not choose to trust me any longer, I should not wish to be obliged to him, but to make a trial of my own skill, which I doubt not would have a very different success from that of the monk." I got my servants to

bring me new thick sheets, and did not send back the
soiled ones. When they asked me for them, I answered,
that I had given them away to some of the poor soldiers;
adding that, if it should be discovered, they would be in
danger of being sent to the galleys. Thus my journeymen and servants, Felice in particular, took the utmost
care to keep the thing secret. I pulled all the straw
out of the tick of my bed, and burned it; for I had a
chimney in the room where I lay. I then cut those
sheets into slips, each about one third of a cubit long, and
when I thought I had made a sufficient quantity to reach
from the top to the bottom of the lofty tower of the
Castle of St. Angelo, I told my servants that I had given
away as much of my linen as I thought proper, and
desired they would take care to bring me clean sheets,
adding that I would constantly return them the soiled
ones. This affair my workmen and servants quickly
forgot.

The Cardinals Santiquattro and Cornaro caused my
shop to be shut up, telling me in plain terms that his
Holiness would not hear of my release, and that the
great favor shown me by the King of France had rather
been of prejudice than of benefit to me. They added,
that the last words Monsieur de Monluc had spoken to the
Pope, by direction of the King, were, that his Holiness
ought to get the cause tried by the ordinary judges of
the court; and that if I had in any way transgressed I
should suffer the punishment ordained by the law, but
in case I were innocent, it was but just they should
discharge me. These words had provoked the Pope to
such a degree, that he had almost formed a resolution
to detain me prisoner the rest of my days. The constable of the castle, on this occasion, espoused my cause
to the utmost of his power.

CHAPTER XXIII

ESCAPE FROM THE CASTLE

MY enemies, when they saw that my shop was closed, took every opportunity to insult and revile my servants and friends that visited me. It happened that Ascanio, who came twice every day, begged that I would have a little waistcoat made for him of a blue satin waistcoat of mine, which I had worn but once, when I walked in procession. I told him it was no time nor place for such finery. The lad was so affronted at my refusing him a rag of a waistcoat, that he declared he would go home to his father's, at Tagliacozzo. I answered that I should be glad if I were never to see his face more; and he swore, in a most furious passion, that he would never again appear in my presence.

The Pope, having received information of what had happened, said with great indignation, "Since it is the King's pleasure that Benvenuto be brought to trial, go, bid him prepare for his defence in three days." The proper officers came to me from his Holiness, and delivered themselves according to his directions. The worthy constable, upon this, repaired to the Pope, and explained that I had nothing at all to do with the affair, and that I had turned off the youth who had committed that rash action; in short, he defended my cause so well, that he prevented me from falling a victim to the Pontiff's resentment. Ascanio fled to his father's house, and wrote to me to beg my pardon, and acknowledged his fault in having added to my sufferings. He concluded by assuring me that if God should ever be so merciful as to deliver me from my confinement, he would never again forsake me. In my answer I requested that he would endeavor to improve, telling him that if the Almighty restored my liberty I should send for him.

The constable of the castle had annually a certain disorder, which deprived him of his senses, and when the fit came upon him he was talkative to excess. Every year he had some different whim: one time he fancied himself metamorphosed into a pitcher of oil; another time he thought himself a frog, and began to leap as such; another time again he imagined he was dead, and it was found necessary to humor his conceit by making a show of burying him. Thus he had every year some new frenzy. This year he fancied himself a bat, and when he went to take a walk he sometimes made just such a noise as bats do. He likewise used gestures with his hands and his body as if he were going to fly. His physicians and his old servants, who knew his disorder, procured him all the pleasures and amusements they could think of; and as they found he delighted in my conversations, they frequently came to me, to conduct me to his apartment, where the poor man often detained me for three or four hours chatting with him. He sometimes kept me at his table, and always made me sit opposite to him; on which occasion he never ceased to talk himself, or to encourage me to join in conversation.

He asked me whether I had ever had a fancy to fly; I answered that I had always been very ready to attempt such things as men found most difficult; and that with regard to flying, as God had given me a body admirably well calculated for running, I had even resolution enough to attempt to fly. He then asked me to explain how I could contrive it. I replied that, when I attentively considered the several creatures that fly, and thought of effecting by art what they do by the force of nature, I did not find one so fit to imitate as the bat. As soon as the poor man heard mention made of a bat, his frenzy

for the year turning upon that animal, he cried out, "It
is very true, a bat is the thing." He then said, "Benvenuto, if you had the opportunity, would you have the
heart to make an attempt to fly?" I answered, that if he
would give me leave, I had courage enough to attempt
to fly as far as Prati by means of a pair of wings waxed
over. He said thereupon, "I should like to see you fly;
but as the Pope has enjoined me to watch over you with
the utmost care, and I know that you have the cunning
of the devil, and would avail yourself of the opportunity
to make your escape, I am resolved to keep you locked
up with a hundred keys, that you may not slip out of my
hands." I then began to solicit him with new entreaties,
putting him in mind that I had had it in my power to
make my escape, but, through regard to the promise
I had made him, would never avail myself of the opportunity. I therefore besought him for the love of
God, and as he had conferred so many obligations on
me, that he would not make my condition worse than it
was. While I uttered these words, he gave instant orders that I should be secured and confined a closer
prisoner than ever. When I saw that it was to no purpose to entreat him any further, I said before all present,
"Confine me as close as you please, I will contrive to
make my escape notwithstanding." So they carried me
off, and locked me up with the utmost care.

Having first of all formed a conjecture of the length
of line sufficient for me to descend by, I took a new pair
of sheets which I had cut into slips and sewed fast together. The next thing I wanted was a pair of pincers,
which I took from a Savoyard, who was on guard at the
castle. This man had the care of the casks and cisterns
belonging to the castle, and likewise worked there as a
carpenter; and as he possessed several pairs of pincers,
and one pair among others that was thick and large,
thinking it would suit my purpose, I took it, and hid it

in my bed. The time being come that I intended to make
use of it, I began, with the pincers, to pull at the nails
that fastened the plates of iron upon the door, and as
the door was double, the clenching of those nails could
not be perceived. I exerted my utmost efforts to draw
out one of them, and at last succeeded. As soon as I had
drawn the nail, I was again obliged to devise some expedient to prevent its being perceived. I immediately
thought of mixing a little of the filings of iron and rust
with wax, and this mixture was exactly the color of the
heads of the nails I had drawn. With it I counterfeited
their resemblance on the iron plates. I left each of the
plates fastened both at top and bottom, and refixed them
with some of the nails that I had drawn; but the nails
were cut, and I drove them in slightly, so that they just
served to hold the plates. I found it very difficult to
effect all this, because the constable dreamed every night
that I had made my escape, and therefore used to send
frequently to have the prison searched. The person
employed on this occasion had the appearance and behavior of one of the city guards. His name was Bozza,
and he constantly brought with him another, Giovanni
Pedignone. The latter was a soldier, the former a
servant. This Giovanni never came to the room where I
was confined without giving me abusive language. The
other was from Prato, where he had lived with an
apothecary. He every evening carefully examined the
plates of iron above mentioned, as well as the whole
prison. I constantly said to him, "Examine me well,
for I am positively determined to make my escape."
These words produced a bitter enmity between us.

With the utmost care I deposited all my tools, that is
to say, my pincers, and a dagger of a tolerable length,
with other things belonging to me, in the tick of my bed,
and as soon as it was daylight swept the room myself,
for I naturally delighted in cleanliness, but on this oc-

casion I took care to be particularly neat. As soon as
I had swept the room, I made my bed with equal care,
and adorned it with flowers, which were brought me every
morning by a Savoyard. This man, as I have observed
before, took care of the cisterns and the casks, and
sometimes amused himself with working in wood. It
was from him I stole the pincers. Whenever Bozza and
Pedignone came, I bade them keep at a distance from it,
that they might not spoil it. Sometimes I would say to
them (for they would now and then, merely for diversion,
tumble my bed), "You dirty wretches, I will draw one
of your swords, and give you such a chastisement as
will astonish you. Do you think yourselves worthy to
touch the bed of a man like me? On such an occasion
I should not spare my own life, but am sure that I should
be able to take away yours; so leave me to my own
troubles and sorrows, and do not make my lot more
bitter than it is. If you act otherwise, I will show you
of what a desperate man is capable." The men repeated
what I said to the constable, who expressly commanded
them never to go near my bed, ordering them at the
same time, when they came to me, to have no words.

One holiday evening the constable's madness being at
the highest pitch, he hardly said anything else but that
he was become a bat, and told his people, that if Benvenuto happened to make his escape, they should take
no notice of it, for he must soon catch me, as he should
doubtless be much better able to fly by night than I;
adding, "Benvenuto is only a counterfeit bat; but I am a
bat in good earnest. Let me alone to manage him, I
shall be able to catch him, I warrant you." I was
chiefly indebted for my information to the Savoyard,
who was very much attached to me.

As I had formed a resolution to attempt my escape
that night, I began with praying fervently to Almighty
God, that it would please his Divine Majesty to befriend

and assist me in that hazardous enterprise. I then went to work, and was employed the whole night in preparations. Two hours before daybreak I took the iron plates from the door with difficulty, for the bolt and the wood that received it made a great resistance, so that I was obliged to cut the wood. I, however, at last forced the door, and having taken with me the slips of linen, which I had rolled up in bundles, I went out and got upon the right side of the tower, and having observed two tiles of the roof, I leaped upon them with ease. I was in a white doublet, and had on a pair of white half hose, over which I wore a pair of light tight boots, that reached halfway up my legs, and in one of these I put my dagger. I then took the end of one of my bundles of long slips, which I had made out of the sheets, and fastened it to one of the tiles of the roof that happened to jut out four inches; and the long string of slips was fastened to the tiles in the manner of a stirrup. When I had fixed it firmly, I addressed myself to the Deity in these terms: "Almighty God, favor my cause, for Thou knowest it is a just one, and I am not on my part wanting in my utmost efforts to make it succeed." Then letting myself down gently, and the whole weight of my body being sustained by my arm, I at last reached the ground.

It was not a moonlight night, but the stars shone with resplendent luster. When I had touched the ground, I first contemplated the great height which I had descended with so much courage; and then walked away in high spirits, thinking I had recovered my liberty. But I soon found myself mistaken; for the constable had caused two pretty high walls to be erected on that side, which made an inclosure for a stable and a poultry-yard: this place was fastened with great bolts on the outside. When I saw myself immured in this inclosure, I felt the greatest anxiety imaginable. Whilst I was walking backward and forward, I stumbled on a long pole

covered with straw; this I with much difficulty fixed
against the wall, and by the strength of my arms climbed
to the top of it; but as the wall was sharp, I could not
get a sufficient hold to enable me to descend by the pole
to the other side. I therefore resolved to have recourse
to my other strings of slips, for I had left one tied to
the great tower; so I took the string, and having
fastened it properly, I went down the steep wall. This
put me to a great deal of pain and trouble, and likewise
tore the skin off the palms of my hands, insomuch that
they were all over bloody; for which reason I rested
myself a little. When I thought I had sufficiently recruited my strength, I came to the last wall, which
looked toward the meadows, and when I had prepared
my string of long slips, which I wished to get about
one of the niched battlements, in order to descend this
as I had the other higher wall, a sentinel perceived what
I was about. Finding my design obstructed, and myself in danger of my life, I resolved to cope with the
soldier, who, seeing me advance toward him resolutely
with my drawn dagger in my hand, thought it most
advisable to keep out of my way. After I had gone a
little way from my string, I quickly returned to it; and
though I was seen by another soldier, the man did not
take any notice of me. I then fastened my string to the
niched battlement, and began to let myself down.
Whether it was owing to my being near the ground,
and preparing to give a leap, or whether my hands were
quite tired, I do not know, but being unable to hold out
any longer, I fell, and in falling struck my head and became insensible.

I continued in that state about an hour and a half,
as nearly as I can guess. The day beginning to break,
the cool breeze that precedes the rising of the sun
brought me to myself; but I had not yet thoroughly recovered my senses, for I had conceived a strange notion

that I had been beheaded, and was then in purgatory. By degrees I recovered my powers; and perceiving that I had got out of the castle, I soon recollected all that had befallen me. As I perceived that my senses had been affected, before I took notice that my leg was broken, I clapped my hands to my head, and found them all bloody. I afterward searched my body all over, and thought I had received no hurt of any consequence; but upon attempting to rise, I found that my right leg was broken three inches above the heel. I thereupon pulled my dagger with its scabbard out of my boot. This scabbard was cased with a large piece of metal at the bottom, which occasioned the hurt to my leg; as the bone could not bend any way, it broke in that place. I therefore threw away the scabbard, and cutting the part of my string of slips that I still had left, I bandaged my leg as well as I could. I then crept on my hands and knees toward the gate, with my dagger in my hand, and, found it shut; but observing a stone under the gate, and thinking that it did not stick very fast, I prepared to push it away; clapping my hands to it, I found that I could move it with ease, so I soon pulled it out, and effected my egress. It was about five hundred paces from the place where I had had my fall to the gate at which I had entered the city.

As soon as I got in, some mastiff dogs came up, and bit me severely. Finding that they persisted in worrying me, I took my dagger and gave one of them so severe a stab that they set up a loud howling; whereupon all the dogs in the neighborhood, as it is in the nature of those animals, ran up to him; and I made all the haste I could to crawl towards the Church of St. Maria Transpontina. When I arrived at the entrance of the street that leads toward the Castle of St. Angelo, I took my way toward St. Peter's gate; but, as it was then broad daylight, I reflected that I was in great danger. I happened to meet a water-carrier, who had loaded his ass and filled his vessels with water, and I begged he would put me upon the beast's back, and carry me to the landing-place of the steps of St. Peter's Church. I told him I was an unfortunate youth, who had been concerned in a love-intrigue, and had made an attempt to get out at a window, from which I had fallen, and broken my leg; but as the house I came out of belonged to a person of the first rank, I should be in danger of being cut to pieces if discovered. I therefore earnestly entreated him to take me up, and offered to give him a gold crown; so saying, I clapped my hand to my purse, which was very well lined. The honest waterman instantly took me upon his back, and carried me to the steps before St. Peter's church, where I asked him to leave me and run back to his ass.

I immediately set out, crawling in the same manner as before, in order to reach the house of the Duchess, consort of Duke Ottavio, natural daughter of the Emperor, who had been formerly married to Alessandro, the late Duke of Florence. I knew that several of my friends were with that princess, who had attended her from Florence; and that I was in her good graces. This last circumstance had been partly owing to the constable of the castle, who, having a desire to befriend me, told the Pope that when the Duchess made her entry into Rome, I prevented a damage of more than a thousand crowns, that they were likely to suffer by a heavy rain; on which occasion, when he was almost in despair, I had revived his drooping courage by pointing several pieces of artillery toward the tract of the heavens where the thickest clouds had gathered; so that when the shower began to fall, I fired my pieces, whereupon the clouds dispersed, and the sun again shone out in all its brightness. Therefore it was entirely owing to me that the day of rejoicing was happily concluded. This coming

to the ears of the Duchess, her Excellency said Benvenuto was one of those men of genius that loved the
memory of her husband, Duke Alessandro, and she
should remember such whenever an opportunity offered
of doing them services. I was, therefore, going directly
to the place where her Excellency resided, which was in
Borgo Vecchio, at a magnificent palace. There I
should have been secure from any danger of falling
into the Pope's hands; but as the exploit I had already
performed was too extraordinary for a human creature,
and lest I should be puffed up with vain-glory, God was
pleased to put me to a still severer trial than that
which I had already gone through.

What gave occasion to this was, that while I was
crawling along, one of the servants of Cardinal Cornaro
recognized me, and, running immediately to his master's
apartment, awakened him out of his sleep, saying,
"My most reverend Lord, here is your jeweler, Benvenuto, who has made his escape out of the castle, and is
crawling along upon all fours, besmeared with blood.
He appears to have broken one of his legs, and we cannot guess whither he is bending his course." The
Cardinal, the moment he heard this, said to his servants,
"Run, and bring him hither to my apartment upon your
backs." When I came into his presence, the good Cardinal bade me fear nothing, and immediately sent for
some of the most eminent surgeons of Rome to take
care of me; among these was Signor Giacopo of Perugia,
an excellent practitioner. He set the bone, then bandaged my leg, and bled me. As my veins were swollen
more than usual, and he wished to make a wide incision,
the blood gushed from me with such violence, and in so
great quantity, that it spurted into his face, and covered
him in such a manner that he found it difficult to continue
his operation. He looked upon this as ominous, and
was with difficulty prevailed upon to attend me after-

ward; nay, he was several times for leaving me, recollecting that he had run a great hazard by having anything to do with me. The Cardinal then caused me to be put into a private apartment, and went directly to the Vatican, to intercede in my behalf with the Pope.

CHAPTER XXIV

SECOND IMPRISONMENT

THE report of my escape made a great noise in Rome; for the long string of sheeting fastened to the top of the lofty tower of the castle excited attention, and the inhabitants ran in crowds to behold the strange sight. By this time the frenzy of the constable had risen to its highest pitch. He wished, in spite of all his servants, to fly from the same tower himself, declaring that there was but one way to retake me, and that was for him to fly after me. Signor Roberto Pucci, father of Signor Pandolfo, having heard the rumor, went to see whether it was as fame had reported. He then visited the Vatican, where he happened to meet with Cardinal Cornaro, who told him all that had passed; that my wounds were dressed, and that I was at his apartments. These two worthy men threw themselves upon their knees before the Pope, who, before they could begin their supplication, cried out, "I know what you want." Signor Roberto Pucci said, "Most holy Father, we come to intercede for that poor man, who, on account of his extraordinary abilities, deserves some compassion. He has displayed such courage, and exerted such extraordinary efforts of ingenuity, as seem to surpass human capacity. We know not for

13

what offences your Holiness has so long confined him. If his crimes are enormous, convinced as we are of your piety and wisdom, we leave him to your decision; but if they are pardonable, we beg you will forgive him at our intercession." The Pope, in some confusion, replied that he had detained me in prison by the advice of some persons at court, because I had been too presumptuous; that, in consideration of my extraordinary talents, he had intended to keep me near his person, and to confer such favors upon me that I should have no occasion to return to France.

The two great personages then came to me from the Pope with this good news. I was visited by the nobility of Rome, by young and old, and persons of all ranks. The constable of the castle, quite out of his senses, caused himself to be carried into his Holiness's presence, and there began to make a terrible outcry, declaring that if the Pope did not send me back to prison, it would be doing him great injustice.

As soon as the constable was gone, the Pope sent for the Governor of Rome, and said, laughing, "This Benvenuto is a brave fellow: the exploit he has performed is very extraordinary; and yet, when I was a young man, I descended from the very same place." In this the Pope spoke the truth, for he had been a prisoner in the Castle of St. Angelo, for forging a papal brief, when he was abbreviator in the pontificate of Pope Alexander, who kept him a long time in confinement, and afterward, as his offence was heinous, determined to have him beheaded. But as he chose to defer the execution till after Corpus Christi Day, Farnese, having discovered the design, got Pietro Chiavelluzzi to come to him with some horsemen, and bribed several of the guards; so that while the Pope was walking in procession on that day, Farnese was put into a basket and with a cord let down to the ground. The precincts of the castle wall had not

then been erected, but the tower only, so that he had
not so many difficulties to encounter in making his
escape as I; besides, he was a prisoner for a real crime,
and I on an unjust accusation. He meant to boast to
the governor only of his having been a brave and gallant
fellow in his youth; but, instead of that, he inadvertently
revealed his own villany. He then said to the Governor, "Go to Benvenuto, and ask him to let you know
who assisted him in making his escape; let him be who
he will, Benvenuto may depend upon being pardoned
himself, and of that you may freely assure him."

The Governor, who two days before had been made
Bishop of Jesi, came to me in consequence of the order
from the Pope, and said, "My friend Benvenuto, though
my office is of a nature that terrifies men, I come to encourage you and dispel your fears, and that by authority of his Holiness, who has told me that he made his
escape himself out of the Castle of St. Angelo; but that
he had been assisted by several associates, otherwise
he could not have succeeded. I swear to you by the
sacrament that I have just now received (and it is but
two days since I was consecrated bishop), that the Pope
has liberated and pardoned you, and that he is sorry
for your sufferings. Therefore, endeavor to recover your
health, and you will find that all has happened to you
for the best, and that the confinement you have suffered,
though innocently, will be the making of you for ever;
for you will thereby emerge from your poverty, and not
be obliged to return to France, or to endure any distress
in foreign countries. So, freely tell me how the whole
affair passed, and who assisted you in your escape;
then be comforted, indulge yourself in repose, and endeavor to recover your health." I thereupon began my
story from the beginning, delivered a circumstantial account of the whole affair exactly as it happened, and
gave him all the tokens of the truth of my narrative that

I could possibly think of, not forgetting even the poor waterman that had taken me upon his back. The Governor, having heard my story to the end, said, "You have achieved too many great things for one person; at least, you are the only man deserving of the glory of such an exploit." So, taking me by the hand, he said, "Be of good cheer; by this hand you are free, and shall be a happy man."

He thereupon withdrew, and left me at liberty to see a considerable number of nobility and gentry, who had been waiting, for they were every day coming to see me as a man that had performed miracles. Some of them made me promises, and others made me presents.

In the mean time, the Governor of Rome told the Pope all that he had heard from me. Signor Pier Luigi, the Pope's son, happened to be present, and all that heard the story expressed the utmost astonishment. The Pope said, "This is certainly one of the most extraordinary events that ever happened." Signor Pier Luigi then said, "Most holy Father, if you liberate this man, he will do something else still more daring, for he is one of the boldest and most audacious of mortals. I must tell you of another exploit of his, which you have not heard of. This favorite of yours, Benvenuto, happening before his confinement to have some words with a gentleman belonging to Cardinal Santa Fiora, occasioned by some expression of that gentleman's, Benvenuto answered with the utmost audacity, and seemed bent on quarreling. The gentleman having informed Cardinal Santa Fiora of all that had passed, the latter said that if he once took Benvenuto in hand, he would soon find means to tame him. After Benvenuto heard of this, he always kept in readiness a fowling-piece, with which he can hit a farthing. The Cardinal happening one day to look out at a window (the shop of Benvenuto being under his palace), the latter took his fowling-piece, leveled it at the Cardinal, and was about to fire, when the latter, being apprised of his intention, left the place. Upon this, Benvenuto, in order to conceal his purpose, took aim at a pigeon, which was hatching its eggs in a hole on the roof of the palace, and shot it through the head, a feat almost incredible. Your Holiness may now act as you think proper with respect to the man. I thought it a duty incumbent on me to tell you what I knew. He may possibly one day, in a persuasion that he was imprisoned unjustly, take it into his head to have a shot at your Holiness. He is a man of too fierce and audacious a spirit. When he killed Pompeo, he gave him two stabs with a dagger in the throat, though he was surrounded by ten of his friends; and then made his escape, to the disgrace of those ten, though they were men of worth and reputation." Whilst he was saying this, the gentleman belonging to the Cardinal Santa Fiora, with whom I had had the dispute, happened to be present, and confirmed to the Pope all that his son had related. The Pontiff swelled with indignation, but said nothing.

The Pope, who was angry at what he had heard from his son, revolved it seriously. Two days later, Cardinal Cornaro went to ask his Holiness for a bishopric for one of his gentlemen, named Signor Andrea Centano. It is true the Pope had promised him the first bishopric that should become vacant: he did not therefore offer to retract, but, acknowledging that he had made such a promise, told the Cardinal he would let him have the bishopric on condition of his doing him one favor, which was, that he would again deliver Benvenuto into his hands. The Cardinal cried out, "What will the world say of it, since your Holiness has pardoned him? And as you have consigned him over to my care, what will the people of Rome say of your Holiness and of me?" The Pope replied, "I must insist upon having Benvenuto, if you have a mind to the bishopric; and let people talk as they will."

The good Cardinal asked that his Holiness would give him the bishopric, and rely upon his doing afterward as his Holiness should think proper. The Pope, appearing to be almost ashamed of his violation of faith, said, "I will send to you for Benvenuto, and, for my own satisfaction, put him into certain apartments of the privy gardens, where he may recover at leisure, and his friends shall be at liberty to visit him. I will myself bear all his expenses till he is thoroughly recovered."

The Cardinal came home, and sent me word that the Pope would fain have me again in his hands; and that he intended to keep me in one of the ground-floor apartments belonging to the privy garden, where I might receive the visits of the nobility and gentry, and of all my friends, in the same manner I had done at his house. I then requested Signor Andrea to ask the Cardinal not to surrender me to the Pope, but to leave the matter to me; adding, that I intended to get myself wrapt up in a mattress, and carried to a place of safety at a distance from Rome; for in delivering me up to the Pope he would consign me to certain destruction. The Cardinal, when he heard this, was on the point of complying with my desire; but Signor Andrea, who was to have the bishopric, discovered the whole affair.

In the mean time the Pope suddenly sent for me, and caused me to be put into one of the ground-floor apartments belonging to his privy garden, as he had said he would. The Cardinal sent me word not to eat anything dressed in the Pope's kitchen, for he would supply me from his own table; at the same time he assured me that he could not possibly avoid acting as he had done, begged I would make myself entirely easy, and promised that he would contrive to procure me my liberty.

While I was in this situation, I was every day visited by many persons of distinction, and received from them valuable presents and offers of service. Food was sent

to me by the Pope, but this I would never touch, instead
of which I ate of that sent by Cardinal Cornaro. Among
my friends, there was a Greek, about five-and-twenty
years of age; he was an active, gay youth, and the best
swordsman at that time in Rome. He was somewhat
deficient in courage, but faithful, honest, and very credulous. He had heard what the Pope had said at first
in my favor, about repaying me for my sufferings, but
perhaps did not know that he had afterward spoken in
a very different style. I therefore resolved to trust this
young Greek, and said to him: "My dear friend, these
people are resolved to take away my life, so that now
is the time to assist me. What! do they think I cannot
perceive that while they show me such external acts of
civility, it is all with an intention to betray me?" The
good youth answered: "My friend Benvenuto, a report
prevails all over Rome that the Pope has given you a
place worth five hundred crowns a year. I therefore entreat you not to let your groundless suspicions deprive
you of so great an emolument." But all this made no
impression on me; I still most earnestly besought him
to take me out of that place, being thoroughly convinced
that, though the Pope had it in his power to do me great
favors, he secretly intended to injure me as much as he
could, consistently with his reputation. I therefore
urged him to be as expeditious as possible in rescuing
me from such a formidable enemy; adding, that if he
would release me from my confinement in the manner I
should point out, I should always consider myself indebted to him for the preservation of my life; and would,
when occasion offered, gladly venture it in his service.
The poor young fellow replied, with tears, "My dear
friend, you are bent on your own destruction; but I cannot refuse complying with your desire; so tell me how
you would have me proceed, and I will do whatever you
require, though much against my inclination." I told

him how to proceed, and what measures to adopt; so that
we should have found it very easy to carry our design
into execution. When I thought he was on the point
of performing all that he had promised, he came to tell
me, that for my own sake, he must disobey me; adding,
that he had been informed, by those who were near the
Pope's person, of the real state of my case. Having no
other means of effecting my purpose, I was in despair.
This happened on Corpus Christi Day, in 1539.

Our dispute being over, and night approaching, a great
quantity of provisions was brought to me from the
Pope's kitchen, and at the same time I received an ample
supply from Cardinal Cornaro. Several of my friends
happening to be with me, I invited them to stay to supper. They consented, and I spent the evening cheerfully, keeping my leg wrapped up in the bed-clothes.
About an hour after sunset, they took their leave; and
two of my servants, having put me to bed, retired to the
antechamber.

I had a shock dog, as black as a mulberry, which had
been of great use to me when I went fowling, and now
would never quit me a moment. As he happened at
night to be under my bed, I called to the servants to
take him away, because he kept howling most hideously.
When the servants came, the dog flew at them like a
tiger. They were frightened out of their wits, and under
terrible apprehensions that the creature was mad, from
its incessant howling. This lasted till one o'clock in
the morning.

As soon as the clock struck the hour, the captain of
the city guards entered my apartment with a considerable number of his followers. The dog then came from
under the bed, flew at them with great fury, tore their
cloaks and their hose, and so terrified them that they
thought he was mad. But the captain said, "Such is the
nature of faithful dogs that they, by a sort of instinct,

foreknow and proclaim any misfortune that is to befall their masters. Two of you take sticks, and defend yourselves from the dog; let the rest seize Benvenuto, bind him fast to that seat, and carry him you know where." The guards obeyed their orders. I was covered and wrapped up, while four of them walked on before the rest, to disperse the few people that might happen to be still walking in the streets.

In this manner they conveyed me to a prison called the tower of Nona, and putting me into that part of it assigned to condemned criminals, laid me upon a piece of a mat, and left one of the guards to watch me. This man all the night lamented my hard fate, saying, "Alas! poor Benvenuto, what have you done to offend these people?" Hence I quickly conjectured what was to be my lot, as well from the circumstance of my being confined in such a place, as because my guard had apprised me of it. I continued part of that night in the utmost anxiety of mind, vainly endeavoring to guess for what cause it had pleased God so to afflict me; and not being able to discover it, I beat my breast in despair. The guard did the best he could to comfort me: but I begged of him, for the love of God, to leave me to myself, and say no more; as I should sooner and more easily compose myself by my own endeavor.

As soon as it was morning my guard awaked me, and said, "O unfortunate though virtuous man! this is no time for you to sleep, for here comes the messenger of dismal tidings." To this I answered, "The sooner I am delivered from the prison of this world the better, especially as I am sure of salvation, being unjustly put to death. The glorified and divine Jesus makes me a companion to his disciples and friends, who suffered death without cause; and I return thanks to the Almighty for the favor. Why does not the person come who is to pronounce my sentence?" The guard replied, "He is grieved on your account, and even now weeps your approaching fate." I then called to him by his name, which was Benedetto da Cagli: "Draw near, my good Benedetto, now that I am ready and prepared for my fate: it is much more for my glory that I should die innocent, than if I were to suffer for my crimes. Come hither, and let me have a priest to talk with for a while before my departure, though I have indeed but little occasion for such assistance, as I have already made my confession to the Almighty. I desire it merely in compliance with the will of our Holy Mother, the Church; for though she has cruelly wronged me, I freely forgive her. Therefore approach me, my dear Benedetto, and despatch me whilst I am resigned and willing to receive my sentence." When I had uttered these words, honest Benedetto bade the guard lock the door, which, without his authority, could not be done.

He went directly to Pier Luigi's lady, who was in company with the duchess above mentioned, and as soon as he was come into their presence he addressed her thus: "I implore you, most illustrious patroness, for the love of God, to send to the Pope, to ask him to appoint another person to pronounce Benvenuto's sentence, and do the office that I was to have done; for I renounce it, and nothing shall ever prevail on me to comply with such orders."

Having thus delivered his sentiments, he departed with the greatest demonstrations of sorrow and concern. The Duchess exclaimed, with an air of indignation, "Is this the justice administered in Rome by God's Vicar upon earth? The Duke, my first husband, greatly patronized this man, on account of his abilities and his virtues, and would not let him return to Rome, because he took great delight in his company." Having spoken thus, she left the place murmuring, and expressing the highest disapprobation of the Pope's proceedings. Pier Luigi's lady,

who was called Signora Jeronima, then repaired to his
Holiness, and falling upon her knees in the presence of
several cardinals, pleaded my cause with such eloquence
that the Pope was covered with confusion and said, "For
your sake, madam, we will proceed no farther against
him—not that we were ever bent on his destruction."

I continued in prison in the most dreadful agitation,
my heart beating violently with terror; and even the men
that were to perform the cruel office of executioners
were in some disorder. At last dinner-time approached,
when all present departed, and my food was brought
me. At this sight I said with surprise, "Now, indeed,
truth has been too powerful for the malignant influence
of the stars! I therefore entreat the Almighty to deliver me from this danger, if it be His divine pleasure."
After sunset the captain of the city guards came with a
considerable number of his followers, who put me again
upon the same seat on which I had been conveyed the
evening before to that prison. He spoke to me in the
most obliging manner, and bidding me banish all fear,
commanded his followers to take care of me. Thus they
carried me to the castle whence I had made my escape;
and when we had ascended pretty high, to a little court,
there for a short time they set me down.

CHAPTER XXV

ESCAPE FROM DEATH

SOON afterward the constable of the castle,
though diseased and afflicted, caused himself to
be carried to the place where I was confined,
and said to me, "So, have I caught you again?"
"'Tis true, you have," said I; "but you see I escaped, as

I told you I would; and if I had not been sold, under the Papal faith for a bishopric, by a Venetian Cardinal to a Roman of the Farnese family, both of whom, in so doing, violated the most sacred laws, you never would have had this opportunity of retaking me; but since they have thus misused me, you also may do your worst, for I now care for nothing more in this world." The poor gentleman then began to make terrible exclamations, crying out, "So, so! life and death are equally indifferent to this man, who is more daring and presumptuous in his present condition than when he was well. Put him there under the garden, and mention not his name any more to me, for he is the cause of my death." I was accordingly carried to a very dark room under the garden, where there was a great quantity of water, full of tarantulas and other poisonous insects. A mattress was thrown to me, covered with a blanket, and that evening I had no supper, but was fast locked in, and so I continued till the next day. At three in the afternoon my dinner was brought, and I asked those who came with it to let me have some of my books. They made me no answer, but mentioned my request to the poor constable, who wished to know everything I said.

The next morning they brought me a Bible of mine in the vulgar tongue, with another book, containing the Chronicles of Villani. On my asking for other books, I was told that I should have no more, and that I had too many already. Thus wretchedly did I drag out my time, lying upon the rotten mattress. In three days everything in the room was under water, so that I could hardly stir an inch, as my leg was broken; and when I wished to get out of bed, I was obliged to crawl along with great difficulty. For about an hour and a half of the day I enjoyed a little of the reflected light of the sun, which entered my wretched cell by a very small aperture; and that was all the time I had to read. I passed the

remainder both of the day and night patiently in the
dark, revolving the most serious thoughts on God and
on the frail condition of human nature. I had hardly
any doubt that I should there in a few days end my miserable life. However, I made myself as easy as I could,
and was comforted with the reflection that it would have
been much worse to feel the excruciating pangs of being
flayed alive.

When I found myself thus reconciled to my condition,
I formed a resolution to bear up under my unhappy lot
as well as I could. I began the Bible at the beginning,
and read it every day with so much attention, and took
such delight in it, that if it had been in my power I
should have done nothing but read; but as soon as the
light failed me, I felt all the misery of my confinement,
and grew so impatient that several times I was about to
lay violent hands upon myself. However, as I was not
allowed a knife, I had not the means of carrying my
design into execution. I once, notwithstanding, contrived to place a thick plank of wood over my head, and
propped it in the manner of a trap, so that if it had fallen
upon me it would have crushed me to death; but when
I had put the whole pile in readiness, and was just going
to loosen the plank, and let it fall upon my head, I was
seized by something invisible, pushed four cubits from
the place, and terrified to such a degree that I became
insensible. In this condition I remained from break of
day till three in the afternoon, when my dinner was
brought to me. The persons that attended me must
have been with me several times before I heard them;
for when I recovered my senses, I heard Captain San-
drino Monaldi enter the cell, exclaiming, "Unfortunate
man, what a pity it is that such merit should have such
an end." On hearing these words, I opened my eyes, and
saw several priests in their sacerdotal robes, who cried
out, "How came you to tell us that he was dead?" Bossa

answered, "I said so, because I found him lifeless." They immediately removed me from the place where I lay, and threw the mattress, which was rotten, out of the cell. On their telling the constable what they had seen, he ordered me another mattress. Having afterward reflected what it could be that prevented me from carrying my design into execution, I believed it was some divine power, or, in other words, my guardian angel.

Afterward at night there appeared to me in a dream a wonderful being, in form resembling a beautiful youth, who said to me in a reprimanding tone, "Do you know who gave you that body, which you would have destroyed before the time of its dissolution?" My imagination was impressed as if I had answered, that I acknowledged I had received it from the great God of nature. "Do you then," he replied, "despise His gifts, that you attempt to deface and destroy them? Trust in His providence, and never give way to despair while His divine assistance is at hand." I began to reflect that this angelic apparition had spoken the truth. So, having cast my eyes round the prison, I perceived a few rotten bricks, which I rubbed together, and made of them a sort of mash. I then crawled along as well as I could to the door of the prison, and gnawed with my teeth till I had loosed a splinter. This done, I waited for the time that the light shone into my cell, which was from half past four till half past five, and then I began to write as well as I could with the composition above mentioned, on one of the blank leaves of my Bible, a dialogue between my soul and my body:

> BODY.—Say, plaintive and desponding soul,
>   Why thus so loth on earth to stay?
>
> SOUL.—In vain we strive 'gainst Heaven's control;
>   Since life's a pain, let's haste away.

BODY.—Ah, wing not hence thy rapid flight.
Content thyself, nor fate deplore:
New scenes of joy and pure delight
Heaven still for thee may have in store.

SOUL.—I then consent to stay a while,
Freedom once more in hope to gain;
The rest of life with ease beguile.
And dread no more the rattling chain.

Having at last recovered my strength, after I had composed myself and resumed my cheerfulness, I continued
to read my Bible, and so used my eyes to that darkness
that though I was at first able to read only an hour and
a half, I could finally read three hours. I then reflected
on the wonderful power of the Almighty upon the hearts
of simple men, who had carried their enthusiasm so far
as to believe firmly that God would indulge them in all
they wished for; and I promised myself the assistance of
the Most High, as well through His mercy as on account
of my innocence. Thus turning constantly to the Supreme Being, sometimes in prayer, sometimes in silent
mediations on the divine goodness, I was totally engrossed by these heavenly reflections, and came to take
such delight in pious meditations that I no longer
thought of past misfortunes; on the contrary, I was all
day long singing psalms and other compositions of mine,
in which I celebrated and praised the Deity.

The constable of the castle sent several times privately
to inquire how I went on. On the last of July I expressed great joy, recollecting the festival that is generally celebrated at Rome on the first of August; and I
said to myself, "Hitherto have I kept this delightful holiday in worldly vanity; this year I will keep it with the
Almighty." At the same time I reflected, how much
happier I was at this festival than at any of the former.
The spies who heard me express these sentiments, repeated them to the constable, who said, "Good God! this
man triumphs, and lives happily in all his distress, while

I am miserable in the midst of affluence, and suffer death
on his account! Go directly and put him into the deep-
est subterranean cell of the castle, in which the preacher
Fojano was starved to death. Perhaps when he sees
himself in so wretched a situation, he will at last come
to himself."

Captain Candrino Monaldi accordingly entered my cell,
attended by about twenty of the constable's servants,
who found me upon my knees praying. I never turned
about, nor took any notice of them; on the contrary, I
worshiped God the Father, surrounded with a host of
angels, and Christ rising victorious over death, which I
had drawn upon the wall with a small piece of charcoal
that I had found there. After the four months that I
had been obliged to keep my bed with my broken leg,
and so often dreamed that angels came to cure it, it had
at length become quite sound, as if it never had been
broken at all.

Hence it was that a band of armed men rushed in upon
me at once, seeming nevertheless to dread me as a poisonous dragon. The captain said, "You see there is a
strong body of us, and we have made noice enough upon
entering the cell; why then did you not turn about?" At
these words I guessed the worst that could befall me,
and being long inured to sufferings, I made this answer:
"To God, the King of Heaven, have I turned my soul,
my contemplation, and all my vital spirits; and to you
I have turned exactly what suits you; for what is good
in me you are neither able to see nor touch. So do whatever you please to that part of me which is in your
power." The captain then, frightened, and not knowing
what I intended to do, said to four of the boldest of his
followers, "Throw your arms on one side." As soon as
they had done so, he cried out, "Fall on him quickly, and
seize him; is he the devil himself, that we should be so
much afraid of him? Hold him fast, and do not suffer

him to escape." I being thus roughly handled and ill-treated, expected much worse than what afterward befel me: I therefore lifted up my heart to Christ, and said, "O just God! Thou who upon that high tree didst expiate all our sins, why is my innocence to suffer for offences of which I am ignorant? Nevertheless, Thy will be done." While they were carrying me off with a lighted torch, I thought they intended to throw me into the sink of Sammalo: that is a frightful place, where many have been swallowed up alive, by falling thence into a well under the foundations of the castle. They put me into the dismal cell in which Fojano was starved to death, and there they left me without doing me any farther harm. As soon as I found myself alone, I began to sing the following psalms:

"Out of the depths I have cried unto thee, O Lord," etc.
"Have mercy upon me, O God, according to thy loving kindness," etc.
"Truly my soul waiteth upon God," etc.

That whole day, which was the first of August, my heart exulted with faith and hope. In two days they took me out of that dungeon, and carried me again to the cell where I had drawn the figures. When I came there, the sight of the images on the wall made me weep with joy. The constable, after that, wished every day to know what I did, and what I said. The Pope having heard all that had passed, and that the physicians had despaired of the constable's recovery, said, "Before my constable departs this life, as Benvenuto is the cause of his untimely fate, I shall be pleased to hear of his putting that fellow to death in what manner he thinks proper, in order that he may not die unrevenged."

The constable, having been informed of this speech by Pier Luigi, said to him, "Is the Pope then willing that I should wreak my revenge on Benvenuto; and does he put him into my power? If he does, leave me to manage

14

him, I shall know how to wreak a proper revenge." As the Pope had borne me the utmost malice and ill-will, so the anger and resentment of the constable were now turned against me with equal fury. At this juncture, the invisible being that had prevented my laying violent hands upon myself came to me, still invisible, spoke with an audible voice, shook me, made me rise, and said, "Benvenuto! Benvenuto! lose no time, raise your heart to God in fervent devotion, and cry to him with the utmost vehemence!" Being seized with a sudden consternation, I fell upon my knees, and repeated several prayers, together with the whole psalm,

"He that dwelleth in the secret place of the Most
    High," etc.

I then, as it were, spoke with God for a while, and in an instant the same voice, clear and audible, said to me, "Take your repose, and now fear nothing."

The reason of this was, that the constable had given cruel and bloody orders to have me put to death, but all on a sudden revoked them, saying to himself, "Is not this Benvenuto whose cause I have so often espoused, whom I know with certainty to be innocent, and to have suffered all that has been inflicted on him unjustly? How can I expect that God should have mercy upon me, and forgive me my sins, if I do not show mercy to those that have offended me? And why should I hurt a man of worth, who has served me and done me honor? Go, tell him that, instead of putting him to death, I grant him his life and liberty, and shall direct in my will that no one shall sue him for the expenses he has been at in this place." When the Pope heard this, he was highly offended.

I continued to put up my usual prayers, kept writing poems, and began to have every night the most encouraging dreams. I likewise constantly thought myself visibly in the company of this divine person, whom I had often heard while he was invisible. I asked but one favor of him, that he would carry me where I could see the sun, telling him that was of all things what I desired most, and that if I could see it but once I should die content, and without repining at any of the miseries and tortures I had gone through; for I was now inured to every hardship, all were become my friends, and nothing gave me any further uneasiness. So I continued to pray with the same earnestness and fervor: "O Thou true Son of God! I beseech Thee by Thy birth, by Thy death upon the cross, and by Thy glorious resurrection, that Thou wouldst deem me worthy to see the sun in my dreams at least, if it cannot be otherwise! But if Thou thinkest me worthy of seeing it with these mortal eyes, I promise to visit Thee at Thy holy sepulcher!" These vows did I make on the second of October, 1539.

The next morning I awoke at daybreak, and having left my wretched couch, I put on a waistcoat, as it began to be cool, and prayed with greater devotion than ever. I earnestly entreated Christ that He would be graciously pleased to favor me with a divine inspiration, to let me know for what offence I was so severely punished. When I had uttered these words, some invisible being hurried me away like a whirlwind to a place where he unveiled himself to me in a human form, having the figure of a youth with the first down upon his cheeks, and of a most beautiful countenance, on which a particular gravity was conspicuous. He remained with me, and showed me what was in that place, saying, "Those numerous men whom you see are all that have hitherto been born and died." I then asked him why he brought me thither? To this he answered, "Come forward, and you will soon know the reason." I had in my hand a dagger, and on my back a coat of mail: he led me through that spacious place, and showing me those who traveled several ways an infinite number of miles, he conducted me forward, went out at a little door into a place that appeared like a narrow street, and pulled me after him. On coming out of the spacious apartment into this street, I found myself unarmed, and in a white shirt, with my head uncovered, standing at the right of my companion. Lifting my eyes, I saw a high wall in the front of a house, on which the sun darted his refulgent rays. I then said, "O my friend, how shall I contrive to raise myself so as to be able to see the sphere of the sun?" He thereupon showed me several steps, which were upon my right hand, and bade me ascend them. I mounted several of those steps backward, and began by little and little to see the approaching sun. I ascended as fast as I could in the manner above mentioned, so that I at last discovered the whole solar orb; and because its powerful rays dazzled me, I, upon perceiving the cause of it, opened my eyes, and looking steadfastly on the great luminary, exclaimed, "O brilliant sun! whom I have so long wished to behold, henceforward I desire to view no other object, though the fierce luster of thy beams quite overpowers and blinds me." In this manner I stood with my eyes fixed on the sun, and after I had continued thus gazing for some time, I saw the whole force of his united rays fall on the left side of his orb; and the rays being removed, I with great delight and equal astonishment contemplated the body of the glorious luminary. While I gazed on this noble phenomenon, I saw the center of the sun swell and bulge out, and in a moment appeared Christ upon the cross, formed of the self-same matter as the sun; and so gracious and pleasing was His aspect, that no human imagination could ever form so much as a faint idea of such beauty. As I was contemplating this glorious apparation, I cried aloud, "A miracle! a miracle! O God! O clemency divine! O goodness infinite! what mercies dost thou lavish on me this morning!" At the very time that I thus meditated and uttered these words, the figure of Christ began to move toward the side where the rays were concentered; and the middle of the sun swelled and bulged out as at first. The protuberance having increased considerably was at last converted into the figure of a beautiful Virgin Mary, who appeared to sit with her Son in her arms in a graceful attitude, and even to smile. She was between two angels of so divine a beauty that imagination could not even form an idea of such perfection. I likewise saw in the same sun a figure dressed in sacerdotal robes. This figure turned its back to me, and looked toward the blessed Virgin.

All these things I clearly and plainly saw, and with a loud voice continued to return thanks to the Almighty. This wonderful phenomenon remained before me about eight minutes, then vanished, and I was instantly conveyed back to my couch. I then began to make loud exclamations, crying out thus: "It has pleased the Almighty to reveal to me all his glory in a splendor which perhaps no mortal eye ever before beheld: hence I know that I am free, happy, and in favor with God. As for you, unhappy wretches, you will continue in disgrace with him. Know that I am certain that on All Saints' Day (on which I was born in 1500, the night of the first of November, exactly at twelve o'clock), know, I say, that on the anniversary of that day you will be obliged to take me out of this dismal cell; for I have seen it with my eyes, and it was prefigured on the throne of God. The priest who looked toward Christ, and had his back turned to me, was St. Peter, who pleaded my cause, and appeared to be quite ashamed that such cruel insults should be offered to Christians in his house. So proclaim it everywhere, that no one has any further power to hurt me; and tell the Pope that if he will supply me with wax or paper to represent the glorious vision sent to me from Heaven, I will certainly convince him of some things of which he now appears to doubt."

The constable, though his physicians had given him up, had recovered a sound mind, and got the better of all those whims and vapors which used to torment him. So he gave his whole attention to the salvation of his soul. And as he felt great remorse on my account, and was of opinion that I had been most cruelly injured, he informed the Pope of the extraordinary things I declared I had seen. The Pontiff (who neither believed in God, nor in any other article of religion) sent him word that I was mad, and advised him to think no more about me, but mind his own soul. The constable sent some of his people to comfort me, and likewise ordered me pen, ink, paper, and wax, with the proper implements to work in wax, as well as his best respects and most courteous expressions of kindness. I fell to work, and at my leisure wrote a poem, inscribed to the worthy constable.

The day following, when that servant of the constable's who was my well-wisher came with my breakfast, I gave him the poem. The good man showed it to the constable, who would gladly have released me, being of opinion that the injury done me was in a great measure the cause of his death. He took the sonnet, and having read it several times, said, "These are not the expressions or thoughts of a madman, but of a worthy and virtuous person." He then ordered his secretary to carry it to the Pope, and put it into his own hand, at the same time requesting him to set me at liberty.

While the secretary was carrying this poem to the Pope, the constable sent me candles, both for day and for night, with all the conveniences that could be wished for in such a place. I thereupon began to recover of my indisposition, which had increased to a very high pitch. The Pope read the poem, and sent word to the constable that he would soon do something that would

please him. While I was drawing a design of the late
wonderful miracle, the constable, sensible of the approach
of death, on the morning of All-Saints' Day sent his
nephew Piero Ugolino to me, to show me some jewels.
As soon as I saw them, I said to myself, "This is a proof
that I shall shortly be at liberty." When I expressed
myself to that effect, the young man, who was a person
of few words, said, "Think no more of that, Benvenuto."
"Take away your jewels," said I, "for I am under so
strict a confinement that I see no light but what glimmers
in this gloomy cell, so that I cannot distinguish the
quality of precious stones; but with regard to my release from this prison, before this day expires you will
come to deliver me from it." In two hours the man returned, attended by two boys to support me; and in that
manner he conducted me to the large apartments that
I occupied at first (I mean in 1538), at the same time
allowing me all the conveniences and accommodation I
could desire.

A few days later, the constable, who thought I was released, being overpowered by the violence of his disorder, departed this life. He was succeeded by Signor
Antonio Ugolino, his brother, who had made the deceased
constable believe that he had discharged me from confinement. This Signor Antonio, as far as I could understand, was ordered by the Pope to keep me a sort of
prisoner at large, till he should let him know how I was
to be disposed of. Signor Durante of Brescia had entered into a conspiracy with that soldier, now a villain
of an apothecary of Prato, to mix something poisonous
with my food, which was to produce its effect in four or
five months.

They at first thought of mixing with my meat the
powder of a pounded diamond. This is not a poison of
itself, but is so excessively hard, that it retains its acute
angles, differing from other stones, which, when they

are pounded, entirely lose the sharpness of their particles, and become round. When it enters the stomach with the meat, and the operation of digestion is to be performed, the particles of the diamond stick to the cartilages of the stomach and the bowels; and as the newly received food is impelled forward, the minute parts of the diamond which adhere to those cartilages, in process of time perforate them; and this causes death. The rascal Durante gave for this purpose a diamond of little value to one of the guards belonging to the castle. I was informed that one Lione of Arezzo, a goldsmith, and my inveterate enemy, was employed to pound the diamond; but, as this fellow was very indigent, and the diamond was worth several scores of crowns, he made the guard believe that a certain dust, with which he supplied him, was the pounded diamond.

On the day that it was administered to me, being Good Friday, they put it into all my food, into the salad, the sauce, and the soup. I ate very heartily, as I had had no supper the night before, and it happened to be a holiday. I indeed felt the meat gritty under my teeth, but never once dreamed of the villainous designs of my enemies. When I had done dinner, as a little of the salad remained on the dish, I happened to fix my eyes on some of the smallest particles remaining. I took them, and advancing to the window, upon examining them by the light, recollected the unusual grinding; then, viewing the particles with attention, I was inclined to think that a pounded diamond had been mixed with my food. I supposed myself to be a dead man, and with the most heartfelt sorrow had recourse to my devotions. As I thought death inevitable, I made a long and fervent prayer to the Almighty, thanking His divine Majesty for so easy a death; and, as my stars had so ordered it, I thought it a great happiness that my life was to terminate in that manner.

But as hope is never totally extinct in the human breast, I had still some glimmering of it left. I therefore laid hold of a little knife, and taking some of the small particles, put them upon one of the irons of the prison, then, pressing upon them with the point of the knife as hard as I could, I heard the little grains crack. I examined them attentively with my eye, and found that it was really so. Hence I conceived new hopes, and said to myself, "This is not the stone that was intended for me by the villain Durante. It is a small brittle stone, which is not likely to do me any manner of injury." I returned thanks to God, and blessed poverty, which was the preserver of my life; for Durante having given a diamond, worth more than a hundred crowns, to Lione to pound, his poverty made him keep it for himself, and in lieu of it he pounded for me a counterfeit diamond, not worth more than twenty pence, thinking it was equally likely to do the business.

At this very time the Bishop of Pavia, brother of the Count of St. Secondo, called Monsignor Rossi, of Parma, was a prisoner in the castle. I called to him with a loud voice, telling him that a parcel of villains had given me a pounded diamond with a murderous intention. I then got one of his servants to show him part of the dust that was left on my plate. Yet I did not let him know that what they gave me was no diamond. I moreover requested him that, for the short time I had to live, he would supply me with bread from his table. He thereupon promised to furnish me every day with provisions. Signor Antonio, the new constable, who certainly was not an accomplice in the design upon my life, made a great stir on the occasion, and asked to see the pounded diamond; but, thinking that the Pope was at the bottom of the affair, he chose to take no further notice of it. I was now so circumspect as to eat only of the food sent me by the bishop, and I continued my stanzas on the prison, setting down every day such new events as befel me. Signor Antonio always sent my meals by one Giovanni, who had been an apothecary at Prato, and was then a soldier on duty at the castle. I told him that I would eat nothing that came through his hands, unless he first tasted it: but he answered that this ceremony was only for Popes. To this I replied that as gentlemen are obliged to perform the office of tasting for the Pope, so, he who was a soldier, a journeyman apothecary, and a low fellow from Prato, was in duty bound to taste for a Florentine of my character. High words thereupon ensued between us.

After this, Signor Antonio chose another of his servants, who was my friend, to carry my meals; and the man readily tasted them for me, without dispute. This servant told me every day, that the Pope was constantly solicited by Monsieur de Monluc, in the name of the King his master, and that his Holiness seemed to be very unwilling to part with me. He added that Cardinal Farnese, who had formerly been so much my friend and patron, had declared that I must not think of being released from my confinement in haste. On hearing this I affirmed that I should recover my liberty in spite of them.

CHAPTER XXVI

LIBERTY AT LAST

AFTER I had led this melancholy life a few days longer, the Cardinal of Ferrara appeared in Rome. On going to pay his respects to his Holiness, he was detained to supper; and the Pope, being a person of taste and genius, chose to converse with him concerning all that he had seen curious and worthy of observation in France. The Cardinal, in the heat of conversation, revealed several things that he would otherwise have concealed; and as he knew how to conform himself to the French King's taste, and was equally possessed of the art of pleasing his Holiness, the latter took a much greater liking to him than he was aware of himself, and seemed to be in high spirits, as well on account of this engaging conversation, as of the debauch he indulged in on the occasion, which he repeated every week. When the Cardinal saw the Pope in good humor, and likely to grant favors, he applied in my behalf, in the name of the King his master, and expressed himself in such terms as demonstrated that the French monarch was very solicitous to obtain his request. The Holy Father thereupon perceiving that the great quantity of wine he had poured down his throat was upon the point of operating, said to the Cardinal laughing, "Take Benvenuto home with you directly, without a moment's delay." Thus, having given proper orders in the affair, he rose from the table, and the Cardinal sent for me that very moment, before the matter could come to the knowledge of Signor Pier Luigi.

The Pope's order was brought to the prison by two of the Cardinal of Ferrara's gentlemen, in the dead of night. They conducted me to the Cardinal, who gave me the kindest reception, and I was well lodged at his house. Signor Antonio, brother of the Governor, who was then possessed of his place, insisted upon my paying all my expenses, as well as the fees and gratuities required by the officers of justice and others. In short, he was resolved to act in every respect contrary to the will of the deceased Governor. This affair cost me many score of crowns. The Cardinal bade me take care of myself, if I valued my life, adding, that if he had not that evening got me out of prison I should, in all probability, have ended my days in confinement, as he was informed that the Pope had already repented his having set me at liberty. While I was in the apartment of the Cardinal, and afterward in the Pope's privy garden, among other friends that visited me, came a cashier of Signor Bindo Altoviti, named Bernardo Galluzzi, whom I had entrusted with the value of several hundred crowns. This young man came to the privy garden with an intention to settle accounts, and restore to me all that I had deposited with him. I told him that I could not put my property into the hands of a dearer friend, nor into any place where it would be more secure. My friend, on this, seemed to decline keeping it, and I, by a sort of violence, obliged him to continue his trust. When I was liberated from the castle this last time, I understood that poor Galluzzi was a bankrupt, and that I had lost all my money.

I had had, moreover, a terrible dream, in which a person appeared to write certain words of great importance on my forehead with a reed, at the same time strictly charging me not to divulge what he had been doing; and when I awoke in the morning I perceived that my forehead was actually marked. In the verses composed during my confinement are several events of a similar nature. I likewise received a circumstantial account, without knowing to whom I owed the intelligence, of all that afterward happened to Signor Pier Luigi; and it was so clear and express in every article that I have often thought I received it from a heavenly angel.

Another circumstance I must not omit, which I mention in justice to God and the wondrous ways of his providence toward me. From the very moment that I beheld the phenomenon, a resplendent light appeared over my head, which has displayed itself conspicuously to all the few to whom I have thought proper to show it. This shining light is to be seen over my shadow from morning till two o'clock in the afternoon, and it appears

to the greatest advantage when the grass is moist with
dew. It is likewise visible at sunset. This phenomenon
I took notice of when I was at Paris, because the air
is exceedingly clear in that climate, so that I could distinguish it there much plainer than in Italy, where mists
are much more frequent; but I can still see it even here,
and show it to others.

CHAPTER XXVII

AN EXCITING JOURNEY

AS I was recovering my health by degrees, I exerted my utmost efforts to become again expert in my profession. I rode out to take the
air, having first asked the good Cardinal's leave,
and borrowed his horses. On these occasions I was
usually accompanied by two young Roman citizens, one
of whom was bred to my own business. When I was
out of Rome, I rode toward Tagliacozzo, thinking to
meet my pupil Ascanio. I found him there, with his
father, his brothers, his sisters, and his mother-in-law.
I met with a kind reception, and remained two days. I
then set out for Rome, and carried Ascanio with me.

On our return to that capital I fell to work with the
utmost assiduity; and happening accidentally to find a
silver basin, which I had undertaken for the Cardinal
just before my imprisonment, I set Paolo to work on
the basin; and I took in hand a cup, which consisted
of round figures in basso rilievo. In like manner the
basin contained little round figures and fishes in basso
rilievo; and it was so rich, and the workmanship so exquisite, that all who saw it expressed the utmost surprise,

as well on account of the force of genius and invention
in the design, as of the admirable polish the young artists
had displayed.   The Cardinal came at least twice every
day to see me, accompanied by Signor Luigi Alamanni
and Signor Gabriello Cesano.   On these occasions we
passed an hour or two merrily, though I had a great deal
of business that required despatch.   He at the same time
put several other works into my hands, and employed me
to make his pontifical seal, which was about the size
of the hand of a child twelve years old.   On this seal
I carved two little pieces of history, one was John preaching in the wilderness; the other was St. Ambrosio routing
the Arians, represented on horseback, and with a whip in
his hand.   The design of this seal was so bold and admirable, the workmanship so exquisite, and the polish so
fine, that everybody said I had surpassed the great Lautizio, whose talents were confined to this branch alone;
and the Cardinal, in the joy of his heart, ostentatiously
compared it with the other seals of the Roman cardinals,
which were almost all by that artist.

At the same time that the Cardinal gave me the other
two works, he employed me to make a model of a salt-
cellar, but desired it should be in a different taste from
the common ones.   Signor Luigi said many excellent
things concerning this salt-cellar.   Signor Gabriello
Cesano likewise spoke admirably upon the subject; but
the Cardinal, who had listened with attention, and
seemed highly pleased with the designs these two ingenious gentlemen proposed, said to me, "Benvenuto, the
plans of Signor Luigi and Signor Gabriello please me so
highly that I am in doubt which to prefer.   I therefore
leave it to you to make a choice, as you are charged with
executing the work."   I then said, "Gentlemen, do but
consider of what importance the sons of kings and emperors are, and what a wonderful splendor and emanation
of the Godhead is conspicuous in them; yet ask but a

poor humble shepherd, which he has the greatest love
and affection for, these children of emperors and kings,
or his own; he will, doubtless, answer you that he loves
his own offspring best.   In like manner, I have a strong
paternal affection for my own child; so that the first
model I intend to show you, most reverend patron, shall
be my own work and invention.   For many plans that
appear very plausible when delivered in words, have but
an indifferent effect when carried into execution."   I
then turned to the two virtuosi, and said, "O gentlemen,
you have given us your plans in words, but I will show
you mine in practice."

Thereupon Signor Luigi Alamanni, with a smiling
countenance, spoke a long time in my favor, and that in
the most complaisant manner imaginable.   In doing this
he acquitted himself with extraordinary grace, for he had
a pleasing aspect, an elegant figure, and a harmonious
voice.   Signor Gabriello Cesano was quite the reverse of
him—as ill-shaped in his person as ungracious in his
manner—and when he spoke he acquitted himself awk-
wardly.   The plan proposed by Signor Luigi was, that
I should represent a Venus with a Cupid, and several
fine devices round them suited to the subject.   Signor
Gabriello was for having me represent Amphitrite, the
spouse of Neptune, and the Tritons, Neptune's attendants, with other ornaments, very fine in idea, but extremely difficult to be carried into execution.

I designed an oval, almost two thirds of a cubit in
breadth; and upon this oval, as the sea appears to embrace the earth, I made two figures about a hand high,
in a sitting posture, with the legs of one within those
of the other, as some long branches of the sea are seen
to enter the land; and in the hand of a male figure, representing the ocean, I put a ship, contrived with great
art, in which was deposited a large quantity of salt;
under this I represented four sea-horses, and in the right

hand of the ocean I put his trident. The earth I represented by a female figure, the most elegant and beautiful
I could form an idea of, leaning with one hand against a
magnificent temple; this was to hold the pepper. In the
other hand I put a cornucopia, adorned with all the embellishments I could think of. To complete this idea,
in that part which appeared to be earth, I represented
all the most beautiful animals that that element produces.
In the part that stood for the sea I designed the finest
sort of fish and shells that so small a space was capable
of containing. In the remainder of the oval I placed
several noble ornaments. Having then waited till the
Cardinal came with the two virtuosi above mentioned, I
produced my model in wax. The first that spoke was
Signor Gabriello Cesano, who said, "This is a work that
the lives of ten men would be hardly sufficient to execute; and you, most reverend Cardinal, who desire to
have it finished in your life-time, are never likely to see
it. Benvenuto has, indeed, thought proper to show you
some of his offspring; but he has not done like us, who
proposed only such things as were feasible; he has
brought you a plan which it is impossible to finish." On
this Signor Luigi Alamanni took my part. The Cardinal, however, said he did not choose to be concerned
in so great an undertaking. I thereupon replied: "Most
reverend Cardinal, I must beg leave to tell you, that I
expect to complete this work at all events, and you will
see it, when finished, a hundred times more luxuriant
in ornaments than its model. I even hope to have more
than sufficient time to bring works of much greater consequence to perfection." The Cardinal said, in a passion,
"If you do not make it for the King of France, to whom
I intend to introduce you, there is no likelihood of your
finishing it for any other person." He then showed me
the letters, in which the King wrote to him to return directly, and bring Benvenuto with him. Seeing this, I

lifted my hands to heaven, and exclaimed, "When will that *directly* come?" He bade me lose no time, but settle my affairs at Rome in ten days.

The time for our departure being arrived, the Cardinal made me a present of a fine horse, to which he gave the name of Tournon, because it was a present from a cardinal of that name. Paolo and Ascanio, my apprentices, were likewise provided with horses. The Cardinal divided his retinue, which was very considerable. The chief part of it he took with him, following the road to Romagna, in order to visit our Lady of Loreto, and then to proceed to his own house at Ferrara; the other part he sent toward Florence.

At Viterbo I was received with the utmost kindness by my sisters and the whole monastery. After leaving that city with the company, we rode on sometimes before and sometimes behind the retinue of the Cardinal, so that by six o'clock on Holy Thursday evening we were come within a stage of Siena. Obtaining a fresh horse, I spurred on, in order to get to Siena half an hour before the rest, that I might have time to visit my friends and transact some business. The horse I sent back to the posthouse, which was without the gate that leads to Camollia; and upon it I had, through forgetfulness, left my stirrups and saddle.

The next day I recollected my stirrups and saddle. On my sending for them, the postmaster answered that he would not return them, because I had overworked his horse. Several messages passed between us, but he persisted in refusing to return them, and that with much opprobrious and abusive language. The innkeeper at whose house I lay said to me, "It is well for you if he does not do something worse than keep your saddle and your stirrups. He is one of the most insolent men that have ever had the place of postmaster in this city; and he has two sons that are soldiers, desperate fellows, and

15

more insolent than their father." He, therefore, advised me to make all the haste I could in buying whatever I might stand in need of, and leave the place directly, without entering into any contest with him. I thereupon bought a pair of stirrups, thinking to recover my saddle by fair means; and as I was extremely well mounted, wore a coat of mail, and had an excellent piece at the pommel of the saddle, I was not in the least intimidated by this report. I had likewise used my apprentices to wear coats of mail under their clothes; and I had great confidence in my young Roman, who seemed never to have neglected this defence while we were at Rome. Even Ascanio, though in his tender years, wore a coat of mail; and, as it was Good Friday, I imagined that the folly of these wretches would for that day subside.

We soon arrived at the posthouse at Camollia; and I immediately saw and knew the postmaster, by tokens that had been given me, particularly by his being blind of an eye. I went up to him, and, leaving my two young fellows and the rest of the company at a little distance, said mildly, "Signor Postmaster, when I assure you that I have not ridden your horse very hard, why do you make a difficulty of restoring me my saddle and stirrups?" He answered with all the violence and brutality I had been prepared for. I thereupon said to him, "What! are you not a Christian, and do you intend to bring a scandal both upon yourself and me this Good Friday?" He answered that he cared neither for Good Friday nor for the devil's Friday, and that if I did not get about my business, he would soon, with his long pike, lay me sprawling upon the ground, musket and all. Upon his speaking to me thus roughly, there came up an old gentleman of Siena, a very polite, worthy man, who had just performed the devotions usual on that day. Having heard what I had to say for myself, and perceiving that I was in the right, he boldly reproved the post-

master, took my part, and reprimanded the two sons for
behaving rudely to strangers, by swearing and blas-
pheming, and thereby bringing a scandal upon the city
of Siena. The two young fellows, sons of the postmaster, shook their heads, and without returning any answer
retired. The incensed father, exasperated by what was
said by the worthy gentleman, ran at me with his long
pike, cursing and plaspheming, and swore he would instantly be the death of me. When I saw him thus determined, I, to keep him off for a while, presented the
muzzle of my piece at him. He, notwithstanding, flew
at me with redoubled fury; and the gun, though in a
proper position for my own defence, was not rightly
levelled at him, but the muzzle being raised, it went off
of itself. The ball hit the arch over the street-door, and
having rebounded, entered the postmaster's windpipe,
who instantly fell dead. His sons thereupon rushed out
of the house, and one having taken down arms from a
rack, while the other seized his father's pike, they both
fell upon the young men in my company. The son that
had the pike wounded Paolo, the Roman, in the left
breast; and the other fell upon a Milanese in our company, a foolish fellow, who would not ask quarter or declare that he had no connection with me, but defending
himself with a short stick against a partisan, he was
unable to parry his adversary's weapon and was slightly
wounded in the mouth. Signor Cherubino was in the
habit of a priest, though he was an excellent clock-
maker, and several benefices were conferred upon him
by the Pope. Ascanio was well armed and stood his
ground bravely, instead of offering to fly like the Milanese, so that these two received no manner of hurt.

I spurred my horse, and while it was in full gallop
quickly charged my piece again. Then I returned in
a passion, thinking that what I had done was but a trifle;
for, as I thought my two young men were killed, I ad-

vanced with a firm resolution to die myself. My horse had not gone many paces back, when I met them coming toward me. I asked them whether they were hurt, and Ascanio answered that Paolo had received a mortal wound with a pike. I thereupon said to the latter, "My dear Paolo, how comes this? Could a pike force its way through a coat of mail?" He told me he had put his coat of mail into his cloak-bag. I replied, "What, this morning? It seems, then, that coats of mail are worn at Rome to make a show before the ladies; but in times of danger, when they might be of use, they are put into the cloak-bag! You deserved all you have suffered, and what you have done is the cause of my destruction also."

While I uttered these words, I continued to ride back resolutely. Ascanio and the other earnestly entreated me to endeavor to save my life, as well as theirs, for I was hurrying on to death. Just then I met Signor Cherubino and the Milanese, the former of whom told me that none of my people had been hurt, that Paolo's wound had only grazed the skin, and that the old postmaster lay dead. He added that the sons had got themselves in readiness, and being assisted by several other persons, would certainly cut us all to pieces. "Therefore, Benvenuto," he continued, "since fortune has saved us from their first fury, let us tempt her no more, for she will not save us twice." I then said, "Since you are satisfied, I am content." So turning to Paolo and Ascanio, I bade them spur their horses hard, and gallop on to Staggia without stopping. The wounded Milanese then said, "A plague of this unlucky adventure. This mischief was owing to a little soup I ate yesterday, when I had nothing else for dinner." We clapped spurs to our horses and left Signor Cherubino and the Milanese, who were for riding on gently, to follow us at their leisure. In the mean time the sons of the postmaster went to the Duke of Amalfi, and requested him to give them a troop of light horse to pursue us. But the Duke, being informed that we belonged to the retinue of the Cardinal of Ferrara, refused.

In a short time we arrived at Staggia, where we were secure. On our arrival we sent for the best surgeon, who, examining Paolo's wound, declared it did not pass the skin, and there was no danger.

We dismounted at the house of my poor sister, where we were most kindly received by her and my cousin. Signor Cherubino and the Milanese went where their respective affairs called them: we stayed four days at Florence, during which Paolo was cured.

CHAPTER XXVIII

A JOURNEY TO PARIS

AFTER four days in Florence, we took the road to Ferrara, and there found the Cardinal, who, having heard of all the accidents that had befallen us, said, "God grant that I may carry you alive to the King, according to my promise to his Majesty!" The Cardinal assigned me an apartment in a palace at Ferrara, a magnificent building, called Belfiore, contiguous to the walls of the city; and there he caused tools and all things necessary to be provided, that I might work at my business. He then ordered his retinue to set out for France without me, and, seeing me very melancholy at being left behind, he said, "Benvenuto, all I do is for your good; for before you leave Italy I should be glad you were upon a certainty with regard to your employment in France. In the mean time proceed as fast as you can with the basin and the little cup; and I will leave orders with my steward to supply you with whatever money you may want."

I assumed those sentiments of gratitude which the favor seemed to deserve, endeavoring to wait with patience and see how this adventure would end. I fell therefore hard to work with my two apprentices, and went surprisingly forward with the basin and the cup.

About this time the Duke of Ferrara adjusted his differences with Pope Paul, relative to Modena and some other cities; and as the claims of the Church were just, the Duke made this peace by dint of money. The sum, I think, exceeded three hundred thousand ducats. The Duke had at that time an old treasurer, who had been brought up at the court of the duke his father, named Signor Girolamo Gibliolo. This old man could not bear that so great a sum should be given to the Pope, and he ran about the streets loudly crying, "Duke Alfonso, our present Duke's father, would rather have taken Rome with his money than have given it to the Pope;" and he would obey no order for paying it. When the Duke at last forced him to pay the money, the old man was attacked with a flux so violent that it brought him to the brink of the grave. While he lay ill, the Duke sent for me and asked me to take his likeness. I accordingly drew his portrait on a round black stone, about the size of a little dish. The Duke was greatly pleased with my performance, and with some agreeable conversations that passed between us. The consequence was, that he usually stayed four or five hours to have his likeness taken, and sometimes he made me sup with him at his own table. In a week I finished this portrait. He then ordered me to make a reverse. The design of this was a female figure that represented Peace holding in her hand a small torch, with which she set fire to a trophy of arms. This figure I represented in a joyous attitude, with garments of the thinnest sort, which flowed with the utmost grace; under her I designed a Fury in despair and bound with heavy chains. In this work I exerted the utmost efforts of my art, and it gained me great honor; the Duke repeatedly expressed the highest satisfaction at my performance, and gave me the inscription for the head of his Excellency as well as for the reverse. The words intended for the reverse were *Pretiosa in conspectu Domini.* This intimated that the peace had been dearly purchased for a large sum of money.

Whilst I was busy about this reverse, the Cardinal wrote to me to get ready, for the King insisted upon my coming at once, and that the next time I heard from him I should receive an order for all he had promised me. I caused the basin and cup to be packed up, having before shown them to the Duke. A gentleman of Ferrara, Signor Alberto Bendidio, agent for the Cardinal, had remained twelve years without stirring out of his house, on account of a lingering disorder. He one day sent for me in a great hurry and said I must that instant take post, and use the utmost expedition to wait upon the King, who had inquired for me with the greatest eagerness and solicitude, thinking I was in France. The Cardinal, to excuse himself, had told the monarch that I had stopped at an abbey of his at Lyons, being somewhat indisposed, but that he would take care I should be shortly with his Majesty; therefore I must take post and repair to the court of France with all speed. This Signor Alberto was a very worthy man, but haughty, and his disorder rendered his pride and humor insupportable. I told him it was not customary with men of my calling to ride post; but that if I were to proceed to the court of France I should choose to go by easy stages, and to carry with me Ascanio and Paolo, my companions and artificers, whom I had brought from Rome; adding that there must likewise be a servant with us on horseback, and that I expected to be supplied with a sum sufficient to defray the charges of the journey. The infirm old man then proudly made answer, that the Duke's sons traveled in the very manner I had described. I replied that the sons of the art that I professed traveled in the manner I had mentioned; and that as I had never been the son of a duke I did not know how such gentry appeared on their journeys; therefore I would not go to France at all, as well because the Cardinal had broken the promise he had made me as that I had now received such insulting language. I then formed a resolution to have no more dealings with the people of Ferrara.

After this, I waited on the Duke with his medal finished. His reception of me was the kindest imaginable, and no man was ever more caressed by a prince. He had given orders to Signor Girolamo Gigliolo, who was then recovered, to look out for a diamond ring worth more than two hundred crowns as the reward of my labor, and put it into the hands of Fraschino, one of the gentlemen of his bedchamber, who was to give it to me. These orders were obeyed. Fraschino, on the same evening that I gave him the medal, put a ring into my hands, with a diamond set in it, which made a great show, and told me from the Duke, that my masterly hand, which had acquitted itself so admirably in consecrating the memory of his Excellency, well deserved to be adorned with such a diamond. The day following I examined the ring, the diamond of which was an inconsiderable one, not worth more than ten crowns; and as I could not conceive that the Duke could use such grand expressions in giving a reward so trifling, or that he imagined he had properly recompensed me, I took it for granted that the rogue of a treasurer had played me a trick. I therefore gave the ring to a friend, asking him to contrive some way to return it to Fraschino, the gentleman of the bedchamber. This friend was Bernardo Saliti, who performed the commission admirably. Fraschino immediately came to me, and made a terrible stir, telling me that if the Duke should discover that I had been so rude as to return a present, which he had made in so kind and gracious a manner, he would certainly resent it, and I might very possibly repent my having taken so indiscreet a step. To this I answered that the ring his Excellency had sent me was not worth more than ten crowns, and the work I had done for him came to more than two hundred; but to show his Excellency that it was his favor alone I set a value upon, he might send me one of those English crab-rings, which are worth only tenpence, and I would keep it in remembrance of him as long as I lived; for I considered my labor abundantly rewarded by the honor of having served so great a prince, whereas a jewel of so little value disgraced me. These words gave the Duke so much displeasure that he sent for his treasurer and reproved him most severely. He at the same time sent me orders not to leave Ferrara without apprising him of my departure, and commanded his treasurer to give me a diamond worth three hundred crowns. The avaricious treasurer found one the value of which was not more than sixty crowns, and maintained that it was worth considerably more than two hundred.

The only valuable acquaintances I made at Ferrara were Cardinal Salviati and the Cardinal of Ravenna, with some of the eminent musicians; for the gentry of Ferrara are not only exceedingly avaricious, but rapacious after the property of others, and endeavor to get possession of it by every expedient they can think of. About ten o'clock Fraschino came and delivered to me the diamond, which was worth no more than sixty crowns; asking me, with a melancholy countenance, to wear it for his Ex-

cellency's sake. I answered that I should do so. I then
set out upon my journey.

Before night I had traveled more than ten miles, trot-
ting all the way, and on finding myself the day following
out of the district of Ferrara I was highly rejoiced; for
I had never met with anything good in that country,
except the peacocks. We steered our course for Mont
Cenis, taking particular care to keep clear of Milan,
and I arrived safe and in health at Lyons with Paolo,
Ascanio, and a servant. We waited for several days
the coming of the muleteer, who was charged with the
silver basin and the cup, as likewise with part of my
baggage. We were lodged in an abbey belonging to the
Cardinal. The muleteer being arrived, we packed up
everything belonging to us in a chest, and continued our
journey to Paris.

CHAPTER XXIX

TO WORK FOR THE KING

WE found the court of the French monarch at
Fontainebleau, where we waited on the Cardinal, who caused apartments to be assigned
us. The next day the wagon came up, so
we took out what belonged to us, and the Cardinal having informed the King of our arrival, he expressed a
desire to see me at once. I waited on his Majesty accordingly, with the cup and basin so often mentioned.
Being come into his presence, I kissed his knee, and he
received me in the most gracious manner. I then returned his Majesty thanks for having procured me my
liberty, observing that every good and just prince like
his Majesty was bound to protect all men eminent for

any talent, especially such as were innocent, like me;
and that such meritorious actions were set down in the
books of the Almighty before any other virtuous deeds
whatever. The good King listened to me till I had made
an end of my speech, and when I had done he took the
cup and the basin and said: "It is my real opinion that
the ancients never were capable of working in so exquisite a taste. I have seen all the masterpieces of the
greatest artists of Italy, but never beheld anything
that gave me such high satisfaction." This the King
said in French to the Cardinal of Ferrara, at the same
time paying me other compliments greater even than
this. He then turned and said to me in Italian: "Benvenuto, indulge yourself and take your pleasure for a
few days. In the mean time I shall think of putting you
into a way of making some fine piece of work for me."

While we followed the court, we may justly be said to
have been in great straits, and the reason is that the
King travels with more than twelve thousand horses, his
retinue in time of peace being eighteen thousand. We
sometimes danced attendance in places where there were
hardly two houses, were often under the necessity of
pitching very inconvenient tents, and lived like gypsies.
I frequently solicited the Cardinal to put the King in
mind of employing me. He answered that it was best
his Majesty should think of it himself, advising me to
appear sometimes in his presence, when he was at table.
This advice I followed, and the King one day called me
to him while he was at dinner. He told me in Italian
that he proposed I should undertake some pieces of great
importance; that he would soon let me know where I
was to work, and provide me with tools and all things
necessary; at the same time, he conversed with me in an
easy manner, on a variety of subjects.

The Cardinal of Ferrara was present, for he almost
always dined with the King. The conversation being

over, his Majesty rose from table, and the Cardinal said,
as I was informed afterward: "May it please your
Majesty, this Benvenuto has a great desire to be at work,
and it would be a pity to let such a genius lose his time."
The King answered that he was very right, and asked
him to settle with me all that concerned my subsistence.
The Cardinal, who had received the commission in the
morning, sent for me that night after supper, and told me
that his Majesty had resolved I should immediately
begin to work; but that he wished first to know my
terms. To this the Cardinal added, "It is my opinion
that if his Majesty allows you a salary of three hundred
crowns a year, it will be abundantly sufficient. Next I
must request that you leave the whole management of
the affair to me, for every day I have opportunities of
doing good in this great kingdom, and I shall be always
ready to assist you to the best of my power." I answered, "Without my ever soliciting your reverence,
you promised, on leaving me in Ferrara, never to let me
quit Italy, or bring me into France, without first apprising me on what terms I was to be with his Majesty.
But instead of acquainting me with the terms, you sent
me express orders to ride post, as if riding post were
my business. If you had then mentioned three hundred
crowns as a salary, I should not have thought it worth
my while to stir for double the sum. I notwithstanding
return thanks to Heaven and your reverence, since God
has made you the instrument of so great a blessing as
my deliverance from a long imprisonment. I therefore
declare that all the hurt you can do me is not equal to
a thousandth part of the great blessing for which I am
indebted to you. I thank you with all my heart, and
take my leave of you; and in whatever part of the world
I shall abide, I shall always pray for your reverence."
The Cardinal then said in a passion, "Go wherever you
think proper to go, for it is impossible to serve any man

against his will." Some of his niggardly followers then
said: "This man must have a high opinion of his merit,
since he refuses three hundred crowns." Others among
the connoisseurs replied: "The King will never find
another artist equal to this man, and yet the Cardinal
is for abating his demands as he would bargain for a
fagot of wood." It was Signor Luigi Alamanni that
said this, the same that at Rome gave the model of the
salt-cellar. This happened at a castle in Dauphiny.

We always took up our quarters at some place not far
from the court, but now they were three miles distant.
I was accompanied by a secretary of the Cardinal of
Ferrara, who happened to be quartered in the same place.
By the way, this secretary was continually asking me
what I intended to do with myself when I got home,
and what salary I had expected. I, who was half angry,
half grieved, never returned him any answer. I said
nothing more to him than that I knew all. On my arrival at our quarters, I found Paolo and Ascanio, who
were waiting for me. I appeared to be in great disorder,
and they, knowing my temper, forced me to tell them
what had happened. Seeing the poor young men terribly
frightened, I said, "To-morrow morning I will give you
money enough to bear your charges home, for I purpose
going by myself about some business of importance.
It is an affair that I have long revolved, and there is
no occasion for your knowing it."

Our apartment was next to that of the secretary, and it
seems very probable that he acquainted the Cardinal
with all that I intended, and was firmly resolved to do;
though I never could discover whether he did or not.
I lay restless the whole night, and was in the utmost impatience for the approach of day. As soon as morning
dawned, I ordered that horses should be in readiness,
and having got myself ready likewise, I gave the young
men all that I had brought with me, with fifty gold

ducats over, and kept as many for myself, together with the diamond the Duke had made me a present of. But I could not get rid of the two young men, who were bent upon going with me by all means. I did my utmost to dissuade them, and said, "One of you has only the first down upon his cheeks, and the other has not even that; I have instructed you to the utmost of my poor abilities, insomuch that you are become the two most expert young men in your way in Italy. Are you not then ashamed that you cannot contrive to help yourselves, but must be always in leading-strings? This is a sad affair, and if I were to dismiss you without money, what would you say? Be gone at once, and may God give you a thousand blessings! so farewell."

I thereupon turned my horse, and left them bathed in tears. I took a delightful path through a wood, intending to ride at least forty miles that day, to the most remote corner I could possibly reach. I had ridden about two miles, and in the little way I had gone formed a resolution to work at no place where I was known, nor did I ever intend to work upon any other figure than a Christ, about three cubits high, willing to make as near an approach as possible to that extraordinary beauty which He had so often displayed to me in visions. Having now settled everything in my own mind, I bent my course toward the Holy Sepulcher, thinking nobody could overtake me.

Just at this time I found myself pursued by horsemen, which occasioned me some apprehension, for I had been informed that these parts were infested by freebooters, called *Venturieri*, who rob and murder passengers, and who, though many of them are hanged almost every day, do not seem to be in the least intimidated. On the near approach of the horsemen, I perceived them to be one of the King's messengers accompanied by Ascanio. The former, on coming up to me,

said, "I command you, in the King's name, to repair to
him directly." I answered, "You come from the Cardinal
of Ferrara, for which reason I am resolved not to go
with you." The man replied that, since I would not go
by fair means, he had authority to command the people
to bind me hand and foot, like a prisoner. Ascanio at
the same time did his utmost to persuade me to comply, reminding me that when the King of France caused
a man to be imprisoned, it was usually five years before
he consented to his release. The very name of a prison so
terrified me that I instantly turned my horse the way
the messenger directed, who never ceased chattering
in French till he had conducted me to court.

On our way to the King's quarters, we passed before
those of the Cardinal of Ferrara, who, being at his door,
called me to him and said, "Our most Christian King
has of his own accord assigned you the same salary that
he allowed Leonardo da Vinci the painter, namely, seven
hundred crowns a year. He will pay you over and above
for whatever you do for him. He likewise makes you a
present of five hundred crowns for your journey; and
it is his pleasure that they should be paid you before
you stir hence." When the Cardinal ceased speaking,
I answered that these indeed were offers worthy of so
great a monarch. The messenger, who did not know
who I was, seeing such great offers made to me in the
King's name, asked me a thousand pardons. Paolo and
Ascanio said, "It is to God we owe this great good
fortune."

The day following, I went to return his Majesty
thanks, and he ordered me to make him models of twelve
silver statues, which he intended should serve as candle-
sticks round his table. He intended they should be the
figures of six gods and six goddesses, made exactly of
his own height, which was very little less than three
cubits. When he had given me this order, he turned to

his treasurer and asked him whether he had paid me five hundred crowns. The treasurer answered that he had heard nothing at all of the matter. At this the King was highly offended, as he had commanded the Cardinal to speak to him about it. He at the same time requested me to go to Paris, and look out for a proper house to work at my business, telling me I should have it at once. I received the five hundred gold crowns and went to Paris, to a house of the Cardinal of Ferrara's, where I began to work zealously, and made four little models two thirds of a cubit high, in wax, of Jupiter, Juno, Apollo, and Vulcan.

At this juncture the King came to Paris, and I waited on him, and carried my models with me, as likewise Ascanio and Paolo. When I perceived that the King was pleased with my performance, and had ordered me to make the silver Jupiter of the height above mentioned with all possible expedition, I informed his Majesty that I had brought those two young men with me from Italy for his service, and as they were my pupils, they were likely to be of much greater use to me, who had instructed them in the principles of my art, than any of the working artists of Paris. The King asked me to settle on the two young men such a salary as should appear to me handsome and sufficient. I then told him that a hundred gold crowns apiece would do, and I would take care that they earned their salary. So it was agreed. I then told the King that I had found a place very proper for carrying on my business. The place I meant belonged to his Majesty, and was then called the Petit Nesle; it was then in the hands of the Provost of Paris, to whom his Majesty had granted it. The King answered: "The place you mention is a house of mine; the person to whom I have granted it does not inhabit or make any sort of use of it. You may therefore take it for the purpose you mention." He thereupon ordered one of his officers to put me in immediate possession of the Nesle. The officer declined this at first, telling the King that it was not in his power to obey him. The King replied in a passion that he would give things to whomsoever he thought proper, and to such men as were of use to him and served him; for, with regard to the provost, he was of no use to him at all. He therefore desired to hear no more objections or demurs. The officer rejoined, that it would be necessary to have recourse to violence. The King then said, "Go thither immediately, and if a little force be not sufficient, you must exert yourself." The officer conducted me to the place, and I was obliged to proceed to violence before I could take possession of it. He then bade me take care of myself, assuring me that my life was in imminent danger. I entered my new habitation, and hired servants and purchased weapons. His Majesty took me into his service in the year of our Lord 1540.

When I found myself liable to daily affronts, I again waited upon the King and requested him to place me somewhere else. The answer was: "Who are you, and what is your name?" At so strange a reception, I was quite disheartened, and could not possibly guess his Majesty's meaning. As I remained in silent astonishment, he repeated his question. I then answered that my name was Benvenuto. The King said thereupon, "If you are that same Benvenuto that has been described to me, act like yourself; I give you free permission." I told his Majesty that it was sufficient for me to continue in his good graces, and then it was impossible for anything to hurt me. The King replied with a smile, "Go your way, and depend upon it that my favor will never be wanting."

He ordered one of his secretaries, De Villeroy, to see me properly accommodated and provided with everything necessary. This Villeroy was an intimate friend

16

of the provost of Paris, in whose possession the place called Nesle had been for some time. It was a large old castle, triangular, contiguous to the walls of the city, but had no garrison. Monsieur de Villeroy advised me to look out for some other building, and at all events to leave that, for as the person to whom Nesle had belonged was a man of great power, he would certainly have me assassinated. To this I answered, that I had come from Italy to France from no other motive but to serve their great monarch. With regard to dying, I was sensible that death is the common fate of all men, and whether it happened a little sooner or a little later, was a matter of indifference to me. This Villeroy was a man of excellent understanding, of most extraordinary qualifications and endowments, and exceedingly rich. He would have done anything to hurt me, but artfully concealed his malice. He had a grave deportment, a good aspect, and spoke deliberately. On this occasion he employed another gentleman, De Marmande, who was treasurer of Languedoc. The first thing this person did was to look out for the best apartments in the building, and get them fitted up for himself. I told him the King had given me the place to work in for his Majesty, and that I was resolved it should be inhabited only by myself and my servants. Whereupon this man declared he would do as he thought proper; that contending with him would be the same thing as running my head against a wall; and that he had Villeroy's authority for all he did. I then replied that I claimed the place by the King's authority, and that neither he nor Villeroy had any right to act in that manner. When I had expressed myself to this effect the haughty treasurer grossly abused me in French, whereupon I told him, in my own language, that he was a liar. At this he was incensed with rage, and by his gestures seemed just going to draw his hanger. I instantly clapped my hand to a large

cutlass, which I constantly wore by my side, and said:
"If you offer to draw that hanger, I will instantly kill
you." He had with him two servants, and I had my two
apprentices. While M. de Marmande remained thus in
suspense, without determining upon anything and was
rather inclined to mischief than otherwise, he muttered
to himself: "I will never put up with this treatment."
As I saw that he had bad intentions, I said to Paolo and
Ascanio: "As soon as you see me draw my cutlass,
fall upon those fellows and kill them if you can; for I
will begin with destroying that villain, and then we shall
make our escape with the assistance of God." When
M. de Marmande perceived that I had formed this resolution, he thought himself happy in getting out of the
place alive.

I wrote an account of all that had happened, in the
most modest terms I could think of, to the Cardinal of
Ferrara, who immediately acquainted the King with the
whole transaction. His Majesty, highly provoked at this
affair, put me under the care of another of his worthless
courtiers, M. d'Orbech. This gentleman provided me
with everything necessary for my business, and that with
the most complaisant officiousness.

CHAPTER XXX

CASTING STATUES

I MADE three models exactly the size they were
to have when executed in silver. These were
Jupiter, Vulcan, and Mars. I made them of
earth well supported with iron, and then went
to the King, who, as nearly as I can recollect, ordered

that I should have three hundred pounds of silver to enable me to begin my work. While I was making these preparations, the cup and the golden basin, which had been several months in hand, were finished. As soon as this was done, I got them well gilt. This appeared to be the finest piece of work that ever had been seen in France. I carried it directly to the Cardinal of Ferrara, who thanked me, and waited on the King to make him a present of it. His Majesty was highly pleased, and lavished greater praises upon me than ever had been bestowed upon any artist. In return for this present, he gave the Cardinal of Ferrara an abbey worth seven thousand crowns a year; at the same time, he was for making me a present, but the Cardinal prevented him, telling his Majesty it was too soon, as I had not yet finished any work for him. This confirmed the King, who was one of the most generous of men, in his resolution; and he said, "For that very reason I will encourage him to exert himself and make something masterly for me." The Cardinal in confusion replied, "Sire, I beg you would leave it to me, for I purpose settling a pension of at least three hundred crowns a year upon him, as soon as I have taken possession of my abbey." These I never received.

I returned to Paris, and being thus become a favorite of the King, I was universally admired. As soon as I received the silver that had been promised me, I began to work at the statue of Jupiter, and took into my service several journeymen. We worked day and night with the utmost assiduity, insomuch that, having finished Jupiter, Vulcan, and Mars, in earth, and Jupiter being pretty well forward in silver, my shop began to make a great show. About this time the King made his appearance in Paris; and I went to pay my respects to him. When his Majesty saw me, he called to me in high spirits, and asked whether I had anything curious to show

I GAVE HIM A KICK, WHICH SENT HIM SPINNING
SEVERAL YARDS, AND HE STUMBLED AGAINST
THE KING

From an Etching by F. Laguillermie

I GAVE HIM A KICK, WHICH SENT HIM SPINNING
SEVERAL YARDS, AND HE STUMBLED AGAINST
THE KING

From an Etching by F. Laguillermie

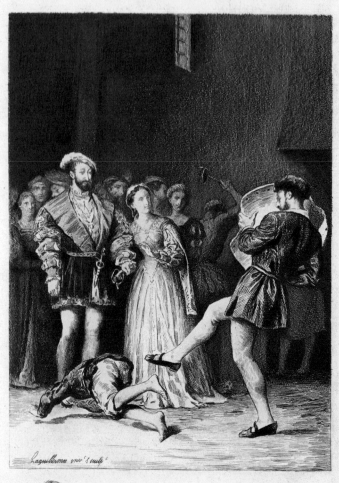

him at my shop, for he intended to call there. I told him of all I had done, and he expressed an earnest desire to see my performances. After dinner he made up a party, consisting of Madame d'Estampes, the Cardinal of Lorraine, and some other great men (as the King of Navarre, cousin to King Francis), and the Queen his sister; the Dauphin and Dauphiness came likewise; in a word, that day all the nobility belonging to the court of France were in my shop.

I had just got home, was beginning to work, when the King appeared at my castle gate. Hearing the sound of so many hammers, he commanded his retinue to be silent. All my people were at work, so that the King came upon us unexpectedly. As he entered the saloon, the first object he perceived was myself, with a large piece of plate in my hand, which I had not yet placed, and which was to make the body of Jupiter; another was employed on the head, another on the legs, so that the shop resounded with the beating of hammers. A French lad working by my side was guilty of a blunder, and I gave him a kick, which sent him spinning several yards, and he stumbled against the King.

The next day the King sent for me after dinner; the Cardinal of Ferrara was present, and dined with him. He began to talk to me, saying that, since he had so beautiful a cup and basin of my making, he must have a handsome salt-cellar to accompany them; that he wished me to draw a design of one, and the sooner the better. I answered that he should see such a design much sooner than he expected; for while I was employed about the basin and the cup, I thought a salt-cellar would be a necessary companion to them, and therefore had already made one, which I should show to his Majesty in a few moments. The monarch turned with great vivacity to the nobleman present, to the King of Navarre, the Cardinal of Lorraine, and the Cardinal of Ferrara, and said: "This is so obliging a man that whoever has heard his character would be desirous to know him." He then told me he would be glad to see my design.

I went for it, and soon returned, for I had nothing to do but cross the Seine. I brought with me a model of wax, which I had made in Rome at the request of the Cardinal of Ferrara. The King expressed great surprise, and said, "This is a much finer design than I expected; it is a most noble production; such a genius should never be unemployed." He then turned to me, and said with great cheerfulness, that he was highly pleased with my model, and should be glad to have a salt-cellar made according to it in gold. The Cardinal of Ferrara winked at me, giving me to understand that he knew this to be the same model I had made for him in Rome. I thereupon repeated what I had before told him, that I had made it for one who would pay for it. The Cardinal, recollecting these words, was nettled, and had a mind to take his revenge: he therefore thus addressed the king: "Sire, this is certainly a great undertaking. I have only one objection to make, namely, that I never expect to see it finished; for men of genius, who have noble and sublime ideas in their own art, are very ready to engage in grand enterprises without duly considering when they can bring them to a conclusion; therefore, if I were to order works of such importance, I should be glad to know how soon they could be executed." The King answered that he who was so anxiously solicitous about the finishing of works would never begin any; and this he said in a manner that intimated that he did not consider such undertakings suitable to men of narrow minds. I then said, "When princes give their servants such noble encouragement as your Majesty does both by words and deeds, they are sure of succeeding in all great undertakings; and since God has blessed me with so munificent a patron, I flatter myself that I shall be able to execute many great and admirable works for your Majesty." "I do not doubt you will," answered the King, rising from table. He sent for me to his apartment, and asked how much gold the making of the salt-cellar would require. I immediately answered him, a thousand crowns. The King called for his treasurer, M. d'Orbech, and commanded him to give me at once a thousand old gold crowns, good weight.

I sent for the two clerks who had caused the money to be given to me for the statue of Jupiter and many other things; and having crossed the Seine, I took with me a little basket, which I had from a nun, a cousin-german of mine, in a convent at Florence; by good luck I took this basket, and not a wallet. I thought to do the business by day, as it was then early, and did not care to disturb my journeymen, nor did I even mind to take a servant with me. I came to the treasurer's house, who had the money ready before him, and had chosen the pieces according to the directions of the monarch. It appeared to me that the villain had recourse to all the little artifices and stratagems he could think of, to delay paying me the money till late at night. I was by no means wanting in diligence, but sent for some of my journeymen to come to me about business of the utmost consequence. When I found that they did not appear, I asked the messenger whether he had obeyed my orders. The scoundrel told me that he had, and that they answered him they could not come; but he would carry the money for me with pleasure. I replied that I chose to carry it myself. In the mean time the receipt was drawn up, and the money being brought, I put it all into the basket, then thrust my arm through the two handles. As it entered with great difficulty, the money was well secured, and I carried it with much greater ease than if I had used a bag. I wore a coat of mail, had my sword and dagger by my side, and set out directly for

my own house. Just then I noticed that some of the
servants were whispering to one another; but they soon
left the house, and appeared to turn down a different
street from that which I had entered. I, being in great
haste, passed the bridge of the Change, and went up by
a little wall in the marshes, which carried me to my own
house at Nesle.

When I was just at the Augustins, a very dangerous
place, though within five hundred paces of my own house,
where, if I had attempted to call out, my voice would not
have been heard by anybody, I suddenly found four
swords drawn against me. I quickly formed my resolution, and covering my basket with my cloak, I clapped
my hand to my sword, and, perceiving that they were
eager to surround me, I told them there was nothing to
be won from a soldier but his cloak and sword. These
I was resolved not to resign tamely, but to defend them
at the risk of my life. While I bravely opposed the villains, I several times opened my arms wide, that in case
they had been set on by the servants who saw me
receive the money, they might have some reason to think
I could not have any such sum about me. Some of them
said in French, "This Italian is a brave fellow; he certainly cannot be the person we wanted, and even if he be
the man, he has no money about him." I spoke Italian,
and dealt my blows with such dexterity that I was near
killing some of them. As I appeared to be an excellent
swordsman, they thought it probable that I was a soldier;
so they crowded close together, and gradually drew off
from me, muttering all the while in their own language.
I at the same time continued to say coolly, and without
any sort of rodomontade, that he who wanted to possess
himself of my arms and cloak must purchase them dearly.
I began to mend my pace, and they followed me slowly;
my fear thereupon increased, and I was filled with apprehensions of falling into an ambush of other villains.

But when I got within a hundred paces of my own house I mended my pace as fast as I could, and cried out, "Help, help, or I am assassinated!" Immediately four of my young men sallied out with long pikes, and offered to pursue the fellows that had attacked me and were still in sight; but I stopped them, saying aloud, "Those four cowardly dogs have not been able to take from a single man a booty of a thousand gold crowns, the weight of which has almost broken his arm. Let us therefore first go and lay them up, and then I will attend you with my great two-handed sword wherever you will."

While we were putting up the money, the young men expressed great concern for the danger I had been exposed to, and said to me in a reprimanding tone, "You have too much confidence in your own courage, which will bring you one day into some scrape, and make us all lament your unhappy fate." I had a long chat with them, and they told me that my adversaries were gone off. So we all supped cheerfully, and were very merry, making a jest of the various turns and changes of fortune, which, whether prosperous or adverse, can affect us but for a time.

The next morning I began the great salt-cellar, and caused that and other works to be forwarded with the utmost expedition. By this time I had provided myself with several journeymen. as well for sculpture as for the goldsmith's business.

While I went on with the silver statue of Jupiter, seeing that I had plenty of that metal, more than what the statue required, I, without the King's knowledge, set about making a large silver vessel with two handles, about a cubit and a half high. I had likewise a fancy to cast in bronze the grand model I had made for the silver Jupiter. I immediately began this arduous undertaking, which was of a nature that I had never attempted before; and having entered into a conversation upon the subject with some of the experienced artists of Paris, I mentioned to them all the methods used in Italy on such a work. They told me they never had made use of that process, but that if I would let them take their own way, they would cast me the model of bronze as fine and as exact as the earthen one. I chose to make a bargain on employing them; and thinking their demand moderate, promised them several crowns more than they asked.

They set about the work, but I soon perceived that they did not take the right method. I therefore began a head of Julius Cæsar, the breast covered with armor, much larger than life, which I took from a little model I had brought with me from Rome, representing an antique head of admirable workmanship. I likewise began another head of the same size, which was the likeness of a fine girl of my acquaintance. I gave her the name of Fontainebleau, from the seat the King had chosen for his favorite residence. Having made a proper furnace to melt the bronze, and arranged and baked our figures, they their Jupiter, and I my two heads, I said to them, "It is my opinion that your Jupiter will not come out, as you have not blown enough under it for the wind to play, so that you labor in vain." To this they answered, that in case their work did not succeed, they would return me the money and make good all my expenses; but they at the same time maintained that the fine heads, which I intended to cast in the Italian manner, would never succeed according to my expectation. The two old artists, who proposed casting the model of Jupiter, occasioned some delay in the preparations for that purpose: they said they would gladly adjust the two moulds of my heads, it being impossible that they could succeed according to my process, and it would be a thousand pities that two such fine pieces should be spoiled. As they had informed his Majesty of this, he requested they would endeavor to learn, and not take upon them to teach a person who was a master of the business.

They with great laughter and merriment put their work into the mould; and I, without any sort of emotion, without either laughing or betraying any uneasiness, put my two heads on each side of the figure of Jupiter. When our metal was thoroughly melted, we poured it out with great satisfaction. The mould of Jupiter was thereupon cleverly filled, as were likewise those of my two heads at the same time. The two old artists were highly rejoiced, while I was very well pleased with my success; in short, it was an equal triumph to us both that we had been mistaken with regard to our opinion of each other's performance. They then were in high spirits, and desired to drink, according to the French custom; which I granted, and readily entertained them with a collation.

The next thing they asked me for was the money I had agreed to give them, and what I had promised them over and above. I answered, "You have been very merry, whereas I suspect you should have been sad; for I have taken it into consideration that there has been a greater consumption of metal upon this work than should have been, so that I am determined not to let you have any more money till to-morrow morning." The poor men began to reflect seriously on this speech of mine, and without making any answer returned home. When they came again in the morning, they without any stir began to take the figures out of the moulds; and because they could not get at their own great figure, without first taking out my two heads, they did so accordingly, and placed them in such a manner that they appeared to the utmost advantage. Soon afterward they set up so loud a cry, that I thought it was a shout of joy, and immediately ran to the workshop. I found them exactly in the attitude of those who guarded Christ's sepulcher, in sorrow and astonishment. I cast my eyes upon the two heads, and seeing that they made a very good appearance, I was partly pleased and partly vexed, while they excused themselves by saying, "We have been unfortunate." I answered, "You have been very fortunate, but you have shown little skill; if I had but instructed you with a single word, the figure would have come out admirably, which would have been greatly to my honor and your advantage; but as to my honor, I can easily find an excuse, for you your parts will gain neither honor nor profit. Therefore another time learn to work. and not to banter and make sport of others."

They begged I would take compassion upon them, acknowledging that I was in the right, and that if I did not show them indulgence, in not obliging them to make good all that great expense, they must be reduced to beggary as well as their families. My answer was, that should the King's treasurers compel them to pay what they had agreed, I would pay it for them; for I saw that they had done their best. By acting in this manner I greatly conciliated the good graces of the King's treasurers and ministers. A full account of the whole affair was given to his Majesty, who was so generous as to order that I should be satisfied in all my demands.

CHAPTER XXXI

A GREAT DESIGN FOR A FOUNTAIN

AT this time arrived at court the great Piero Strozzi, who put the King in mind of his letters of naturalization, and his Majesty gave orders that they should be made out at once. He at the same time said, "Prepare letters of naturalization for

Benvenuto likewise, *mon ami*, carry them to his house, and let him pay no fee whatever." Those of the great Piero cost him several hundred ducats; mine were brought me by one of the King's first secretaries, Anthony Masson. This gentleman put the letters into my hands with many expressions of kindness from the King, and said, "His Majesty makes you a present of these to encourage you to serve him with a greater zeal; they are letters of naturalization." He at the same time told me that letters of the like nature had been granted after much solicitation, and as a great favor, to Piero Strozzi; but the King gave me those of his own accord—a mark of distinction never shown before to any foreigner in that kingdom. I returned my royal benefactor thanks with all possible demonstrations of gratitude, and requested the secretary to inform me what those letters of naturalization meant. The secretary was a very polite, well-bred man, who spoke Italian incomparably well. He first laughed heartily, and then resuming his gravity, told me in my own language the meaning of letters of naturalization; that it was the highest honor that could be conferred on a foreigner, and something of much greater consequence than being made a Venetian gentleman. When he related to his Majesty all that had passed between us, the monarch laughed and said, "He shall know presently why I sent him the letters of naturalization. Go and make out his patent of lord of the castle of Nesle, which is a part of my demesne: he will understand this much more easily than he did the letters of naturalization." A messenger came to me from the King with such a patent, and I was for giving him a gratuity, but he refused it, telling me that he had his Majesty's express orders to the contrary. The letters of naturalization, together with those of the grant of the castle, I took with me, when I returned to Italy; and wherever

I reside, or wherever I am to finish my days, I shall always endeavor to have them with me.

Having upon my hands the works of which I have already spoken, I proceeded with expedition, and gave orders to have a base cast for the statue of Jupiter. This I caused to be made of bronze, enriched with a variety of ornaments, among which I carved, in basso rilievo, the Rape of Ganymede, and on the other side, Leda with her Swan. I made another of the same sort, intending to place upon it the statue of Juno, expecting soon to begin that likewise, if the King furnished me with silver for such an undertaking. Continuing to work with the utmost assiduity, I had completed the silver Jupiter, and had also cast the golden salt-cellar; the cup was very forward, and the two heads of bronze were finished. I had likewise executed several little pieces for the Cardinal of Ferrara, and moreover, a small silver vase of very rich workmanship, which I designed as a present to Madame d'Estampes. At the same time, I had done some work for Italian noblemen, as for Signor Piero Strozzi, the Count d'Anguillara, the Count of Pitigliano, the Count of Mirandola, and many others.

When I was well advanced with these works for my gracious monarch, he returned to Paris, and three days later came to my house, with the chief nobilities of his court. They all expressed great surprise at my being so forward with so many performances; and as Madame d'Estampes was with him, they began to talk of Fontainebleau. The lady advised his Majesty to order me to make some fine ornament for his favorite residence. The King answered, "What you say is very just; I will presently determine upon something handsome for him to execute." Then, turning to me, he asked what I thought would be a proper ornament for that charming fountain. I proposed some of my fancies; his Majesty likewise told his opinion, and he mentioned, at the same

time, that he intended going to take his pleasure, for
fifteen or twenty days, at St. Germain-en-Laye, which
was twelve leagues from Paris, desiring that I would in
the mean while make a model for his seat at Fontainebleau, with the finest designs I could think of, that being
the most delightful place of recreation in his whole kingdom. He concluded with ordering me to exert my utmost efforts to produce something masterly, and I promised to do my best. The King, seeing such a number
of works so far advanced, said to Madame d'Estampes,
"I never knew a man in his way that pleased me more,
or that deserved to be more encouraged. We must endeavor to keep him here; he spends a great deal of money,
is a good companion, and works hard. I am, indeed,
under a necessity of thinking for him myself, for in all
the times that he has been with me, or that I have been
here, he has never asked me for anything; his mind seems
to be entirely taken up with his business. I must confer some favor on the man, for fear of losing him." Madame d'Estampes replied, "I will take care to put you
in mind."

In about six weeks the King returned to Paris, and I,
who had worked night and day, waited on his Majesty
with my model. The figures were so elegantly executed
that it was very easy to understand the design. The
fatal disputes between the King of France and the Emperor being renewed, I found him very pensive; and
therefore addressed myself to the Cardinal of Ferrara,
telling him that I had brought some models which the
King had employed me to make; and I requested him
to take the first opportunity of mentioning them to his
Majesty, as I was inclined to think they would afford
him pleasure. The Cardinal complied with my request,
and spoke of the models to the King, who quickly came
to the place where I kept them.

First of all I had designed the palace gate of Fontainebleau; and made as little alteration as possible in the form of it, which, according to the whimsical taste of the French, appeared to be an odd mixture of greatness and littleness; for its form was almost square, with a semicircle over it bent like the handle of a basket, in which the King wished to have a figure to represent Fontainebleau. I gave a beautiful proportion to the gate, and over it I put an exact semicircle, with some agreeable projections on each side. Instead of two pillars, which the order of architecture seemed to require for their support, I placed two satyrs. One of these, something above half-relief, appeared to sustain with one arm that part of the pile which touched the columns; in the other it held a massive club; the countenance was so stern and fierce as to strike terror into the beholders. The other satyr had the same attitude, but differed from the former in the head and some other parts; it held in its hand a whip, with three balls fastened to certain chains. Though I call these figures satyrs, they had nothing in common with those sylvan gods but certain little horns and heads resembling that of a goat; in all other respects they were of the human form. In the same circle I represented a female figure in a reclining attitude, with her left arm upon the neck of a hart, which was a device of the King's. On one side of her I designed, in half-relief, little goats, boars, and other wild beasts; and on the other, in stronger relief, greyhounds, and other dogs of different sorts, such as are to be seen in the delightful wood where the fountain rises. I drew the whole plan in an oblong form, and at each corner I designed a victory in basso-rilievo, holding little torches in their hands, as they are represented by the ancients. On the top I placed the figure of a salamander, the King's own emblem, with several other ornaments pleasing to the eye and adapted to the nature of the work, which was of the Ionic order.

The sight of this model raised the King's spirits, and diverted him from that disagreeable conversation in which he had been engaged two hours. Finding him in this good humor, I showed him another model, which he little expected, for he imagined he had seen ingenuity enough in the first. This model was more than two cubits in height. It represented a fountain in the form of a complete square, with five steps round it, which intersected each other—a thing almost unexampled in any country whatever. In the midst of this fountain I placed a solid mass, which rose a little above its brim; upon this mass stood a naked figure of most graceful shape. It had a broken lance in its right hand, raised aloft, and the left it kept upon the handle of a scimitar, the form of which was exceedingly beautiful. It rested upon the left foot and held the right upon the crest of a helmet, the workmanship of which was the richest and most elegant that could be conceived. At the four sides of the fountain, I had designed a high raised figure, seated, with many ingenious devices and ornaments to each. The King began to interrogate me about the fancy of this elegant work, telling me that he had himself understood my whole plan of the gate, without asking a single question; but as for my present design, though it appeared to him exceedingly beautiful, he could not so much as form a conjecture concerning its meaning. He added, that he was very sure I had not acted like some foolish artists, who produced works that had some beauty and elegance, but were void of significance.

My explanation was this: "May it please your Majesty, this little work was designed on a small scale, but when it is carried into execution there will be the same symmetry and exactness in great as in miniature. That figure in the middle is fifty-four feet high." At this the King appeared to be greatly surprised. "Next," continued I, "is represented the god Mars. Those other four figures are made for the Virtues, in which your Majesty so highly delights, and which you so much favor. The figure on the right hand is the emblem of Science; observe its symbol, which denotes philosophy with all its train of attendant virtues. That other signifies the art of designing, which comprises sculpture, painting, and architecture. That next figure represents Music, a proper companion for all the other sciences. This, which appears so kind and courteous, is intended for Liberality, since without her aid none of those virtues or talents given us by the Almighty can ever become conspicuous. The great statue in the middle represents your Majesty, who are the Mars of this age, the only valiant prince in the world, a prince who exerts that valor in supporting and asserting the glory of his crown."

Hardly had he the patience to hear me out, when he exclaimed, "I have at last found a man after my own heart." He immediately sent for his treasurer, and ordered him to supply me with all I required, however great the expense. He then clapped me on the shoulder, and said to me in French, "*Mon ami*, I do not know which pleasure is the greater, that of a prince who meets with a man after his own heart, or that of the artist who finds a prince that gives him all the encouragement necessary to carry his great and sublime ideas into execution." I made answer, that if I was the artist meant by his Majesty the happiness was entirely on my side. He answered laughing, "Let us then reckon it equal on both sides."

I left the monarch in high spirits, and returned to my work. It happened unluckily for me that I had not been apprised to act the same farce with Madame d'Estampes, who having in the evening heard from the King himself all that passed, conceived so deep a resentment at the neglect, that she said with indignation, "If Benvenuto

had shown me his fine works I should have had reason
to remember him at the proper time." The King endeavored to excuse me, but without success. Having
received this information about a fortnight later, when
the court was returned to St. Germain-en-Laye, I took
with me the fine piece of plate I had wrought at the
desire of Madame d'Estampes herself, in hopes that, by
making her a present of it, I might recover her good
graces. Accordingly I carried it to her, and having mentioned my intention to her waiting-woman, showed her
the cup I purposed presenting to her lady. She said she
would just speak a word to Madame d'Estampes, who
was not yet dressed, but that as soon as ever she had
apprised her of my coming she would introduce me.
When she told her lady of my arrival, and the present
I had brought, the latter answered disdainfully, "Tell
him to wait." Having heard this, I armed myself with
patience, and continued in suspense till she was going to
dinner. It grew late, and hunger provoked me to such
a degree that, unable to resist its cravings any longer,
I gave the lady a hearty curse, and, going directly to the
Cardinal of Lorraine, made him a present of the cup,
begging he would stand my friend with the King, and
prevent me from being deprived of his good graces. He
answered that I did not want a friend at court, and in
case I had, he would have espoused my cause without
being solicited. Then, calling to his steward, he whispered something in his ear.

The steward, having waited till I left the Cardinal's presence, said, "Benvenuto, come this way, and I
will treat you with a bottle of good wine." As I was
not well aware of his meaning, I answered, "For God's
sake, my good steward, do but give me a single glass of
wine, and a bit of bread, for I am ready to sink for want
of sustenance. I have waited fasting since the morning
early at Madame d'Estampes' door, with an intention to

make her a present of that fine gilt cup; and when I sent
her word that I was there, she, to drive me to distraction,
ordered me to be told to wait. At present hunger attacks me, and I find my powers begin to fail; so, as it
was God's will, I have bestowed my property and my
work on one that deserved it much better, and all I desire
of you is to give me something to drink; as I am of a
temper rather impatient, and hunger also pinches me to
such a degree that I am almost ready to faint." While
I uttered these words with great difficulty, a servant
brought in some excellent wine and other delicacies for
a collation. I refreshed myself very well, recruited my
spirits thoroughly, and my peevishness and impatience
subsided. The worthy steward put into my hands a hundred gold crowns, but I declined accepting them on any
account. He went and told the Cardinal, who reprimanded him severely, and commanded him to force them
upon me, or not appear again in his presence. The
steward came back highly offended, declaring that the
Cardinal had never rated him so before. He then endeavored to persuade me to accept of his master's
bounty: and upon my making some resistance, he said,
in a passion, that he would compel me to take the
money. I at length accepted it, and proposed going to
return the Cardinal thanks; but he gave me to understand by one of his secretaries that whenever he had
it in his power to befriend me he should do it with
pleasure.

I returned to Paris the same evening. The King was
informed of all that had passed, and Madame d'Estampes
was very much rallied upon the occasion; but this only
increased her resentment against me, whence my life was
afterward in danger.

I won the friendship of one of the most learned and
most amiable acquaintances that I ever had. This was
Signor Guido Guidi, an excellent physician and eminent

citizen of Florence.   He came to Paris while I resided in
that capital.   Upon our first acquaintance I conducted
him to my castle, and assigned him an apartment in it,
so that we enjoyed each other's company several years.
Thither also came the Bishop of Pavia, Monsignor de
Rossi, brother of the Count of St. Secondo.   I made this
prelate leave his inn, and took him with me to my castle,
where I gave him an apartment, in which he was hand-
somely accommodated, with all his retinue, several
months.   On another occasion I accommodated Signor
Luigi Alamanni and his sons for some months.

I enjoyed the friendship of Signor Guido as many
years as I resided at the castle, and we often boasted to
each other that we had acquired some improvement in
our respective professions at the expense of the great and
munificent King who had invited us to his capital.   My
castle had a tennis-court, from which I derived great
benefit; at the same time that I used it for exercise there
were many habitations in it, occupied by men of different
trades, among whom there was an excellent printer.   Almost his whole shop was within the precincts of my
castle, and it was he that first printed the excellent medical treatise published by Signor Guido.   As I had use
for the shop, I made him leave it, but not without difficulty.   There was likewise in the same place a person
that made gunpowder.   I wanted the habitation he occupied for some of my German artists, but the powder-
maker would on no account dislodge, though I several
times civilly asked him to let me have the apartment.
The more humble my remonstrances, the more insolently
the brute answered me.   At last I allowed him three
days to remove; but he laughed and told me that he
would begin to think of it in about three years.

I did not know at first that this fellow was a domestic of
Madame d'Estampes; and if it had not been that the affair
between that lady and me had rendered me particularly

cautious, I should instantly have dislodged him; but I
thought it advisable to have patience for the three days:
these being expired, I took with me several armed men—
Germans, Italians, and French, as likewise some menial
servants, who in a short time cleared the house, and
threw all he had in it into the street. I treated him with
this particular rigor because he had told me that he did
not think any Italian had the courage to move the least
thing belonging to him out of its place. I then said to
him, "I am the least of all the Italians, but I have done
nothing to you yet, in comparison with what I find myself disposed to do, and what I certainly shall perform,
if you speak another word," with many more angry and
menacing expressions. The man, in terror and astonishment, gathered up his effects as well as he could, and
ran to Madame d'Estampes, to whom he gave a most
terrible account of the whole transaction. That grand
enemy of mine, an enemy the more dangerous in proportion to her greater influence and credit, represented the
affair in the worst light to his Majesty. The monarch,
as I have been informed, flew into a violent passion, and
was on the point of giving very severe orders against
me; but as his son Henry the Dauphin, and his sister,
espoused my cause so warmly that the King turned the
whole affair into ridicule.

CHAPTER XXXII

VEXATIOUS LAWSUITS

AFTER I had thus got rid of my Frenchman, I
found myself obliged to proceed in the same
manner with another tradesman, but did not
demolish the house; I only caused the goods
to be thrown out of the window. This provoked Ma-

dame d'Estampes so highly that she said to the King,
"I believe this outrageous fellow will one day ransack
the city of Paris." The King answered, in a passion, that
I did very right in ridding myself of a rabble that would
have prevented me from executing his orders. The fury
of this cruel woman rising every day to a higher pitch,
she sent for a certain painter who lived occasionally at
Fontainebleau. This painter was a native of Bologna,
by which name he was universally known; but his real
name was Francesco Primaticcio. Madame d'Estampes
bade him apply to the King for the work that he had
resolved to put into my hands, and said she would second
him to the utmost of her power: this was agreed upon
between them. Bolonga was master of the art of designing, and had agreed with certain workmen who had
learned their business under Rosso, our celebrated painter
of Florence, who must be acknowledged to have been a
man of great genius; and Primaticcio himself, in whatever he had produced of any degree of merit, had followed the excellent manner of that Rosso, who was at
this time no more. These very plausible reasons had
such weight, being backed by Madame d'Estampes, and
conspiring with the continual dinning in the King's ears
day and night, either by Primaticcio or the lady, that this
great prince at last began to listen to their suggestions.

They said to him, "How is it possible that your sacred
Majesty, while employing Benvenuto to make you twelve
statues of silver, of which he has not yet finished one,
can think of engaging him in so great an undertaking?
You must resolve to give up the other plans which you
are so much bent upon, because a hundred men of first-
rate talents would be unable to finish all the great works
which this one enterprising genius has taken in hand. It
is obvious, at the same time, that he exerts himself too
much, and is indefatigable in the business, which may
very probably be the cause of your losing both him and

the works he is employed in." These and many other arguments of the like sort produced their effect upon the mind of the King, so that he complied with their desires; and yet he had not hitherto seen any designs or models by Primaticcio.

At this juncture the second person whom I had driven out of the precincts of my castle had begun a lawsuit against me at Paris, affirming that I had robbed him of several of his effects at the time that I dislodged him. This suit occasioned me a great deal of trouble, and took up so much of my time, that I was frequently on the point of forming a desperate resolution to quit the kingdom. It is customary in France to make the most of a suit with a foreigner or with any other person who is not used to law-transactions. As soon as they have any advantage in the process, they find means to sell it to certain persons who make a trade of buying lawsuits. There is another villainous practice which is general with the Normans, I mean that of bearing false witness; so that those who purchase the suit immediately instruct five or six of these witnesses, as there happens to be occasion. By such means, if their adversary cannot produce an equal number to contradict and destroy their evidence, and happens to be ignorant of the custom of the country, he is sure to have a decree given against him. Both these accidents having happened to me, I thought the proceeding highly dishonorable. I therefore made my appearance in the great hall of the Palais at Paris in order to plead my own cause; where I saw the King's lieutenant for civil affairs seated upon a grand tribunal. This man was tall, corpulent, and had a most austere countenance. On one side he was surrounded by a multitude of people, and on the other with numbers of attorneys and counsellors, all ranged in order upon the right and left; others came one by one, and severally opened their causes before the judge. I observed that

the counselors, who stood on one side, sometimes spoke
all together. To my great surprise, this extraordinary
magistrate, with the countenance of a true Plato, seemed
by his attitude to listen now to one, now to another, and
constantly answered with the utmost propriety. As I
always took great pleasure in seeing and contemplating
the efforts of genius, of what nature soever, this appeared
to me so wonderful that I would not have missed seeing
it for any consideration. As the hall was of a prodigious
extent, and filled with a great multitude of persons, particular care was taken that none should enter but such as
came about business; so the door was kept locked, and
the avenues were guarded by door-keepers. These men,
in opposing those who were for forcing in, sometimes
made such a noise that the judge reprimanded them very
severely. I stooped down several times to observe what
passed. The words I heard the judge utter, on seeing
two gentlemen who wished to hear the trial, and whom
the porter was endeavoring to keep out, were these: "Be
quiet, be quiet, Satan, get hence, and leave off disturbing
us." The words in French were, *Paix, paix, Satan, allez,
paix.* As I had by this time thoroughly learned the
French language, on hearing these words I recollected
what Dante said, when he with his master, Virgil, entered the gates of hell; for Dante and Giotto, the painter,
were together in France, and visited Paris with particular
attention, where the court of justice may be considered
as hell. Hence it is that Dante, who was likewise perfect master of the French, made use of that expression;
and I have often been surprised that it was never under
stood in that sense; so that I cannot help thinking that
the commentators on this author have often made him
say things he never dreamed of.

   To return to my suit: I found that when verdicts
were given against me, and no redress was to be expected from the law, I must have recourse to a long

sword, which I had by me, for I was always particularly careful to be provided with good arms. The first that I attacked was the person who brought that unjust and vexatious suit; and one evening I gave him so many wounds upon the legs and arms, taking care, however, not to kill him, that I deprived him of the use of both his legs. I then fell upon the other, who had bought the cause, and treated him in such a manner as quickly caused a stop to be put to the proceedings. For this and every other success, I returned thanks to the Supreme Being, and began to conceive hopes that I should be for some time unmolested. I earnestly entreated my young journeymen, especially the Italians, to be attentive to their business, and to work hard for a time, till I could finish the works I had undertaken; for I purposed to return to Italy as soon as they were completed, not being able any longer to bear the villainy of the French; at the same time seriously considering that if the monarch should once happen to be angry with me I might meet with severe treatment for having revenged myself in the manner I had done.

These Italian journeymen were as follow:—The first and highest in my favor was Ascanio, born in the kingdom of Naples, at a place called Tagliacozzo: the second was Paolo, a Roman, a person of mean birth, who did not so much as know his own father: these two I had brought from Rome, where they had lived with me. The third was likewise a Roman, who came from Italy, on purpose to enter into my service: his name was also Paolo, and he was son of a poor Roman gentleman of the Maccherani family. This young man had but little proficiency in the business; but he was brave, and an excellent swordsman. The fourth journeyman was a native of Ferrara, whose name was Bartolommeo Chioccia. The fifth was a Florentine, named Paolo Micceri, who had a brother, surnamed Gatta, a very able clerk, but guilty of extravagance when he managed the business for Tommaso Guadagni, a rich merchant; he afterward kept my books, which contained my accounts with his most Christian Majesty and others by whom I was employed. Paolo Micceri, having learned his brother's method of bookkeeping, continued to follow it, and I allowed him a good salary. He appeared to me to be a very pious youth, and showed a great turn for devotion, sometimes singing psalms, sometimes telling his beads, so that I conceived great hopes from such an appearance of virtue. I therefore called him aside, and spoke to him thus: "My dear friend Paolo, you see how happily you are settled with me, and may remember you were before out of business: you are a Florentine, which makes me confide in you; and what gives me high satisfaction is to see you so devout, and so regular in all acts of religion. I therefore, putting more trust in you than in the others, request you to give your attention to two things, in which I am in a particular manner concerned: one is, that you would carefully watch over my property, and be always upon your guard to prevent anybody from medding with it, as likewise that you avoid touching it yourself. At the same time you see the poor girl Caterina, whom I keep in the house chiefly on account of my business, and without whom it would be impossible for me to conduct it. Now I have particular reasons for wishing that she should be extremely circumspect in her conduct; therefore I wish you to watch her attentively, and inform me of any improprieties you may observe. I have no desire to provide for other people's children, nor would I tamely put up with such a thing. Were I to detect so scandalous an outrage, I would sacrifice both to my insulted honor. Therefore be prudent, and obey my injunctions; let me know if you observe anything wrong, and I will dismiss both her and her mother with disgrace." This traitor crossed himself from head to foot; and made the most solemn asseverations that such an idea as that of injuring so great a benefactor in the smallest particular could never enter his mind. His appeals to all that was sacred and his apparent devotion to me completely imposed upon me. Two days afterward my countryman Maltio de Nasaro invited me and all my establishment to partake of his hospitality at his country house. When I proposed to take Paolo with me to enjoy himself, he observed how dangerous it would be to leave the house unprotected, and such gold, silver, and jewels lying all about; and that there were thieves on the look-out day and night. "Go then, and enjoy yourself, dear master," he added, and "I will keep watch."

So, taking Ascanio and Chioccia with me, I set out and spent the greater part of the day with infinite satisfaction. But toward evening I began to feel uncomfortable and out of humor; the words used by Paolo kept recurring to my mind; I could not master my uneasiness, and at last I took horse, and with two of my attendants returned to my castle. I had very nearly taken the villain by surprise; for as I entered the court I heard the wretch of a mother crying, "Pagolo, Caterina, here is the master." Soon they both appeared, terror and confusion depicted in every feature, scarcely knowing what they said or did, and evidently guilty. Overpowered by momentary rage, I seized my sword, resolved to kill them upon the spot. One fled, the other fell at my feet beseeching mercy, a movement that allowed me time to recover my reason. I determined then to turn them both out of the place. Turning to Paolo, I exclaimed, "Thou basest of wretches, had my eyes been a little sharper, I would have passed this weapon through thy craven heart. Now thank thy stars, up and away!" And with every opprobrious epithet, cuffs and kicks, I chased both mother and daughter out of my castle.

In conjunction with a low attorney, a Norman, these wretches entered into a foul conspiracy against me, which caused me the greatest uneasiness, and compelled me to seek redress in a court of justice. I began to think of adopting one of two alternatives, either to quit France altogether or to exhaust her full vengeance, and see what strange destiny heaven had yet in store for me. I persevered, and as I threatened to appeal to the King, my enemies took the alarm, and I came off victorious.

So, giving thanks to God, I returned joyfully to my castle, with my young assistants, who had appeared in my behalf. I resolved no longer to tempt my evil fortune in France, though I could not abandon my prospects without extreme regret. I sat alone in my little studio to consider the matter, having requested those of my young men who advised me to take my departure to leave me a while to my own thoughts; though aware at the same time that they had taken a correct view of the subject. I knew that I could much better justify myself to the King by letters, and thus prove their malignant and assassin-like design than by any other method, and I decided accordingly. But no sooner had I done so than it seemed as if some one slapped me on the shoulder and exclaimed in a cheering voice: "Courage, Benvenuto! Do as you are wont, and fear nothing." Such an effect had this that I recovered all my confidence, and determined to put off my journey for a time.

The first vengeance I took on my persecutors was to compel Paolo to marry Caterina, thinking so infamous a couple well suited to each other. This hypocritical fellow had undertaken what I requested with such solemn assurances of fidelity and devotion to my interest, that I was induced to place implicit confidence in him. Nevertheless, he very soon betrayed me; and after I drove them out of my house they vented a horrible accusation against

me, which, according to the laws of France, endangered
my life; but their conspiracy failed, and my innocence
was clearly established.

CHAPTER XXXIII

A STRUGGLE FOR MONEY

WHEN once adverse fortune, or the influence of
our evil stars, begins to persecute a man, it is
never at a loss for means to distress him.
When I thought myself extricated from one
troublesome and dangerous affair, and flattered myself
that my evil genius would leave me at rest for a while,
I was involved again in perplexing difficulties, and in
a few days two accidents befel me, by both of which I
was in imminent danger of my life. I was obliged to go
to Fontainebleau to wait upon the King, who had written me a letter, asking me to undertake to strike the
coins for his whole kingdom. He had inclosed some
little designs, but at the same time he left me at liberty
to follow the dictates of my genius. In compliance with
his Majesty's orders, I had drawn new designs, in my
own taste, and with the utmost elegance of art. On my
arrival at Fontainebleau, one of the King's treasurers,
Monsieur de la Faye, who had received orders to provide
me with whatever I wanted, said to me: "Benvenuto,
Primaticcio the painter has been ordered by the King to
make your colossal statue; and all the other great works
that had been put into your hands, his Majesty has now
given to him. We are all very sorry for it, and think
this countryman of yours has acted very presumptuously,
and behaved extremely ill to you; for you had been en-

trusted with the works on account of the excellence of
your models and your masterly performance; but this
man has supplanted you merely through the interest of
Madame d'Estampes. It is now several months since
he undertook those works, and he has not yet so much
as done a stroke." I exclaimed with surprise, "How is
it possible I should never have heard a word of all this?"
He answered that Primaticcio had kept the affair as
secret as possible, and obtained his request with the
utmost difficulty, the King being very unwilling to grant
it; but that Madame d'Estampes had been so earnest in
her solicitations as to extort, in some measure, his compliance.

Finding myself so cruelly wronged, so unjustly treated,
and deprived of a work that was due to me in consideration of the pains I had taken, I resolved to perform some
signal feat of arms, and went with eager haste in quest
of Signor Primaticcio. I found him in his chamber, ab-
sorbed in study. He bade me come in, and with some of
his Lombard civilities asked me what was the best news,
and what had brought me thither. I answered that it
was an affair of the last importance. He thereupon ordered his servants to bring wine, and said, "Before we
talk about business we must drink together, for that is
the custom here in France." "I must inform you," I
said, "Signor Francesco, that there is no occasion for our
conversation to be begun with drinking—that, perhaps
may come afterward." I then continued: "All those
who profess themselves to be men of worth and virtue
show by their actions that they are such; and when they
behave otherwise they can no longer be considered in
that light. I am sensible that you were not ignorant of
the King's having employed me to make the colossus,
which has been talked of these eighteen months, and
neither you nor anybody else said anything about it
during that time. I had by my labors made myself

known to that great prince, who was so pleased with my models as to commit this grand undertaking to me, and for many months I heard nothing of his having a different intention.   It was not until this morning that I heard it was given to you, and that you had basely undermined me, though I had obtained the work by my successful performances, and you have taken it from me by empty words." "My friend Benvenuto," answered Primaticcio, "every man endeavors to do the best he can for himself; and if it be the King's pleasure, what objection can you make?   Say what you will, you will only lose your labor in talking against the grant; it has been made to me, and cannot be disputed: now speak as much as you please, and I will listen to you in my turn."   I thereupon replied: "I have a great deal to say to you, Signor Francesco, and could by many strong and convincing arguments make you confess that such methods of acting and reasoning as yours are not customary among rational animals; but I will be brief, and come directly to the point.   Listen attentively, for what I am going to say is of great consequence."   He was ready to rise from his seat, seeing that I changed color and discovered symptoms of great emotion; but I told him it was not yet time for him to stir, and bade him sit still and attend to what I had to say.

I then proceeded thus: "Signor Francesco, you know very well that the work was at first put into my hands, and that, according to the practice of the world, it was no longer a proper time for any other person to apply for it.   I now declare to you that I am willing you should make a model, and I will make a new one.   We then will carry them both to our great monarch, and he who on that occasion acquits himself best, shall be looked upon as entitled to the honor of making the colossus.   If it should happen to be your lot, I will lay aside all resentment of the injury you have done me, and bless your

hands as more worthy than mine of so great an honor.
Let us therefore make this agreement, and we shall be
friends; otherwise we must be enemies; and God, who
always assists the just cause, and I, his instrument, will
find means to convince you of your error." Francesco
answered, "The work is mine; and since it has been
given to me, I do not choose to take any further risk."
To this I replied: "Signor Francesco, since you will not
accept the alternative proposed, which is both just and
reasonable, I will offer another to you, which will resemble your own proceeding in its harshness and deformity.
I must tell you plainly that, if I ever hear you have said a
word of this work of mine, I will kill you as I would a
mad dog. We are neither in Rome, Florence, Naples,
nor Bologna, and the manner of living in this country is
quite different. If I ever hear that you have uttered but
a word about it to the King, I will instantly put you to
death without mercy. Think therefore seriously which
proposal you choose to accept—the first, which is fair;
or the last, which exposes you to destruction."

The man was at a loss what to say or how to act, and
I was almost preparing to put my design instantly into
execution. He said nothing further than this, "So long
as I behave like a man of honor and principle, I shall
be free from all fear and apprehensions." To this I replied, "What you say is very just; but when you act
in a contrary manner, you have reason to be afraid. Remember my words." I thereupon left him, to wait on the
King, and had a long conference with his Majesty concerning the coins, in which we could not agree; for his
privy council, being there present, persuaded him that
money should still be coined in the same manner that it
always had been coined in France. I answered, that his
Majesty had invited me from Italy to work for him so as
to deserve approbation; and even if he should give me
contrary directions, I could never find it in my heart to

18

obey him. Further conversation on the subject was deferred to another opportunity, and I returned to Paris. I had hardly dismounted when one of those busy persons who delight in mischief-making came to inform me that Paolo Micceri had taken a house for Caterina and her mother, and that he made use of the most injurious and contemptuous expressions toward me. "Poor Benvenuto; he paid the piper while I danced; and now he goes about boasting of the exploit. He thinks I am afraid of him—I, who can wear a sword and dagger as well as he; but I would have him to know my weapons are as keen as his. I, too, am a Florentine, and come of the Micceri, a much better house than the Cellini." In short, the vile informer painted the things in such colors to my disadvantage that it fired my whole blood. I was in a fever of the most dangerous kind. And feeling it must kill me unless it found vent, I had recourse to my usual means on such occasions. I called to my workman, Chioccia to accompany me, and told another to follow with my horse. On reaching the wretch's house, finding the door half open, I entered abruptly. There he sat with his *chère amie*, and his boasted sword and dagger beside him, in the very act of jesting with the elder lady upon my affairs. To slam the door, draw my sword, and present the point to his throat, was the work of a moment, giving him no time to think of defending himself. "Ah! thou vile poltroon, recommend thy soul to God; thou art a dead man." In the excess of his terror, he cried out thrice, in a feeble voice, "Mamma, Mamma, Mamma!—help! help me!" At this ludicrous appeal, so like a girl's, and the ridiculous manner in which it was uttered, though I had a mind to kill, I lost half my rage, and could not forbear laughing. Turning to Chioccia, however, I bade him make fast the door; for I was resolved to inflict the same punishment upon all three. Still with my sword-point at his throat, and pricking him a

*I GAVE HER THIRTY SOUS A DAY . . . AND OBLIGED
HER TO POSE FOR ME*

From an Etching by F. Laguillermie

little now and then, I terrified him with the most desperate threats; and, finding that he made no defence, was rather at a loss how to proceed. It was too poor a revenge—it was nothing; when suddenly it came into my head to do it effectually, and make him espouse the girl upon the spot. "Up! and off with that ring on thy finger, villain!" I cried, "marry her this instant; and then I shall have my full revenge." "Anything, anything you like, provided you will not kill me," he eagerly answered. Removing my sword a little: "Now, then," I said, "put on the ring;" and he did so, while trembling all the time. "This is not enough. Chioccia, go and bring me two notaries to draw up the contract." Then addressing the girl and her mother in French: "While the notaries and witnesses are coming I will give you a word of advice. If any one of you utters a word about my affairs, I will kill you—all three—so keep it in mind." I afterward said in Italian to Paolo: "If you offer the slightest opposition to the least thing I choose to propose, I will cut you up into mincemeat with this good sword." "It is enough," he interrupted in alarm, "that you will not kill me. I will do whatever you wish." So this singular contract was duly drawn up and signed; my rage and fever were gone; I paid the notaries, and went home.

The next day Primaticcio came to Paris and sent Mattio del Nasaro for me. I waited upon him accordingly, when he asked me to consider him in the light of a brother, and declared he would not mention a word concerning the great work to the King, as he was sensible that I must be in the right.

Not satisfied with making Paolo marry Caterina, I completed my revenge by inviting her to sit to me as a model. I gave her thirty sous a day, paid in advance, and a good meal, and obliged her to pose before me.

When the salt-cellar was finished, the King returned to Paris. I paid him a visit, carrying the salt-cellar with me, which was entirely of gold, and admirably engraved with the chisel.

When I showed the King this piece of work, he burst into an exclamation of surprise, and could not sufficiently admire it. He then bade me carry it home, telling me he would soon let me know what to do with it.

I invited several of my most intimate friends to dinner, and put the salt-cellar upon the table. Thus we were the very first to make use of it, and spent the day very cheerfully. After this I continued to work on the statue of Jupiter, and the great silver vase, on which were engraved several pretty mottoes, with a variety of figures.

About this time the Bolognese told the King that it would be proper for his Majesty to send him to Rome, and give him letters of recommendation, that he might take designs of the first-rate antiques of that city, the Laocoön, the Cleopatra, the Venus, the Commodus, the Apollo, and the Zingara; which are indeed the finest things in Rome. He at the same time told the monarch that his Majesty, by seeing those admirable masterpieces, would be able to form a judgment of the art of drawing; for all the works of modern artists that had been shown him were infinitely inferior to the masterly performances of the ancients. The King approved of his proposal, and gave him all the encouragement he desired. So the fool went off in this manner, and not having the spirit to rival me, had recourse to this artifice, worthy of a Lombard, of pretending to praise the works of the ancients in order to depreciate mine; but though he took excellent drawings of them, his success proved quite the reverse of what he had flattered himself it would.

Having discontinued my connection with that wretch Caterina, and the poor unfortunate young man who had conspired with her to wrong me being gone from Paris, I intended to have my ornament for Fontainebleau, which was of bronze, properly cleaned, and likewise to get the two figures of Victory, which extended from the side angles to the middle circles of the gate, furbished up. For this purpose I took into my house a poor girl about fifteen years of age. She was extremely well-shaped, lively, and of a complexion rather swarthy; and as she was somewhat rustic, spoke little, walked rapidly, and had a sort of wildness in her eyes, I gave her the name of Scozzona; but her name was Gianna. With her assistance, I finished my Fontainebleau and the two Victories intended for ornaments to the gate. By this Gianna I had a daughter, on the seventh of June, at three in the afternoon, in 1544. I gave this child the name of Constantia, and she was held upon the font by Signor Guido Guidi, one of my most intimate friends, physician to the King. He alone stood godfather; for the custom of France is, that there should be but one godfather and two godmothers. One of these was Signora Maddalena, wife to Signor Luigi Alamanni, a gentleman of Florence, and an admirable poet, the other godmother was a French lady of good family, wife of Signor Riccardo del Bene, also a citizen of Florence and an eminent merchant. This was the first child that I ever had, to the best of my remembrance. I assigned the mother such a maintenance as satisfied an aunt of hers, into whose hands I put her; and never had any acquaintance with her afterward.

I continued my works with all possible expedition, and by this time they were well forwarded. The Jupiter was as good as finished, so was the vase, and the gate began to display its beauties. At this time the King arrived in Paris; and though I have spoken of the birth of my daughter as having happened in 1544, at the time now under consideration the year 1543 had not quite elapsed. The King immediately came to my house, where my works gave him great satisfaction. He was as much

pleased with them as an artist could wish him to be.
He also recollected of himself, that the Cardinal of Ferrara had given me none of the money that he had promised should be paid to me; so, speaking low to his admiral, he said the Cardinal of Ferrara had done
very wrong in not paying me; but that he himself would
see justice done me; for he perceived that I was a man
of few words and would leave the kingdom if I were not
satisfied. After dinner the King bade the Cardinal tell
the treasurer to pay me, with all possible expedition,
seven thousand gold crowns in three or four instalments,
according as he found it convenient, and not to fail, at his
peril. He then concluded with these words, "I had put
Benvenuto under your care, and you have quite forgotten
him." The Cardinal assured the King, that he would
punctually obey his orders; but his natural malignity
made him stay till the monarch's fit of generosity was
over.

In the mean time France was threatened more and
more with the calamities of war, and the Emperor with a
large army appeared to be on the point of marching to
Paris. The Cardinal, perceiving that money was very
scarce in the kingdom, took occasion one day to speak
to the King in these terms: "I thought it best not to
give Benvenuto the money your Majesty ordered him;
and one of my reasons was, that you now stand but too
much in need of it yourself; the other, that so generous
a present would have deprived us of him the sooner, for
if once he had found himself rich, he would have purchased an estate in Italy, and when the whim took him
would certainly have left you. So I have considered
that it is most advisable your Majesty should assign him
some settlement in your own dominions, if you desire
that he should continue any considerable time in your
service." The King seemed to approve of what was said;
but with a greatness of soul worthy of such a mon-

arch, he considered that the Cardinal had acted as he had done rather to gratify his own temper than because he had so long before had the sagacity to foresee the distressed state of so great a kingdom. Thus, though the King appeared to assent outwardly to the reasons assigned by the Cardinal, his private sentiments were very different; for he soon returned to Paris, and the day after his arrival he came of his own accord to my house, when I conducted him through several apartments, in which there was a variety of works.

Beginning with those of least value, I showed him several pieces of bronze, which surpassed anything of the kind he had ever beheld. I then led him to the silver Jupiter, and he was pleased to find it almost finished, with all its beautiful ornaments. This indeed he admired much more than any other man would have done, on account of an unlucky accident that had happened to him a few years before, when the Emperor, planning an expedition against the town of Tunis, passed through Paris with the consent of the French monarch. Francis, being desirous of making Charles a present worthy of so great an emperor, caused a silver Hercules to be cast for that purpose, exactly of the same size with my Jupiter. This Hercules was a most ordinary piece of work; and when the King found fault with it, the artists whom he had employed, and who pretended to be the greatest masters in the world, maintained that nothing more complete could be made of silver, insisting upon two thousand ducats for their bungling piece of work. For this reason, when his Majesty saw my performance, he was surprised at its admirable finish. To such a degree was he pleased that he valued it at two thousand crowns, and said, "Those ignorant artists received no recompense from me. For this I will give a thousand crowns, and it is well worth the money. I then took his Majesty to see some other models of new works. When he was on the point of departing, I conducted him through the castle garden, where I showed him my statue of the giant.

The King expressed the greatest astonishment imaginable, and spoke thus to the Admiral, M. d'Annebaut: "Since the Cardinal has not yet supplied this man with money, and the latter is so backward to ask it, I must without more delay take care to provide for him myself; for when artists are too modest to ask any recompense, their works seem sufficiently to claim it. Therefore give him the first abbey that becomes vacant, the revenue of which amounts to two thousand crowns a year, and in case you cannot let him have it in one benefice, give it to him in two or three; it will be the same thing to him." I was present, heard all that was said, and immediately returned thanks to his Majesty, as if I had the abbey already in my possession; telling him that I intended, when that work was finished, to serve his Majesty without any other reward, salary, or recompense for my labor, till old age should render me incapable of working, when I might be allowed to retire to necessary repose, happy in the remembrance of having served so great a monarch. To this he answered, "So be it!"

CHAPTER XXXIV

THE STATUE'S TRIUMPH

MADAME d'ESTAMPES, having heard of my encouragement, was more incensed against me than ever, and said, "I govern the whole kingdom, and yet this insignificant fellow sets my power at defiance." In a word, she left no stone unturned to effect my destruction. A great distiller gave her certain odoriferous waters of an extraordinary virtue for the skin, which never had been used in France before that time. This man she introduced to the King, to whom he showed certain operations in distilling, with which his Majesty was highly delighted. During these amusements she made the distiller apply to the King for a tennis-court at my castle, with certain little apartments belonging to it, of which he said I made no use. The King, who knew with whom this application originated, returned no answer. Madame d'Estampes thereupon began to solicit him, and made use of all those insinuating arts with which women know how to work upon men; and so successful did she prove that, happening to find the King in an amorous mood, to which he was very subject, he granted the lady all she desired.

Thereupon the distiller came, accompanied by the treasurer Grolier, one of the first nobility of France, who understood Italian incomparably well. In this language he talked to me at first in a jocular manner, and then, coming to the point, told me that in the King's name he put the other man in possession of that tennis-court, and the little apartments adjoining to it. To this I answered, "His sacred Majesty is master of this house, and of everything in it. You might therefore enter with the utmost freedom. But this taking possession in the manner of notaries and courts appears to be rather a trick than the order of so great a monarch. I therefore protest to you that instead of going to complain to his Majesty, I will defend myself in the manner that he commanded me the other day; that is, I will throw this man whom you have placed here out of the window, if I do not see a commission signed with his Majesty's own hand."

The treasurer went away menacing and muttering to himself, and I remained in equal ill humor. Soon after he was gone, I went in quest of the notaries that had put the man in possession. These, being my intimate acquaintances, gave me to understand that it was a ceremony performed by the King's authority, but not of much consequence; and if I had made ever so little resistance, the man would not have taken possession as he did; adding that these were acts and customs of the court, which did not concern the obedience due to the King, insomuch that, if I thought proper to dispossess him in the same manner as he had taken possession, I should do very well, and need not be under any apprehensions with regard to consequences. Being thus sufficiently instructed, I the next day had recourse to open violence. Though there were some difficulties in the way, I took pleasure in contending with them, and every day made some assault with stones, pikes, or muskets. I, however, fired without ball; but even so, struck such terror into my adversary's adherents that nobody chose afterward to stir to his assistance. One day, finding his resistance feeble, I entered the house by force, and drove him out, throwing all his goods and furniture after him. I then went to the King, and told him I had done what he had commanded me, and defended myself against all that offered to impede me in his Majesty's service. The King laughed, and caused new letters to be issued, to secure me from being molested for the future.

In the mean while, having finished the beautiful statue of Jupiter, with its gilt pedestal, I placed it upon a wooden socle, which hardly made any appearance, and within that socle I fixed four little globes of wood, which were more than half hidden in their sockets, and so admirably contrived, that a little child could with the utmost ease move this statue of Jupiter backward and forward, and turn it about. I took it to Fontainebleau, where the King then resided. About this time Primaticcio had brought the figures already mentioned from

Rome, and caused them to be cast in bronze with the utmost care. I knew nothing at all of the matter, for he had transacted the business with great secrecy, and Fontainebleau is more than thirty miles from Paris. On my inquiring of the King, in the presence of Madame d'Estampes, where I was to place the statue of Jupiter, she told his Majesty that there was not a more proper place than his beatiful gallery. This was what we might call a corridor. It was about two hundred paces long, adorned with pictures by the admirable Rosso of Florence, and with several pieces of sculpture, some detached and others in basso rilievo. The breadth was about twelve paces. Here Primaticcio had assembled all his bronze figures, and placed them in the most regular order on their pedestals. Here also I introduced my Jupiter; and when I saw this great display of the wonders of art I said to myself, "This is like passing between the pikes of the enemy. Heaven protect me from all danger!" Having put the statue into its place, and fixed it in the most advantageous situation I could, I awaited the coming of the great monarch.

This figure of Jupiter had a thunderbolt in his right hand, and appeared to be just about to throw it. In his left hand I had placed a globe, and among the flames I had with great dexterity put a white torch. Madame d'Estampes had detained the King till night, intending to make mischief, either by preventing his coming or contriving to make my work appear unfavorably in the night. As God, however, has promised that He will be the friend of such of his creatures as put their trust in Him, it happened quite the contrary to her expectations; for, on the approach of night, I lighted the torch in the hand of Jupiter, and as it was raised somewhat above his head, the light fell upon the statue, and caused it to appear to much greater advantage than it would otherwise have done. The King came, accompanied by Madame d'Estampes, the Dauphin his son, now King of France, and the Dauphiness, the King of Navarre his cousin, the Princess Margaret his daughter, and several great lords and noblemen, who had all been instructed by Madame d'Estampes to speak against me. When I saw his Majesty enter, I ordered my boy Ascanio to push the statue of Jupiter before him, and this motion being made with admirable contrivance, caused it to appear alive: thus the above-mentioned bronze figures were left somewhat behind, and the eyes of all the beholders were first struck with my performance. The King immediately cried out, "This is one of the finest productions of art that ever were beheld. I who take pleasure in such things and understand them, never could have conceived a piece of work the hundredth part so beautiful."

The noblemen who had been directed to rail at my performance, seemed now to vie with each other in praising it; but Madame d'Estampes said, with the utmost confidence, "It appears to me that you are very much at a loss for something to commend, when you lavish encomiums upon that statue. Don't you see those beautiful antique figures, which stand a little beyond it? In these the utmost perfection of art is displayed, and not in those modern pageants." The King then advanced, as did the rest likewise, and cast an eye upon the other figures, which appeared to great disadvantage, the light being placed below them. His Majesty observing this, said, "Those who have endeavored to hurt this man have done him the greatest service imaginable; for, from a comparison with these admirable figures, it is evident this statue is in every respect vastly superior to them. Benvenuto is, therefore, worthy of the highest esteem, since his performances, instead of being barely upon a par with those of the ancients, greatly surpass them." In answer to this, Madame d'Estampes observed that my

statue would not at another time appear a thousandth
part so well as it did by night; and that it should be
further taken into consideration that I had thrown a veil
over the figure to conceal its blemishes. This was an
exceedingly thin drapery, which I had placed so grace-
fully that it gave additional majesty to the figure. On
hearing these words, I took hold of the veil, and, pulling
it away, revealed the parts it was intended to conceal.
The lady thought I had done this out of contempt. The
King perceived her resentment; and I, being overcome
with passion, was about to speak, when the wise monarch uttered these words deliberately, in his own language: "Benvenuto, I must interrupt you—therefore be
silent—and you shall have a thousand times more treasure than you could wish." Not being allowed to speak,
I betrayed my emotion by my contortions. This caused
the lady to be more highly incensed than ever, and made
her mutter her indignation to herself. The King left the
place much sooner than he otherwise would, declaring
aloud, for my encouragement, that he had brought over
from Italy one of the ablest men that the world had
ever produced, and one who was endowed with the greatest variety of talents.

I left my statue there, and as I chose to leave the place
that morning, the King ordered me a thousand crowns,
partly as a recompense for my labor, and partly in payment of sums that appeared from my accounts to have
been disbursed by me. Having received the money, I
returned to Paris, and made merry at my own house.
After dinner I caused all my clothes to be brought me,
which were of the finest furs, or the very best cloth.
Out of these I made presents to all my workmen, dis-
tributing them according to their deserts, and even
giving some to the maids and the stable-boys; thereby
encouraging them to assist me with alacrity. I set about
finishing my statue of Mars, which I had made of

pieces of wood well fastened together, over which the flesh was represented by a covering, in thickness about equal to the eighth part of a cubit, made of plaster, and of the most elegant workmanship. I afterward resolved to make up the figure of several different pieces, and to put them together according to the rules of art; and this I with great ease effected.

I had given strict orders to all those who lived with me not to bring any women into my castle, and was particularly careful to see my orders obeyed. My boy Ascanio was in love with a girl of extraordinary beauty, who answered his passion with equal ardor. The girl, having on that account fled from her mother, came one night to Ascanio, and as she did not care to return home, he was at a loss where to conceal her; but, necessity sharpening his wit, he bethought himself of the odd expedient of hiding her in my Mars, and let her sleep in the head of the statue. There he stayed to watch her, and in the night he took her out sometimes, without making any noise. I had almost finished that head, and vanity prompted me to leave it uncovered, so that it was every day exposed to the view of the inhabitants of Paris. The neighbors began to climb upon the roofs of their houses to see it, and great numbers went thither on purpose to indulge their curiosity. At the same time a report became current in Paris, that my old castle was haunted by a ghost; but, for my part, I never could perceive that it was well founded. This ghost was universally called Lemmonio Boreo. As the girl concealed in the head could not but be sometimes seen through the eye-holes to move, some of the credulous populace affirmed that the ghost had entered the body of the great statue, and that it made the eyes and mouth move as if it were just going to speak. Accordingly, many went away frightened out of their wits; and some persons of penetration and sagacity, who came to see the figure, could not doubt the truth of what they had heard, when they contemplated the movements in the eyes of the figure. So they declared in their turn that there was a spirit within it; not being aware that there was not only spirit in it, but likewise good flesh and blood.

CHAPTER XXXV

LONGING FOR HOME

HIS Majesty about this time consulted me concerning the means of expeditiously fortifying Paris. He led me all round the city, and, perceiving how judiciously I spoke on the subject of fortifications, empowered me to cause all I proposed to be instantly carried into execution. At the same time, he told his Admiral, Sieur Annebaut, to order the people to obey me. The Admiral was a man of no genius, who owed his exalted dignity to the favor of Madame d'Estampes, well-deserving his name, which they pronounced Ane-et-bo, "*ass and ox.*" This blockhead having told Madame d'Estampes of all that had passed between the King and me, she commanded him to send at once for Girolamo Bellarmato. The latter was an engineer of Siena, who lived not more than a day's journey from Paris. He instantly came, and had recourse to the most slow and tedious method of fortification. I concerned myself no longer in the affair; and if the Emperor had advanced briskly to Paris, that city might have been easily taken. It was said with great truth that, in the treaty afterward concluded, Madame d'Estampes, who was the person most concerned in negotiating it, had betrayed the King, and exposed him to the enemy.

I then set about finishing my gate, and likewise my great vase, and two other middle-sized ones, made of my own silver. The good King, after all his various distresses, came to rest himself for a while at Paris; and as his pestilential mistress seemed born for the destruction of the kingdom, I think I may justly value myself upon her hating me as her capital enemy. Having entered into conversation with the King concerning my affair, she spoke so ill of me, that the easy monarch swore he would never show me the least favor, no more than if he had not known any such person. These words were immediately repeated to me by a page of the Cardinal of Ferrara, named Ville; he told me he had himself heard them.

This intelligence put me into so violent a passion that, having thrown down my tools and all my work, I formed a resolution to quit the kingdom immediately. I went at once to the King, and entered an apartment where his Majesty was with a very few persons attending him. When he saw me, I bowed to him with the respect due to a king, and he nodded to me with a cheerful countenance. I then began to conceive some hopes, and gradually approached his Majesty, because they were showing him some things connected with my profession. After some little conversation concerning these matters, the monarch asked me whether I had anything worth seeing to show at my house; adding, that he would go thither to see it, whenever I thought it convenient. I answered that I was then ready to show him something curious, if agreeable to his Majesty. He then ordered me to go home, and said he would follow me without delay. I went accordingly, and waited the coming of the good monarch, who was gone to take his leave of Madame d'Estampes. The lady, having heard where he was going, told his Majesty that she did not choose to accompany him; and moreover requested him not to go to my house that day himself. She used reiterated entreaties to dissuade him from his purpose, and that day he did not come near me.

The day following, I returned to his Majesty at the very same hour. The instant that he saw me, he swore he would go directly to my house. While he was taking his leave of his dear Madame d'Estampes, she, through spite at not having influence enough to prevent his going, spoke as bitterly of me as if I had been an inveterate enemy to the crown. The King declared that his sole intention in going to see me was to scold and reproach me in such terms as could not fail to throw me into a panic. He faithfully promised Madame d'Estampes that he would act in that manner. When he came to my house, I showed him into some ground-floor apartments, in which I had put together the several parts of the gate of Fontainebleau; the King was seized with such astonishment that he could not find in his heart to load me with abuse, as he had promised Madame d'Estampes. He did not, however, choose entirely to swerve from his word, as appears from his having expressed himself to this effect: "It is something extraordinary, Benvenuto, that you men of genius are not sensible of your inability to display your talents without our assistance, and that you show yourselves great only by means of the opportunities that we afford you. It would become you to be a little more humble, and less proud and opinionative. I remember I gave you express orders to make twelve silver statues for me, and that was all I required of you; but you took it into your head to make me a salt-cellar, vases, heads, and a thousand other fancies of your own; insomuch that I am quite surprised you should neglect all that I required of you, and mind nothing but pleasing yourself. If you continue to be-

19

have thus, I will show you in what manner I am used to proceed when I wish to have things done in my own way. I must therefore repeat it to you, that I insist upon your showing yourself obedient, when I lay my commands upon you, because, if you continue obstinate in your whims, you will only run your head against the wall."

While his Majesty uttered these words, the noblemen stood with the most profound attention, perceiving that he shook his head, knit his brows, and used a variety of gestures, sometimes with one hand, and sometimes with the other; all present, therefore, began to tremble for me, but I myself was not at all alarmed. As soon as he had made an end of reprimanding me, as he had promised Madame d'Estampes, I knelt with one knee upon the ground, and kissing his mantle, addressed him in the following terms: "Sire, I acknowledge the truth of what you say. All I have to allege in my defence is, that my heart has been constantly attentive day and night to obey and serve you, to the utmost extent of all my faculties. Whatever appears to the contrary to your Majesty, you may depend upon it, does not come from Benvenuto, but is the work of my adverse fate, which has rendered me unworthy of serving the greatest prince that the world ever beheld. I therefore humbly entreat you to pardon me. But it appeared to me that your Majesty gave me silver for one statue only, and, as I had none of my own, I could make only that; so with the little silver that was left, I made the vase, to give your Majesty an idea of the beautiful manner of antiquity which in that species of work was perhaps unknown to you before. With regard to the salt-cellar, it seems to me, as well as I can recollect, that you one day requested me to make one, in consequence of some conversation concerning a salt-cellar that was shown to you; upon which I produced you a model I had formerly made in

Italy, solely at your Majesty's request, and you were pleased to order me a thousand ducats for making it, declaring yourself highly pleased with my performance; I thought you even went so far as to thank me, when I gave it to you finished. As for the gate, I apprehend that your Majesty, in some occasional conversation, gave orders to Monsieur de Villeroy, to direct the Messieurs Marmande and Fay to employ me in such a work, and supply me with money; for without that assistance, that I might try the different nature of French clays, I could not possibly have gone on with the work. With regard to the heads, I should not have thought of casting such large pieces, except to try my hand at that branch of business. The bases I made in the belief that they were admirably suited to such figures. In all I undertook I endeavored to do my best, and never lost sight of what your Majesty intended. True it is, I made the great colossal statue, and brought it to its present degree of perfection at my own expense; for it appeared to me that it would become the dignity of so great a monarch, and reflect some honor on my slender abilities, that such a statue should be made in your kingdom as had never been seen by the ancients. But since I perceive that God has not thought proper to render me worthy of so honorable a service, I request of your Majesty that, instead of the noble recompense you intended to make me for my labors, you would only give me a small share of your good-will, and leave to depart. If you condescend to grant me this favor, I will instantly set out for Italy, returning thanks to the Supreme Being for the happy hours that I have been in your Majesty's service."

The King took me by the hand, and raised me from the ground. He told me that I ought to be contented to remain in his service, and that he was highly pleased with all I had done for him. Turning to the noblemen present, he deliberately uttered these words: "I really believe that if there were to be gates to Paradise, they never could be finer than such as this." When I saw that he had made an end of his angry speaking, though his words were highly favorable to me, I again in the most respectful manner returned him thanks, at the same time repeating my request to be dismissed, as my resentment had not yet entirely subsided. Perceiving that I made such a return to his extraordinary compliments, he commanded me, in a loud voice, not to utter another word, for that if I did I should repent it. He added that he would smother me in gold, and that he gave me leave to depart; that the works he had employed me upon were not so much as begun; but with respect to what I had done of my own head, he was very well pleased; that I should never more have any difference with him, because he knew me thoroughly; and that I should endeavor to study his temper, and know him, as duty required of me.

After answering that I thanked God and his Majesty for everything, I requested him to come and see the colossal statue, which was by this time in great forwardness; so he came to my house. I caused the statue to be uncovered, and nothing could equal his astonishment at beholding it. He gave orders to one of his secretaries instantly to reimburse me the money I had spent out of my own pocket, let the sum be never so great, provided I gave him an account written with my own hand.

When he returned to his palace, he could not help thinking of my words, some of which were so very humble, and others so proud and haughty, that they had nettled him. Some of the latter he repeated before Madame d'Estampes, when M. de St. Paul, one of the great barons of France, happened to be present. That nobleman, who had always warmly professed himself my friend, upon that occasion proved the sincerity of his professions like a true Frenchman. After a good deal of conversation the King was complaining of the Cardinal of Ferrara, that, when he had put me under his care, he gave himself no longer any concern about me; and though I had not left the kingdom, it was not the Cardinal that had prevented me; therefore he had serious thoughts of putting me under the care of some other person, as he did not choose to be any longer in danger of losing me. At these words M. de St. Paul offered his service, telling the King that he would take particular care that I should no longer be any way tempted to leave the kingdom. The King replied that he consented, if St. Paul would tell him the method he would pursue to prevent me from deserting his service. Madame d'Estampes all this while was in very ill humor, and St. Paul for a time declined answering his Majesty. But the King asked the question a second time, and St. Paul, to please Madame d'Estampes, answered, "I should order Benvenuto to be hanged, and then you would be sure of his not making his escape out of the kingdom." Madame d'Estampes burst into a loud laugh, and declared it was what I very well deserved. The King thereupon began to laugh to keep her company. He agreed, he said, to St. Paul's hanging me, provided the latter could first find an artist of equal abilities; and though I never had done anything to deserve hanging, he in that case left him entirely at liberty to act as he thought proper.

Several months had passed since I had recived any money, or any order to work, insomuch that I had dismissed all my journeymen except the two Italians, whom I employed in making two little vases of my own silver, because they did not understand working in bronze. As soon as these pieces were finished I carried them to Argenton, which is a distance of several days' journey south from Paris, about one hundred and sixty miles.   On arriving at the place, I found the King indisposed.   The Cardinal of Ferrara informed his Majesty of my arrival; but the King made him no answer, so that I was obliged to stay there several days in great perplexity.   Not long afterward I presented myself one evening before his Majesty, and showed him the two vases, with which he was highly delighted.

When I saw him in good humor, I requested him to let me make a tour to Italy, for pleasure and recreation; and engaged to leave seven months' salary which his Majesty was in arrears to me, to be remitted to me in Italy, in case I wanted it.   I begged that he would be graciously pleased to grant me that favor, as it was then a time to think of military operations, and not of making statues.   I added that, as his Majesty had granted Primaticcio the painter such a favor, I hoped he would show me the same indulgence.   While I uttered these words, the King looked attentively at the vases, and sometimes frowned on me so sternly that I was shocked. I, however, continued to request the favor in the most persuasive manner I could.   He appeared to be in a great passion, and, spoke to me thus in Italian: "Benvenuto, you are a great fool; carry those vases at once to Paris, for I wish to have them gilt," and without making me any other answer, he departed.

I went to the Cardinal of Ferrara, and requested him to procure leave for me to return to Italy.   The Cardinal answered that he would gladly do anything in his power to oblige me, and that I might leave the affair entirely to him.   Nay, that if I chose, I might go at once, and he would take care to excuse me to the King.   I then said that since his Majesty had put me under his care, if he were pleased to give me leave I would set out, and return whenever he should think proper.   The Cardinal told me to go to Paris, and stay there a week, assuring me that he would in that time obtain leave for me;

that in case the King should disapprove of my going he would let me know it by letter, but if I did not hear from him in that time I might set out for Italy.

CHAPTER XXXVI

A TERRIBLE STORM

ON my return to Paris, I followed the Cardinal's directions, and made very fine cases for the two pieces of plate. Twenty days being expired, I put the two vases upon a mule of burden, which had been lent to me to go as far as Lyons, by the Bishop of Pavia, to whom I had again given an apartment in my castle. I departed, in an unlucky hour, with Signor Ippolito Gonzaga, who received the King's pay, and was likewise in the service of Count Galeotto of Mirandola, with some other gentlemen belonging to the count. Leonardo Tedaldi, a Florentine, went with us. I left under the care of my journeymen my castle and all my effects, among which were some little vases just begun, so that they had no occasion to remain idle. There was in my house a good deal of furniture of great value, for I made a considerable figure at Paris. The value of these effects was more than fifteen hundred crowns.

I told Ascanio to remember all the favors he had received from me; that hitherto he had been only a giddy youth, but it was high time for him to think seriously, and behave like a man; that I chose to leave under his care all my effects, and even my honor; adding that, in case he happened to be ill-used by any of those French rascals, he had only to write to me, and I would instantly ride post to Paris. Ascanio said, with the counterfeit tears of a thief, "I never had a more indulgent ar.d tender father than you. I will therefore always behave to you like a most dutiful son." Matters being thus settled, I set out, attended by a footman and a little French boy. Six hours after my departure, some of the treasurers came to my house. These villains ordered Signor Guido and the Archbishop of Pavia to send after me directly for the King's vases, otherwise they would despatch a person for them in a manner that I should not like. The Archbishop and Signor Guido, much more alarmed than was necessary, immediately sent after me the treacherous Ascanio, whom I saw about midnight. I was kept awake by my anxiety, and said to myself, "To whose care do I leave my effects and my castle? What strange decree of fate obliges me to undertake this journey? The Cardinal must certainly be in a conspiracy with Madame d'Estampes, who desires nothing more earnestly than that I should forfeit that good King's favor."

Hearing myself called by Ascanio, I rose, and asked him whether he brought me good or bad news? The thief answered, "I bring you good news; but you must send back the vases, for those rogues of treasurers make a terrible stir about them; so that the Bishop and Signor Guido insist upon your sending them back by all means. Be under no apprehensions about anything else, but make your tour, and enjoy all the pleasures that life can afford." I thereupon put the two vases into his hands; but the money and other effects I carried to the abbey of the Cardinal of Ferrara at Lyons; for though it was given out that I intended to carry them with me to Italy, it is well known that no specie, either gold or silver, can be conveyed out of the kingdom without special permission. It should therefore be well considered, whether it would have been possible for me to carry off the two large beautiful vases, which with the boxes that contained them loaded a mule. They were very fine things, and of great value, and I was apprehensive of the, King's death, having left him very much indisposed; but I comforted myself with the reflection that if anything were to happen I could not lose them, as they were in the hands of the Cardinal. I sent back the mule with the vases and other things of value, and continued my journey. But all the way I could not refrain from sighing and weeping.

When we were within a day's journey of Lyons, it being almost ten o'clock at night, some thunder-claps were heard, and lightning flashed. I was about a bow-shot before my companions. After the lightning such a terrible peal of thunder was heard in the sky that I thought it was the day of judgment. I stopped a while, when a thick shower of hail began to fall. The hail-stones, though small, hurt me. The shower grew thick-er and the hailstones at last became as big as the balls of a cross-bow. As my horse was frightened, I rode back till I came up with my company, who had taken shelter in a grove of pines. The hailstones at length rose to the size of lemons, and I cried out, "Have mercy upon me, O God!" While I was devoutly addressing the Deity, an enormous hailstone broke off a large branch of the pine-tree under which I thought myself in safety. Another great hailstone fell upon the head of my horse, which seemed ready to drop; and one of them struck me, but not directly, or it would have killed me.

After we had been all terribly pelted, we remounted, and while we were traveling on to the inn where we intended to lodge, and showing each other our hurts and bruises, we found, at about a mile's distance, a scene of distress so much deeper than our own that it is almost impossible to describe. All the trees were broken down, and all the cattle killed. We also found a great many shepherds killed; and we saw several hailstones that a man would have found it difficult to grasp with both hands. We were then sensible that calling upon God and singing those psalms had done us more good than we could have done ourselves. We therefore returned thanks to the Supreme Being, and continued our journey the next day to Lyons, where we made a stay of a week.

When we had been a day in Italy, we were joined by Count Galeotto of Mirandola, who had traveled post. He remained a while with us, and told me that I had erred in leaving France; that it would be advisable for me not to proceed farther, because my affairs might suddenly change their aspect, and take a more favorable turn than ever. He said that by continuing my journey I should open a field to my enemies; whereas by returning at once I should defeat their stratagems. He added, that those in whom I put the greatest confidence were the very persons that imposed upon me. Taking leave of me, he traveled on with post-horses, while I, with my company above mentioned, chose to ride forward also. I was in an irresolute state till at last I formed a resolution to take post to Florence. As I could not reconcile my mind to go back to France, I determined to go and pass a melancholy life at Florence. As I could not agree with the first post, I parted company with Signor Ippolito Gonzaga, who took the road to Mirandola, while mine was through Parma and Piacenza.

At Piacenza, I happened to meet in the street the Duke Pier Luigi, who, examining me attentively, knew me again. Sensible that all I had suffered in the Castle of St. Angelo arose from this man, I felt the utmost indignation at the sight of him; but not being able to think of any expedient to get out of his power, I at last resolved to pay him a visit. I entered just as the servants were clearing the table; with him were some persons

belonging to the family of Landi, the same by whom he
was afterward murdered. At my arrival he lavished
compliments upon me. He told those present that I
was the first man of the age, and that I had been a long
time in prison at Rome. He said, "My good friend
Benvenuto, I was very sorry for your misfortune, from
my consciousness of your innocence, but it was not in
my power to relieve you. My father persecuted you
at the instigation of some of your enemies, who had in-
sinuated that you had spoken ill of him, though I am
certain you never did; and I was very much concerned
for your sefferings." To these words he added so many
more, of the same tendency, that he seemed almost to
ask my pardon. He inquired next about the several
pieces of work that I had done for King Francis. When
I gave him an account of them, he seemed to be all attention. This being over, he asked me whether I was
willing to enter into his service? I answered that I could
not, consistently with the laws of honor; adding, that
when I had once finished the great works that I had
begun for the King, I would refuse the service of all the
greatest lords to devote myself entirely to his Excellency.

On my return to my inn I found that the Duke had
sent me presents of meats and wines. I ate heartily; and
having mounted on horseback, bent my course toward
Florence. On my arrival in that city, I found my sister
with six daughters, one of whom was marriageable, and
one still in the nurse's arms. I likewise found her
husband there, who, on account of a variety of accidents,
no longer continued his business. A twelvemonth before,
I had sent them jewels and French presents to the value
of more than two thousand ducats, and had then brought
with me to the amount of a thousand crowns. I discovered that, though I allowed them four gold crowns
a month, they every day raised money upon my presents,

which they were continually selling. My brother-in-law, for fearI should be angry with him when the money I sent proved insufficient, pawned all he had in the world, and borrowed upon the most exorbitant interest, purely to avoid meddling with money that was not intended for him. In consequence of this, I knew him to be a man of strict integrity, conceived a greater desire to serve him than ever, and grew impatient to provide for all his little daughters before I left Florence.

CHAPTER XXXVII

IN THE SERVICE OF COSMO DE' MEDICI

THE Duke of Florence happening to be, at this time, which was August, 1545, at Poggio Cajano, ten miles from Florence, I waited on his Excellency merely to compliment him, as my ancestors had been very much attached to the House of Medici. I, therefore, repaired to Cajano, solely to pay my respects to Duke Cosmo, for whom I had an affection, and not with an intention to make any stay. But, as God orders all things for the best, it was his Divine will that when the Duke saw me, after receiving me with the greatest kindness, both he and the Duchess began to inquire about the works that I had executed for the King of France. I told them of all I had done for that monarch; and when the Duke had heard me to an end, he said he had been informed of this before, and that all I had related was true. He then exclaimed, "How ill have so many great and beautiful works been rewarded! My good friend Benvenuto, if you would do something for me, I would pay you far more satisfactorily than that king upon whom you lavish your praises." I replied that I had great obligations to his Majesty for delivering me from an unjust confinement and afterward giving me an opportunity of signalizing myself by the most admirable performances that were ever done by any artificer. While I expressed myself in this manner, the Duke made strange contortions, and seemed hardly to have patience to hear me out. As soon as I had ceased speaking, he said, "If you are willing to work for me, I will pay you in such a manner as will, perhaps, surprise you, provided I am pleased with your performance, as I have no doubt I shall be." I, like a poor, unfortunate creature as I was, being desirous of showing that since I left that admirable school, I had cultivated talents it did not think of, answered the Duke that I would gladly undertake to make a great statue of marble or bronze for his fine square at Florence. He replied, that all he desired for a specimen was a Perseus, and ordered me to make him a little model of one. In a few weeks I finished one about a cubit in length, of yellow wax.

The Duke came to Florence, and, before I could have an opportunity of showing him this model, several days passed, during which he behaved as if he never had seen or known me. But having one day, after dinner, carried the model into his wardrobe, I found him with the Duchess and some of the nobility. As soon as he saw it he was pleased with it, and praised it to excess. When he had sufficiently viewed it, his satisfaction was greatly increased, and he expressed himself to this effect: "My friend Benvenuto, if you were to make a great work according to this little model, it would surpass everything in the square." I replied, "Most excellent sir, in the square of Florence are the works of the great Donatello and the admirable Michelangelo, the two greatest statuaries since the day of the ancients. Your Excellency, therefore, pays me a high compliment; for I will undertake that the execution of the work shall be three times as masterly as that of the model." The Duke, who maintained that he was a great connoisseur in these things, disputed the matter with me for a while, saying he knew exactly what could be done. I answered that my works would decide the question and put his Excellency out of all doubt. I at the same time asked him to afford me the means of carrying my design into execution, because, without such assistance, it would be impossible for me to perform my engagement. He bade me submit a written account of all I had occasion for, and I should be supplied. Certain it is, that if I had been sufficiently cautious to make an agreement in writing for all that I had occasion for in my works, I should not have had half the trouble and perplexity that I brought upon myself by my negligence; for the Duke seemed to have a great desire to have works done, and to supply those employed in them. But I, not being aware that he intended to engage in great undertakings, proceeded in the most liberal manner. I made out the account in writing, which was answered with the greatest liberality imaginable. Whereupon I said, "Most noble patron, contracts do not properly consist in verbal agreements or in such writings as this; all that is required is, that I should keep my promise with your Excellency. In case I succeed, I take it for granted you will remember me, and perform all that you have promised." The Duke was so highly pleased with my words and my behavior, that both he and the Duchess lavished upon me the most extraordinary compliments.

As I had a strong desire to set about my work at once, I told his Excellency that I had occasion for a house in which I might conveniently set up my furnaces, and carry on a variety of works, both of clay and of bronze, and of gold and silver separately; for I knew how likely he was to make use of me in the various branches of my

business. I told him at the same time that, to convince
his Excellency how zealous I was to serve him, I had
already selected a house that would answer my purpose;
but as I did not intend to trouble him for money or anything else till he had seen my performance, I had brought
two jewels from France, with which I asked his Excellency to purchase that house for me; and that he would
keep them in his possession till I had earned them. The
workmanship of these jewels was exquisite, and was
done by my journeymen from my own designs. After
looking at them for a time, the Duke said: "Take your
jewels again, Benvenuto, for it is you I want, and not
them; you shall have the house you mention, without
its costing you anything." He then wrote a line under
my memorial, which I have ever since kept by me, the
purport of which is as follows: "Let the house be examined, and the price and title inquired into; for we intend it for Benvenuto."

When I read this order, I thought myself sure of the
house, as I fancied that my works would not fail to give
the highest satisfaction to my employer. His Excellency
at the same time gave express orders about the affair to
his steward, Pier Francesco Riccio (who was a native
of Prato, and had been tutor to the Duke). I spoke to
this fool of a fellow, and gave him an exact account of
all I stood in need of; for I intended to erect a shop on a
piece of ground that was then laid out in a garden. The
steward immediately employed a close, artful agent, Lattanzio Gorini, a little man, who seemed to crawl like a
spider, had a feeble voice, resembling that of a gnat, and
was as slow as a snail. He caused so small a quantity of
stones, sand, and mortar to be brought to the spot as
would hardly have made a pigeon-house. Perceiving
that things went on so ill, I began to be alarmed. I
however thought little beginnings sometimes lead to a
great end. I likewise conceived some hope from seeing

how many thousand ducats the Duke had squandered
upon some little ordinary works of sculpture done by the
stupid Baccio Bandinello.   So I did my utmost to stim-
ulate Lattanzio; and, the better to excite him, I employed some other mean fellows, who had an influence
over him, to remind him of his duty.   But it was like
talking to lame asses, with a blind man for their guide.
Although I had so many difficulties to encounter, I, with
my own money, caused a place to be marked out for a
shop; ordering vines and trees to be plucked up by the
roots, with my usual ardor, and even with a degree of
fury.   At the same time I employed one Tasso, a carpenter, who was my intimate friend, to make certain
props and supports of wood, that I might begin my great
statue of Perseus.   This Tasso was an excellent workman. I do not think he was ever equalled in his business; he was also remarkably facetious and merry, for
every time I went to him he came up smiling, singing
some ballad or other.   I was by this time half desperate,
as well from having heard that my affairs were in a very
untoward situation in France, as because I had little
hope from my employers here, on account of their cold-
ness.   I constantly put a constraint upon myself, to hear
one half of my carpenter's ballad; but at last I grew
cheerful in his company.

I had now given directions concerning all the things
above mentioned, and began to hurry the workmen.   Already part of the mortar had been used, when I was sent
for by the Duke's steward, and I found him, just after
the Duke had dined, in the hall of the palace where
the clock stood.   As I approached him with respect, he,
with great rudeness and asperity, asked me who had put
me in possession of that house, and by what authority
I had begun to build there, adding that he was quite
surprised at my boldness and presumption.   I answered
that I had been put in possession of the house by his

Excellency, who had upon the occasion employed one
Lattanzio Gorini as his agent; that the said Lattanzio
had caused stones, sand, and mortar to be carried to the
house, and had supplied me with all that I wanted. I
added that for all this I had received his own order,
though he questioned me about my authority. When I
had expressed myself in this manner, the vile fellow flew
into a more violent passion than at first, and told me
that neither he nor any of those I mentioned had spoken
the truth. This behavior at last provoked my resentment, and I replied to him in these terms: "Signor steward, so long as you speak in a manner agreeable to the
dignity of your character, I shall have a due regard for
you, and address you with the same respect that I do
the Duke himself; but in case you behave otherwise, I
shall speak to you only as Francesco Riccio."

Hereupon the old man flew into such a passion that I
thought he would instantly have been deprived of his
senses. He told me, with much opprobrious language,
that he was surprised he should condescend so far as to
speak to such a person as I. At these words I felt the
highest indignation, and said, "Hear me a word or two,
Francesco Riccio, and I will tell you who are my equals,
and who are yours; yours are pedagogues, that teach
children to read." The old man thereupon, with a countenance inflamed with choler, raised his voice, and repeated the very same words as before. I began in my
turn to look big, and, assuming somewhat to myself,
told him that such men as I were worthy of speaking to
popes, emperors, and mighty monarchs; that there was
perhaps but one such as I in the world, whereas there
were dozens such as he to be met with at every corner.
When he heard this, he went up toward a window in the
hall, and asked me to repeat my words once more. I
accordingly repeated them more boldly than at first, adding that I no longer cared to serve the Duke, and that I

20

would go back to France, where I was sure of being welcome. The fool remained thunderstruck, and as pale as ashes, while I went off in a violent passion, with a resolution to leave the place; and would to God I had put my design into execution. The Duke certainly did not immediately hear of this broil, for I stayed a few days, having laid aside all thoughts of Florence, except so far as related to my sister and my nieces, whom I provided for as well as I could with what little money I had left. I was then for returning to France, without any inclination ever to see Italy again, being resolved to go off with all possible expedition, and that without taking my leave of the Duke or anybody else.

One morning the steward sent for me of his own accord, and with an air of great civility began to make a long, pedantic oration, in which I could perceive neither method, nor meaning, head nor tail; all I could gather from it was, that, as he professed himself to be a Christian, he did not care to harbor malice against any man, and now he asked me, in the Duke's name, what salary I required for my support. I continued for a time wrapt in meditation, without returning any answer, and the reason was, that I did not intend to remain at Florence. Perceiving that I did not answer immediately, he carried his complaisance so far as to say: "Benvenuto, a duke expects an answer; what I say to you is by the Duke's orders." I then requested him to tell his Excellency that I could by no means submit to be below any of those of my profession whom he had at his court. The steward immediately said: "Bandinello has a pension of two hundred crowns a year; so that, if that sum will satisfy you, your salary is fixed." I told him it would, and if I deserved anything over, it might be given to me after my works had been seen, and should be left entirely to his Excellency's judgment and pleasure.

CHAPTER XXXVIII

CORRESPONDENCE WITH THE KING

BY this time I had received several letters from France, from my faithful friend Signor Guido Guidi. The King was informed that I had entered into the service of the Duke of Florence, and as he was the best-natured prince in the whole world he often said, "Why does not Benvenuto return?" When he inquired in a particular manner of my two young men, they told him that I had often written that I was greatly encouraged and very happy where I was, and that they did not suppose I would ever come back to serve his Majesty. The King, highly incensed upon hearing these disrespectful words, which never came from me, replied: "Since he has quitted my service without any cause, I will never again inquire after him; so he may stay where he is." Thus these villains and assassins brought affairs to the crisis they desired; for in case I had returned to France, they must again have become my journeymen and dependents; but they thought that, if I never returned, they should be their own masters, and have all my business.

While I was getting my shop erected, in order to begin the statue of Perseus, I worked in a room on the ground floor, in which I made a model in plaster, of the intended size of the work. When I found that this method was likely to prove somewhat tedious, I had recourse to another expedient; for by this time I had a shop made of bricks piled one upon another in so miserable a manner that the very remembrance of it makes me uneasy. I began the arrangement of the bones, or rather the figure of the Medusa, and made the skeleton of iron.

I afterward made the figure of clay, and when I had done this I baked it hard by the fire, with the assistance of some of my little apprentices, one of whom was a boy of extraordinary beauty, son of a woman named Gambetta. I kept this child with a view of drawing his likeness (for there are no books that teach this art like Nature herself), and I inquired for journeymen in order to despatch the work the sooner; but I could find none, and it was morally impossible for me to execute the work myself in all its branches. There were some in Florence that would willingly have entered into my service, but Bandinello found means to prevent them. He also told the Duke that I endeavored to decoy his workmen, because I could never of myself contrive to put a great figure together. I complained to the Duke of the ill offices done me by this fool; and begged he would procure me some journeymen. This made the Duke believe what was told him by Bandinello. Perceiving this, I resolved to do the best I could by myself, and fell to work under the greatest difficulties conceivable.

While I labored in this manner night and day, my sister's husband was taken ill, and died in a few days. He left to my care his wife, a young woman, with six daughters, some of them grown up, and some very little. This was the first great trouble I had in Florence, to be left father and guardian of a whole afflicted and disconsolate family. Seeing my garden full of rubbish, I sent for two porters, who were brought to me from the Old Bridge; one of these was a man of seventy, the other a stripling of eighteen. When they had been with me about three days, the young porter told me the old fellow would not work, and advised me to turn him off, for he was not only idle himself, but the cause of idleness in others. He added that the little there was to be done, he was able to do himself. When I saw him so well disposed to work, I asked him whether he was willing to live with me as my servant; and we soon agreed. This young man, whose name was Bernardino Manellini of Mugello, took care of my horse, worked in the garden, and even endeavored to assist me in the shop; at last he began to learn the art so well that I never in my life had a better servant. I resolved to do the whole business by his assistance, and began to convince the Duke that Bandinello was a liar, and that I could do very well without his journeymen.

I was about this time troubled with a pain in my back, and, being unable to work, was glad to pass my time in the Duke's wardrobe, with two young goldsmiths, Giovan Paolo and Domenico Poggini, whom I set to make a little golden vase, wrought with a basso rilievo of figures and other ornaments. This belonged to the Duchess, and her Excellency had it made for a drinking-cup. She likewise desired me to make her a golden girdle, and to adorn this work with jewels and many pretty inventions of figures and other things of that kind, which was done accordingly. The Duke came from time to time to the wardrobe, and took great pleasure in seeing the work carried on, and in talking to me about it. When I found myself somewhat better, I caused clay to be brought me, and while the Duke was thus occupied, I took his likeness, making a head of him much larger than the life. His Excellency was greatly pleased with this work, and he told me it would be highly agreeable to him if I would work at his palace; and he would look out for apartments of a proper size for me, which I might have fitted up with whatever I had occasion for. I told his Excellency it was impossible, for I should not then finish my work in a hundred years.

The Duchess was lavish of her compliments to me, and would gladly have had me work for her alone, and neglect the statue of Perseus and everything else. I, who saw myself possessed of this vain shadow of favor, knew to a certainty that my inauspicious star could not long bear to see me happy, and would soon involve me in new perplexities; for every moment I had present to my thoughts the great injury I had done myself in endeavoring to better my condition. I speak with regard to my affairs in France. The King could not digest the mortification that my departure had occasioned him; and yet he would have been glad of my return, but would have me look upon it as an obligation. I thought that I had many good reasons to decline making any submission; for I believed that had I descended so low as to serve the French again with humility and complaisance, they would have said I knew myself to be in fault, and would have given credit to certain calumnies. I therefore wrote to France like a man that knew himself to be in the right. My conduct was highly agreeable to my two young disciples; for in my letters to them I boasted of the many works I was employed in by two great personages, who were the chief in power in my native city. As soon as they had received this intelligence, they went to the King, and persuaded his Majesty to make over to them my castle. The King, who was a prince of great generosity and honor, would never comply with the presumptuous demands of these two young villains; for he began to perceive the malicious tendency of their application. But, that he might seem to afford them some faint hope, and induce me to return quickly, he caused a treasurer of his, Giuliano Buonaccorsi, a citizen of Florence, to write to me in a style somewhat angry: the purport of the letter was, that if I wished to retain that reputation of a man of honor which I had before enjoyed, as I had quitted the kingdom without any cause, I should give an account of all I had done for his Majesty.

On the receipt of this letter, I was so highly pleased that I could not have wished for one couched in terms

more to my mind. When I sat down to write, I filled
nine leaves of common paper, and in these I specified all
the works that I had been concerned in, with the several
accidents that had befallen me in the prosecution of
those undertakings, and all the money expended on them,
which was paid by two clerks and one of the King's
treasurers, and signed by the persons through whose
hands it had passed, some of whom had contributed their
property, and others their labor. I added, that I had
not pocketed a single farthing of the money, and that
when I had finished my work I was not in the least a
gainer; that I had carried with me to Italy only a few
favors and promises, truly worthy of his Majesty; and
though I could not boast of having acquired by my works
anything more than certain salaries settled upon me by
his Majesty for my support, and there remained above
seven hundred crowns of my salary still due, which I
never touched, but left behind me in France, that they
might be remitted me to defray the charges of my return, yet as I had discovered that ill offices had been done
me by certain malevolent persons, excited thereto by
envy, I appealed to his most Christian Majesty. "I am
not excited," said I, "by avarice. I am conscious of
having done for your Majesty more than ever I engaged
to perform, and I have never received the promised reward. I desire nothing more in this world than to
remain in the opinion of your Majesty a man of a fair
and unblemished character, such as I have always shown
myself; and if your Majesty retains the smallest doubt
of my integrity, I will, upon your signifying the least
desire of it, return to France to give an account of my
conduct, at the hazard of my life. But, as I saw myself
held in so little consideration, I did not care to make a
new offer of my services, being sensible that I can earn
a livelihood in any part of the world; and whenever I
am written to, I shall send a proper answer."

About this time Bernardone Baldini, who was employed by his Excellency as broker in the jeweling business, had brought with him from Venice a diamond of more than thirty-five carats. He had with him Antonio di Vittorio Landi, whose interest it was to prevail on the Duke to purchase it. This diamond had its upper face terminating in a point: but, as it did not appear to have the luster required in a jewel of that sort, the owner got the point made flat, which spoiled the beauty of the stone. Our Duke, who was passionately fond of jewels, held out to that rogue Bernardone some hope that he would purchase the diamond; and as the fellow wished for himself the honor of putting a trick upon the Duke of Florence, he never spoke a word of the affair to his partner Antonio Landi. This Antonio had been intimate with me ever since we were boys, and as he saw I was so familiar with the Duke, he one day called me aside and said: "Benvenuto, I know full well that the Duke will show you a diamond which he seems to be desirous of purchasing. You will see a very fine stone: endeavor to promote the sale of it; I could sell it for seventeen thousand crowns. I am positive his Excellency will ask your advice, and it is very possible he may purchase it." I promised, that in case it should be shown to me, and my opinion should be asked, I would speak of it to the best of my judgment, without saying anything to depreciate its value. Somewhat more than a week from the day that Antonio Landi had the conversation with me, his Excellency showed me the diamond in question. I, seeing of what sort it was, would certainly have advised the Duke not to purchase it. Therefore, when his Excellency showed it to me, I asked him what he would have me say of it, as jewelers had two different methods of appreciating a jewel, one after a great man had bought it, and another in order to excite him to be a purchaser. The Duke told me that he had bought it,

and only wished to know my opinion concerning it. I
thereupon declared my sentiments of the diamond to the
best of my judgment. He asked me to consider well the
beauty of the great facets in it. I answered that he
was quite mistaken in considering that as a beauty, for
it was nothing else but a flattened point. The Duke who
perceived that what I said was true, then with a look of
great displeasure bade me examine the jewel carefully,
and give my opinion concerning its value. I imagined
that as Antonio Landi had valued it at seventeen thousand crowns, the Duke might have given at most fifteen
thousand for it; and, therefore, as I saw that he was
offended at my speaking the truth, I thought it advisable
to favor his mistake, and so returning him the diamond,
said, "It cost you eighteen thousand crowns." Upon my
speaking thus, he made an exclamation of surprise—an
Oh! with a mouth as wide as a draw-well, and said,
"Surely you can be no connoisseur in jewels." I answered, "My Lord, you are mistaken; endeavor to continue in a good humor with your diamond, and I will
endeavor to understand these things better: at least be
so good as to let me know how much it cost you, that
I may the better enter into your Excellency's method of
purchasing these things." The Duke thereupon said to
me with a sneer, "It cost five-and-twenty thousand
crowns and upward," and so went away.

During this conversation were present Giovan Paolo
and Domenico Poggini, both goldsmiths; and Bacchiaca
the embroiderer, who worked in the next apartment, ran
to us on hearing it. I then said that I would not have
advised him against purchasing it, but that Antonio
Landi had a week before offered it to me for seventeen
thousand crowns; and I apprehended that I might have
bought it for fifteen thousand or less: but the Duke was
resolved to keep up its reputation at any rate.

Having already sketched the figure of the great Medusa, I made the skeleton of iron, then forming the figure of clay about half an inch thick, I caused it to be well baked, and over it I put a covering of wax in order to finish it completely in the manner it was intended to remain.   The Duke, who came several times to see me, was greatly disgusted at its not being of bronze, and would have had me send for some master to cast it.

His Excellency was constantly speaking in the most advantageous terms of my genius and skill, while his steward was as constantly watching for some opportunity to hurt me.   This man, though a native of Prato, the natural enemy of our state, was by a surprising turn of fortune, only because he had been the pedagogue of Duke Cosmo de' Medici, invested with a command over the city guards and all the public offices in Florence. He was always on the watch to do me some injury, but found it a very difficult matter to form his plans with any probability of success.   He at last thought of a sure way to ruin me, by bribing the mother of my young apprentice (whose name was Cencio, as hers was Gambetta) to charge me with a horrible crime, in hope that the fear of a prosecution would induce me to leave the city.   But I was not to be so easily intimidated, and thrust them out of my house.

CHAPTER XXXIX

A TRIP TO VENICE

HAVING reflected on the villainy as well as power of that wicked pedagogue, I thought it advisable to keep for a time out of the way of such machinations; so in the morning early I put into the hands of my sister jewels and effects of the value of nearly two thousand crowns, and mounting on horseback, bent my course toward Venice, carrying with me my journeyman Bernardino di Mugello. On my arrival at Ferrara, I wrote to the Duke that, though I had left Florence without taking leave of him, I would return without being sent for.

I passed my time very agreeably in Venice, that beautiful and opulent city, where I visited the great painter Titian, and Signor Giacopo Sansovino, an excellent statuary and architect of Florence, who had a considerable pension from the Senate of Venice. As we had been acquainted in our youth I was highly entertained by these two ingenious artists. The day following I met Signor Lorenzo de' Medici, who received me with the greatest affection imaginable. We had known each other in Florence, when I was stamping coins for Duke Alessandro, and afterward at Paris, when I was in the service of the King of France. He had resided at the house of Signor Giuliano Buonaccorsi; and because he did not know where else to go for amusement, without taking a considerable risk, he passed a great deal of his time at my house, in observing the process of the great works above mentioned. On account, therefore, of our former acquaintance, he carried me to his own house, where was the Prior degli Strozzi, brother to Signor Piero; they were very merry, and asked me how long I purposed staying at Venice, thinking that I intended to return to France. I told them of the affair that had made me quit Florence; and added that I purposed returning to that city in two or three days, to enter again into the service of my sovereign the Grand Duke. The Prior and Signor Lorenzo looked so sternly at me that I was quite disconcerted. They then said, "You would act much more wisely in returning to France, where you have both money and friends: if you go back to Florence, you will lose all your interest in France, and at Flor-

ence you will meet only with disgust and disappoint-
ment." I made no answer, but set out the next day
with all possible secrecy, taking the road to Florence.

In the mean time the diabolical plot that had been
hatched against me was pretty well over, for I had written the Duke a full account of the affair, and the reason
of my having gone to Venice. I waited on him without
ceremony; and though he showed some displeasure at
first he at last turned to me with a placid countenance,
and asked where I had been. I answered that my heart
had always been with his Excellency, though a certain
troublesome affair had obliged me to ramble for a while.
His good humor growing upon him, he asked me to give
him some account of Venice; so we entered into conversation for a while, till at last he bade me mind my work,
and finish the statue of Perseus. I returned to my house
in high spirits, which caused great joy to my family,
that is, to my sister and her six daughters. I then resumed my work.

The first thing I cast in bronze was the great head
of his Excellency in my workshop, when I had the pain
in my back, which has been mentioned above. This
work gave high satisfaction, and I made it with no other
view than to try the clay used in casting bronze; and
though I perceived that the admirable Donatello had cast
his works in bronze with the clay of Florence, it appeared to me that he had great difficulties to struggle
with. Thinking, therefore, that this proceeded from the
ill condition of the clay, before I set about casting my
Perseus I chose to make those experiments, by which I
found the clay to be good, though the nature of it was
not understood by the great Donatello, for I observed
he had been under great difficulties in finishing his pieces.
Thus did I contrive by great art to make a compound
clay, which was of infinite service to me. With this I
cast the head; but as I had not yet made a furnace, I

used that of Signor Zanobi di Pagno, a bell-founder. Seeing that the head had come out very exact, I immediately set about making a little furnace in the shop that the Duke had caused to be erected according to my own plan. After making the furnace with all possible expedition, I began casting the statue of Medusa, that distorted female figure which is now seen under the feet of Perseus: and as this was a matter of great difficulty, I found it necessary to use all the precautions I had learned. Thus had I the most complete success at the first time of my casting in this furnace, and the bronze came out of it so neat and clean that my friends did not think I should have occasion to retouch it.

This work highly pleased the Duke, who came to see it at my house, and encouraged me to exert myself; but the unquenchable envy of Bandinello had such power, for he was constantly misrepresenting me to his Excellency, as to persuade him that, though I cast some of those figures, I should never be able to put them all together, because I was quite a novice in the art, and his Excellency should take care how he threw away his money. These words had such an effect upon my noble employer, that part of the money allowed me for journeymen was withheld, insomuch that I found myself under a necessity of coming to an explanation with his Excellency. One morning I took occasion to wait his coming, in the Via de' Servi, and addressed him in these terms: "My Lord, I am not assisted in my business as my occasions require: I therefore begin to suspect that your Excellency doubts my being able to perform my promise; yet I must repeat it to you again, that I desire to finish the work in a manner far more masterly than the model, as I have already promised." When I perceived that all I said had no effect upon him, as he returned no answer, I immediately conceived such resentment and fell into so violent a passion, that I said,

"My Lord, this city has been indeed the school of every ingenious art; but as soon as a person has made himself known and learned something, if he desires to be a credit to his country and his illustrious prince, he would do well to seek for work elsewhere. I am convinced, my Lord, that this is true: I know that your Excellency has been acquainted with Donatello and Leonardo da Vinci, and at present is so with the admirable Michelangelo Buonarroti; men who by their genius add greatly to your Excellency's glory and renown. I also hope that I shall contribute my share toward it; therefore, my good Lord, suffer me to depart. But take care never to let Bandinello move away; rather let him have greater supplies than he requires of you; for, if he should go abroad, so great is his presumption and ignorance that he would probably bring this illustrious school into discredit. Dismiss me then, my Lord. The only reward I desire for my past labors is your Excellency's good will."

The Duke, seeing me thus resolute, turned to me with some emotion, and said, "Benvenuto, if you are willing to finish the work, you shall want no assistance." I answered that I desired nothing more than to show those detractors of my reputation that I had a spirit to perform my promise. Having left his Excellency, I received some little assistance; but found myself under a necessity of opening my purse, as I wished that my work should go on briskly. In the evening I often went to his Excellency's wardrobe, where Domenico and Giovanni Poggini his brother were at work on a golden vase for the Duchess, and on a golden girdle. His Excellency likewise caused a little model to be made of a pendant, in which was to be set that great diamond which Bernardone and Antonio Landi persuaded him to purchase; and though it was what I should willingly have declined, the Duke used such insinuations and arguments that he used to prevail upon me to work there till ten o'clock at night, and by the same alluring arts would fain have persuaded me to work also by day. This I could never consent to, for which I at last thought his Excellency was angry with me. As I happened one day to come a little later than usual, the Duke said, "You are *malvenuto*." I answered, "My Lord, that is not my name, for I am called Benvenuto; and as I apprehend that your Excellency jests with me, I shall say nothing more." The Duke replied that he was not in jest, but quite in earnest, adding, that he advised me to take care how I behaved, for it had come to his knowledge that I had availed myself of his favor to presume rather too much. I requested his Excellency to name a man that I had ever wronged. He immediately flew into a passion and said, "Go and restore what you have had from Bernardone: that is one man you have wronged." I answered, "My Lord, I thank you, and beg you would just hear me say four words in my defence. It is true he lent me a pair of old scales, two anvils and three little hammers, which goods I, fifteen years ago, asked his agent Giorgio da Cortona to send for, whereupon Giorgio came for them himself. If your Excellency, on inquiry and sifting the evidence on both sides, finds that I ever had anything else from any person, either in Rome or in France, punish me with the utmost severity."

The Duke, seeing me very warm, became quite mild and gentle, and said that those who have not done amiss should not be reprimanded; so that, if the case were as I represented it, I should continue to be as much in favor with him as ever. I then answered, "The knaveries of Bernardone force me to entreat your Excellency to tell me sincerely, what you gave for the great diamond with the flattened point; for I hope to make you sensible of this rogue's motive for doing me ill offices with your Excellency." The Duke replied, "The diamond cost me twenty-five thousand crowns: why do you ask?" I told him, "Because, my lord, on such a day, and at such an hour, Antonio di Vittori Landi, speaking to me of this diamond, valued it at sixteen thousand crowns. Your Excellency now knows what sort of bargain you have had; and for the truth of what I say, I appeal to Domenico Poggini and Giovan Paolo, his brother, who are here present, for I immediately apprised them of the affair; but since that, I have never said a word more about it, because your Excellency told me that I did not understand jewels, which made me think you had a mind to keep up the reputation of your purchase. Be assured, my Lord, that I do understand jewels, and that I profess myself a man of principle, and of as much honor as any person living. I shall never attempt to rob you of eight or ten thousand crowns at a time, but rather try to earn them. I agreed to serve your Excellency as a sculptor, a goldsmith, a stamper of coins, but never as a talebearer, nor do I wish the fourth part of the fine that is due to an informer. What I say to you at present is in my own defence, and in the presence of several persons of worth, that your Excellency may no longer believe what is said by Bernardone."

The Duke thereupon fell into a passion, and sent for Bernardone, who was obliged to fly to Venice, and Antonio Landi with him. When they returned from Venice, Antonio said that the diamond sold to the Duke was not the one he showed me in the market-place. I again waited on his Excellency, and said to him, "My Lord, all I told you is true, and all that Bernardone mentioned concerning the goods I borrowed is false, and you would do well to examine the affair to the bottom, and I will go to give order to the city guard." The Duke turned to me, and said, "Benvenuto, live like a man of honor, and fear nothing." The affair ended here.

I set about finishing the jewel, and when I had done it I carried it to the Duchess, who told me she set as high a

value on my work as on the diamond that Bernardone
had made the Duke purchase. She then asked me to
fasten it to her breast with my own hand; and when she
gave me a large pin, I pinned it on, and departed very
much in her good graces. I afterward heard they caused
it to be set again by a German, or some other foreigner,
because Bernardone had said that the simplest manner
of setting it was best.

Domenico and Giovan Paolo Poggini, goldsmiths and
brothers, worked in his Excellency's wardrobe, after my
designs, upon certain little cases of gold, carved with historical figures in basso rilievo, and other things of importance. I one day took occasion to say to the Duke,
"My Lord, if you would enable me to keep several journeymen I would stamp the coins in your mint, as likewise medals of your Excellency, in which I should rival
if not surpass those of the ancients; for since I was employed in making medals for Pope Clement the Seventh,
I have improved so considerably in this art that I come
much nearer to perfection than I did at that time; I am
even able to surpass the coins that I stamped for Duke
Alessandro, though they are still looked upon as very
fine. I would likewise make great vases of gold for you,
as I did for the great King Francis the First, who afforded me all manner of assistance in my business, and
I never lost my time either in making colossuses or other
statues." To this the Duke replied, "Work, Benvenuto,
and I will take care to see you properly supplied." Yet he
never gave me any assistance, or supplied me with conveniences for working.

One day his Excellency sent me several pounds of fine
silver, said it was from his silver mines, and asked me
to make him a beautiful cup with it. As I did not choose
to neglect my Perseus, and yet had a great desire to
serve the Duke, I put it into the hands of a fellow called
Piero de Martini the goldsmith, together with my de-

signs and models in wax. He set about it most awk-
wardly, and did not go on with it, so that I lost more
time by employing him than if I had undertaken it myself. Having been thus plagued and disappointed for
several months, when I saw that Piero would neither
work at it himself nor get others to do it, I made him
return it; and it was with great difficulty I could get
back the body of the vase and the remainder of the silver
I had put into his hands. The Duke having heard something of the affair, sent for the vase and the models,
without telling me why or wherefore. He, however,
from my designs, got men to work for him at Venice and
other places, but was extremely ill served. The Duchess
was incessantly requesting me to work for her in the
jeweling way; and I as constantly answered, that it was
well known to all the world in general, and to all Italy
in particular, that I was a master of the jeweler's business, but that Italy had not hitherto seen a piece of
sculpture of my workmanship; and that several statuaries, provoked at my vying with them, called me in derision the upstart sculptor. However, I hoped to show
them that I had the skill of an old and experienced
sculptor, if God should so far indulge me as to enable
me to exhibit my statue of Perseus in his Excellency's
grand square. So I went home, worked hard both day
and night, and no more made my appearance at the
palace. But that I might not be entirely deprived of
the Duchess's favor, I got certain little vases of silver
made for her, about the size of a two-penny pot, adorned
with fine figures in the antique taste. When I carried
her these little vases, she gave me the kindest reception
imaginable, and paid me for the gold and silver that I
had used in making them. At the same time I solicited
her Excellency's interest, and begged she would inform
the Duke that I was not properly assisted in my great
work; and that she would likewise advise him to be

upon his guard against the malicious insinuations of Bandinello, by which he hindered me from finishing my Perseus. The Duchess, shrugging her shoulders, exclaimed, "Surely the Duke should by this time know what a worthless fellow that Bandinello is!"

CHAPTER XL

WORKING IN MARBLE

I NOW stayed almost constantly at home, and worked with the utmost assiduity to finish my statue. I was obliged to pay my workmen out of my own pocket; for the Duke, having caused them to be paid for me by Lattanzio Gorini about eighteen months, at last grew tired of it, and ordered payment to be stopped. I thereupon asked Lattanzio why he did not pay my men as usual? He answered with the shrill voice of a gnat, and using some odd, fantastic gestures with his spider hands, "Why don't you get your work finished? It is the general opinion that you will never finish it." I answered him passionately, uttering horrid imprecations against him and all those that thought I should not complete it. Thus in deep despair I returned home to my unfortunate statue of Perseus, not without shedding tears.

Once I mounted a little nag, and taking a hundred crowns with me, set out for Fiesole, to see a natural son whom I had at nurse with a gossip of mine, wife of one of my journeymen. I found the child in good health; and though I was greatly dejected, and uneasy in my mind, I embraced him. When I was departing, he would not let me go, but held me fast with his little hands, at the same time crying and screaming so loud that it was something surprising in an infant two years old. But, as I had formed a resolution in case I could meet with Bandinello, who went every evening to visit his farm above St. Domenico, to attack him and punish his insolence, I disengaged myself from my child and bent my course toward Florence. Just as I arrived at the square of St. Domenico, Bandinello entering it on the other side, I came up to him with a full resolution to take a sanguinary vengeance on the spot. I looked up, and saw him on a little mule, quite unarmed; and he had with him a boy about ten years of age. As soon as he perceived me he turned as pale as death, and trembled. I, who knew what a cowardly wretch he was, cried out, "Fear nothing, vile poltroon, I do not think you worth striking." He gave me a look of the most abject pusillanimity, and returned no answer. I thereupon resumed just and virtuous sentiments, and returned thanks to the Almighty for preventing me from perpetrating the rash action I intended.

In three days I received information that the nurse had accidentally smothered my only son, which occasioned me as poignant a grief as ever I had felt. Hearing the news, I fell upon my knees, and returned thanks to God with a profusion of tears, according to my custom, saying, "Lord, thou gavest that infant to me, and now thou hast deprived me of him: for all thou hast done I return thanks to Thy divine majesty."

About this time a young man had quitted Bandinello's service, whose name was Francesco, son of Matteo Fabbro. This young man applied to me for work, and I employed him to clean the statue of Medusa, which was already cast. The same person, about a fortnight later, told me that his master, meaning Bandinello, had asked him to tell me that if I were willing to make a marble statue he would furnish me with a fine block. I in-

stantly answered, "Tell him I accept his offer, and it may
prove an unlucky piece of marble for him, for he is always provoking me, and does not remember what passed
between us upon the square of St. Domenico. Let him
know I insist upon having the marble by all means. I
never speak ill of him, while he is always backbiting and
traducing me; nay, I verily believe that your coming to
work with me was a mere pretext, and that in fact you
were sent by him to be a spy upon my conduct. So go
and tell him I will have the marble in spite of him, and
you may return again to his service."

As I had not for several days made my appearance at
the ducal palace, I went thither one morning through a
sudden caprice, and the Duke had just done dinner when
I entered. I was afterward given to understand the
Duke had that morning spoken much of me; in particular, he had extolled me highly for my masterly manner
of setting jewels. When the Duchess saw me, she sent
Signor Sforza to call me, and upon my presenting myself before her Excellency, she requested me to set a
little rose diamond for her in a ring; adding, that she
intended to wear it constantly. She gave me the measure
of her finger, together with the diamond; which was
worth about a hundred crowns, and begged I would be
as expeditious as possible. The Duke thereupon said to
the Duchess, "It must be acknowledged that Benvenuto
was formerly unrivaled in this branch; but now that he
has dropped it, I apprehend it would be too much trouble for him to make such a ring as you require. Therefore I beg you would not break in upon his time with
this trifling affair, which is now so much out of his way."
I returned the Duke thanks for his obliging speech, and
requested him to let me do the Duchess this little service; so I undertook the work, and finished it in a few
days. The ring was intended for the little finger. I
therefore made four small figures of boys, with four little

grotesques, which completed the ring, and I added to it a few fruits and ligatures in enamel, so that the jewel and the ring appeared admirably suited to each other. I carried it directly to the Duchess, who told me that I had acquitted myself extremely well, and that she would not forget me. This ring she sent as a present to King Philip, and afterward was constantly employing me in one work or other, but in so complaisant and obliging a manner, that I always exerted myself to the utmost to serve her, though I saw but very little of her money. And yet Heaven knows I wanted money very much; for I earnestly desired to finish my Perseus, and I had found some young men to assist me, whom I paid out of my own pocket.

One holiday I went to the palace immediately after dinner, and entering the hall in which the great clock stands, I saw the door of the wardrobe open. As I presented myself, the Duke beckoned to me, and addressed me thus: "You are welcome to court; take this little chest, which was sent to me as a present by Signor Stefano, of Palestrina; open it, and let us see what it contains." I opend it, and answered, "This, my Lord, is the figure of a little boy, in Greek marble, and is indeed a very extraordinary piece. I don't remember ever having seen amongst the antiques so beautiful a performance, or one of so exquisite taste; I therefore offer your Excellency to restore its head, arms, and feet, and make an eagle for it, that it may be called a Ganymede; and though it is by no means proper for me to patch up old statues, as that is usually done by a sort of bunglers in the business, who acquit themselves very indifferently, the excellence of this great master is such that it powerfully excites me to do him this piece of service." The Duke was highly pleased to find the figure had such merit, and asked me several questions about it. "Tell me," said he, "Benvenuto, in what precisely consists the extraordinary excellence of this great master, which excites in you such wonder and surprise." I endeavored to give him an idea of the extraordinary beauty of the statue; of the great genius, skill, and admirable manner of the artist, conspicuous in his work; topics on which I enlarged a long time, and that with the greater earnestness, as I perceived that his Excellency took pleasure in listening to me.

While I amused him so agreeably with my conversation, a page happened to open the door of the wardrobe; and just as he came out Bandinello entered. The Duke asked him, with a stern look, what he was about. Bandinello, without answering, fixed his eyes on the little chest, in which the statue was very plainly to be seen; then shaking his head, he turned to the Duke, and said with a sneer, "My Lord, this is one of those things I have so often spoken to your Excellency about. Depend upon it, the ancients knew nothing of anatomy, and for that reason their works abound with errors." When the fool had made an end of his nonsensical harangue, the Duke said, "Benvenuto, this is quite the reverse of what you awhile ago so much boasted, and seemed to prove by so many specious arguments; so endeavor to defend your own cause." I answered: "My Lord, your Excellency is to understand that Baccio Bandinello is a compound of everything that is bad, and so he has always been; insomuch that whatever he looks at, however superlatively good in itself, is, by his fascinating eyes, immediately converted into something supremely evil. But I, who am inclined to good alone, see the truth through a happier medium: so that all I mentioned awhile ago to your Excellency concerning that beautiful figure is strictly and literally true, and what Bandinello has said of it is purely the result of his own innate malevolence." The Duke seemed to hear me with pleasure; and while I expressed myself thus, Bandinello

writhed himself into a variety of contortions, and made
his face, which was by nature very ugly, quite hideous
by his grimaces. Immediately the Duke, quitting the
hall, went down to the ground-floor apartments, and
Bandinello after him; the gentlemen of the bedchamber,
pulling me by the cloak, encouraged me to follow him;
so we followed the Duke till he sat down in one of the
rooms, and Bandinello and I placed ourselves one on his
right, the other on the left. Many of the Duke's servants, who stood round, kept their eyes on Bandinello,
tittering when they recollected what I had said to him in
the hall. Bandinello again began to chatter, and said
that when he exhibited his Hercules and Cacus to the
public, he really believed more than a hundred lampoons
were published against him, which contained all the
vilest ribaldry that could enter into the imagination of
the rabble. To this, I answered, "My Lord, when your
great artist, Michelangelo Buonarroti, exhibited his
Sacristy, in which so many beautiful figures are to be
seen, the members of the admirable school of Florence,
which loves and encourages genius wherever it displays
itself, published more than a hundred sonnets, wherein
they vied with each other which should praise him
most: and as Bandinello deserved all the censure that
was passed on his work, so Michelangelo merited the
encomiums that were bestowed on his performance."

At this, Bandinello was ready to burst with fury, and,
turning to me, said, "What faults have you to find with
my statues?" I answered, "I will soon tell them, if you
have but the patience to hear me." He replied, "Tell
them, then." The Duke and all present listened with attention. I began by premising that I was sorry to be
obliged to lay before him all the blemishes of his work,
and that I was not so properly delivering my own sentiments, as declaring what was said of it by the ingenious school of Florence. But as the fellow at one

time said something disobliging, at another made some
offensive gesture with his hands or his feet, he put me
into such a passion that I behaved with a rudeness which
I should otherwise have avoided.

"The ingenious school of Florence," said I, "declares
what follows: if the hair of your Hercules were shaved
off, there would not remain skull enough to hold his
brains. With regard to his face, it is hard to distinguish whether it be the face of a man, or that of a creature something between a lion and an ox; it reveals
no attention to what it is about; and it is so ill set upon
the neck, with so little art and in so ungraceful a manner, that a more shocking piece of work was never seen.
His great, brawny shoulders resemble the two pommels
of an ass's pack-saddle; his breasts and their muscles
bear no similitude to those of a man, but seem to have
been drawn from a sack of melons. As he leans directly against the wall, the small of the back has the
appearance of a bag filled with long cucumbers; it is
impossible to conceive in what manner the two legs are
fastened to this distorted figure, for it is hard to distinguish upon which leg he stands, or upon which he exerts
any effort of his strength; nor does he appear to stand
upon both, as he is sometimes represented by those masters of the art of statuary who know something of their
business. It is plain, too, that the statue inclines more
than one third of a cubit forward; and this is the greatest and the most insupportable blunder which pretenders
to sculpture can be guilty of. As for the arms, they both
hang down in the most awkward and ungraceful manner
imaginable; and so little art is displayed in them, that
people would be almost tempted to think that you had
never seen a naked man in your life. The right leg
of Hercules and that of Cacus touch at the middle of
their calves, and if they were to be separated, not one
of them only, but both, would reman without a calf in

the place where they touch: besides, one of the feet of the Hercules is quite buried, and the other looks as if it stood upon hot coals."

Thus I went on, but the man could no longer stay with patience to hear the defects of his figure of Cacus enumerated. One reason was, that what I said was true; the other, that I made the Duke acquainted with his real character, as well as the rest of those present, who showed the greatest symptoms of surprise and began to be sensible that all I said was true. The brutish fellow then said, "O thou slanderer, dost thou say nothing of my design?" I answered that he who drew a good one could never work ill, and that I was convinced his design was of a piece with his works. Seeing that the Duke and all present showed by their sarcastic looks and gestures that they thought the censure of his performance to be just, he let his insolence get the better of him, and, turning to me with a most brutish physiognomy, called me by the basest and most infamous epithets.

The Duke endeavored to restrain him by one of his severest frowns; all present appeared shocked, and fixed their eyes upon him, but said not a word. I was seized with one of my transports of rage, and at first deprived of speech. Recovering myself, "Madman!" I exclaimed, "you exceed all bounds of reason and truth. Would to God I was so happy as to belong to that fraternity of illustrious delinquents who boast a title even from Jove to commit the greatest crimes with impunity, and perpetrate their enormities and oppressions under such a plea. But I am only a man, a poor humble creature who can lay claim to no such special order of merit and hereditary gift of oppressing others and sinning with impunity. It is too wonderful and inexplicable for me— quite beyond the range of my humble art." At these words the Duke, and all who were present, could not conceal their approbation, which expressed itself in a loud burst of merriment directed against my adversary, who stood quite aghast. Yet, though capable of expressing myself in this strain of sarcastic pleasantry, you may believe me, gentle reader, my heart was almost bursting with grief and indignation. But the reader should take it into consideration, that on this occasion the Duke was affronted, and not I; for had I not been in his august presence, I should have killed the villain on the spot.

Perceiving that the noble personages present never once ceased laughing, this wretch began to change the subject, and said, "This Benvenuto goes about making it his boast that I promised him a block of marble." "How!" said I, interrupting him, "did you not send word by your journeyman, Francesco Matteo Fabbro, that, if I chose to work in marble, you would make me a present of a piece? Did I not accept the offer, and don't I still require of you the performance of your promise?" He replied, "Then depend upon it, you shall never have it." Thereupon I, suddenly deprived of my reason, as it were, forgot for a moment that I was in the presence of the Duke, and cried out: "In plain terms, either send the marble to my house, or think of another world; for I will certainly send you out of this." Recollecting immediately that I was in the presence of so great a prince, I turned with an air of humility to his Excellency, and said, "My Lord, one fool makes a hundred. The folly of this man has made me forget your Excellency's glory, and myself, for which I humbly beg your pardon."

The Duke asked Bandinello whether it was true that he had promised me the marble. Bandinello answered that it was. The Duke thereupon said to me: "Return to your work, and take a piece of marble to your liking." I replied that he had promised to send me one to my house. Terrible words passed upon the occasion, and I insisted upon receiving it in that manner and no other.

The next morning a piece of marble was brought to my house, and I asked the porters from whom it came. They told me it was sent by Bandinello, being the piece of marble which he had promised me. I ordered it to be carried into my shop, and took it in hand that moment; and while I was working upon it, I made my model; so eager was I to be employed in marble, that I had not the patience to take the necessary time for making a model. Perceiving the marble crack, I several times began to repent that I had undertaken the work; yet I made what I could out of it, I mean the Apollo and Hyacinthus, which, though imperfect, are still to be seen at my shop.

While I was employed in this manner, the Duke came to my house, and said several times, "Let the bronze alone for a while, and work a little in marble, that I may see how you do it." I took the tools, and began to use them. The Duke inquired about the model I had made for this work, and I told him the marble was quite broken, but I would warrant to make something of it notwithstanding; for though I could not resolve upon a model, I would still work on, and do the best I could. The Duke, hearing this, caused a piece of Greek marble to be conveyed with expedition from Rome, to enable me to restore the antique Ganymede that had given rise to the dispute between me and Bandinello. When the Greek marble arrived, I considered that it was a sin to break it into pieces, for the sake of making and repairing the Ganymede. I therefore provided myself with another block, and for this piece of Greek marble I made a little waxen model, to which I gave the name of Narcissus. As this marble had two holes, which were more than a quarter of a cubit in depth and fully two inches broad, I had recourse to the attitude seen in that work, by which the figure avoids them. But for many years it had rained constantly on the marble; these holes were always left full of water, and the moisture had penetrated to such a degree that the marble became weak and almost rotten in the upper hole, and so it appeared when the water rose more than a cubit and a half in my shop at the great inundation of the Arno. This piece of marble was placed on a square piece of wood, and the water made it turn about, by which accident the breasts were broken, so that I was obliged to mend them; and that the cleft might not appear where they were fastened on, I placed there a garland of flowers. This work I executed at certain hours before day, or else on holidays only, that I might not delay my great work of the statue of Perseus. As I was one morning preparing some tools to work at it, a little bit of steel flew into my right eye, and entered so far into the pupil that it was impossible to get it out, so that I was in very great danger of losing that eye. Several days later I sent for Maestro Raffaello de Pilli, a surgeon, who took two live pigeons, and making me lie upon my back, with a little knife opened a vein under their wings, so that the blood ran into my eye, and I was thereby greatly relieved. In two days the bit of steel issued from my eye, and I in a great measure recovered my sight.

The feast of St. Lucia approaching, I made a golden eye of a French crown, and got it offered to that saint by one of the daughters of my sister Liperata, a girl about ten years of age. In this manner did I testify my gratitude to God and to St. Lucia. For some time after this I discontinued working upon the Narcissus, but went on with my Perseus, for I was resolved to finish it and then to leave Florence.

CHAPTER XLI

A FEAT IN CASTING

AS I had been particularly successful in casting my Medusa, I made a model of my Perseus in wax, and flattered myself that I should have the same success in casting the latter in bronze, as with the former. On its appearing to such advantage, and looking so beautiful in wax, the Duke took occasion to say to me, "Benvenuto, this statue cannot be cast in bronze; it is not in the power of your art to compass it." Hearing him express himself in that manner, I betrayed great vexation, and said, "My Lord, I know that your Excellency places very little confidence in me, and that you have but too good an opinion of those who speak ill of me; or else you do not understand things of this nature." Hardly did he suffer me to utter these words, when he answered, "I profess to understand them and I do understand them perfectly." I replied, "You may understand them as a prince, but not as an artist; for if you had that skill in these matters which you think you have, you would believe me on account of the fine bronze head that I cast for your Excellency, which was sent to Elba; as likewise for having restored the beautiful figure of Ganymede, a work that gave me infinite trouble, insomuch that it would have been easier for me to make a new one; likewise for having cast the Medusa, which stands here, a performance of immense difficulty, in which I have done what no other man has done before me in this most laborious art. Consider, my Lord, I have constructed a new sort of furnace, in a manner unknown to other artists; for, besides many other particulars and curious

inventions to be seen in it, I have made two issues for
the bronze; for otherwise that difficult and distorted
figure never could come out, and it was only by means
of my skill and invention that it came out as well as it
did.   And do not imagine that every common artist
could have done as much.   Know likewise, my Lord, that
all the great and difficult undertakings I have been employed in by the renowned King Francis, were attended
with admirable success, purely on account of that king's
generous encouragement of my labors in providing me
with everything I wanted, and allowing me as many
assistants as I required.   At certain times I had under
me more than forty journeymen, all of my own choosing;
and this was the reason that I finished so many undertakings in so short a time.   Therefore, my Lord, take
my advice, and afford me the assistance I want, for I
have great hopes of producing a work that will please
you: whereas, if your Excellency discourages me, and
does not supply me with the necessary helps, it is impossible that either I or any man living can produce
anything worth notice."

The Duke hardly had patience to hear me out, but
sometimes turned one way, sometimes another; and I
was in despair when I recollected the circumstances in
which I had lived in France.   At last he suddenly said,
"Tell me, Benvenuto, how is it possible that this fine
head of Medusa, which Perseus holds aloft, should ever
come out cleverly?"   I answered, "It is clear, my lord,
that you are no connoisseur in statuary, as your Excellency boasts yourself; for if you had any skill in the art,
you would not be afraid of that fine head not coming
out, but would express your apprehensions concerning
that right foot, which is at such distance below."   The
Duke, half angry, addressing himself to some noblemen,
said, "I really believe it is a practice of Benvenuto's to
contradict and oppose everything he hears advanced;"

then turning to me, as it were in derision, in which he was imitated by all present, he expressed himself thus: "I am willing to have patience to hear what reason you can allege that can possibly induce me to believe what you affirm." I answered, "I will give your Excellency a reason so satisfactory that you will be able to conceive the full force of it. You know, my lord, that the nature of fire is to fly upward; I therefore assure you that the head of Medusa will come out perfectly well. But as it is not a property of fire to descend, and it is here necessary to force it down six cubits by art, hence, I affirm that it is impossible that yon foot should ever come out; but it will be an easy matter for me to make a new one." * The Duke thereupon said, "Why did you not think of contriving to make that foot come out as well as the head?" "I must then," said I, "have made the furnace much bigger with a conduit as thick as my leg, and with that weight of hot metal I should have made it come out by force; whereas, my conduit, which goes down to the feet six cubits, as I mentioned before, is not more than two inches thick. But that is not worth notice, for it can soon be rectified. When my mould is something more than half full, I have good hopes that from that half upward, the heads of Perseus and Medusa will come out admirably; and this you may depend upon."

I still flattered myself that if I could but finish my statue of Perseus, all my labors would be converted to delight, and meet with a glorious and happy reward. Though I had but little money left, I purchased several

---

* Cellini first formed his model of clay more slender than the statue was intended to be. He then baked it, and covered it with wax of the thickness of a finger, which he modeled into the perfect form of the statue. He covered the wax with clay, and baked this second covering. Thus the wax dissolving, and escaping by fissures left open for the purpose, he obtained between the first model and the second covering a space for the introduction of the metal.

loads of pine wood, and while I was waiting for it, I
covered my Perseus with the clay that I had prepared
several months beforehand, that it might have its proper
seasoning. After I had made its coat of clay, covered
it well, and bound it properly with irons, I began by
means of a slow fire to draw off the wax, which melted
away by many vent-holes; for the more of these are
made, the better the moulds are filled: and when I had
entirely stripped off the wax, I made a sort of fence round
my Perseus, that is, round the mould above-mentioned,
of bricks, piling them one upon another, and leaving
several openings for the fire to exhale at. I next began
gradually to put on the wood, and kept a constant fire
for two days and two nights, till, the wax being quite
gone off, and the mould well baked, I began to dig a
hole to bury my mould in, and observed all those fine
methods of proceeding that are prescribed by our art.
When I had completely dug my hole, I took my mould,
and by means of levers and strong cables directed it with
care, and suspended it a cubit above the level of the
furnace, so that it hung exactly in the middle of the hole.
I then let it gently down to the very bottom, and placed
it with all the care and exactness I possibly could.
After I had finished this part of my task, I began to make
a covering of the earth that I had dug out, and as I
raised the earth, I made vents for it, with tubes of
baked clay. As soon as I saw that I had placed it properly, and that this manner of covering it, by putting
these small tubes in their proper places, was likely to
answer, as also that my journeymen thoroughly understood my plan, which was very different from that of
all other masters, and I was sure that I could depend
upon them, I turned my thoughts to my furnace. I had
caused it to be filled with pieces of brass and bronze,
and heaped them upon one another in the manner taught
us by our art, taking particular care to leave a passage

22

for the flames, that the metal might the sooner assume its color and melt. Thus, with great alacrity, I excited my men to lay on the pine wood, which, because of the oiliness of the resinous matter that oozes from the pine-tree, and that my furnace was admirably well made, burned at such a rate that I was continually obliged to run to and fro, which greatly fatigued me. I bore the hardship; but the shop took fire, and we were all very much afraid that the roof would fall in and crush us. From another quarter, that is, from the garden, the sky poured in so much rain and wind that it cooled my furnace.

Thus did I struggle with these adverse accidents for several hours, and exerted myself to such a degree that my constitution, though robust, could no longer bear the severe hardship, and I was suddenly attacked by a most violent intermitting fever: in short, I was so ill that I found myself under a necessity of going to bed. This gave me great concern, but it was unavoidable. I thereupon addressed myself to my ten assistants, masters who melted bronze, helpers, men from the country, and the journeymen that worked in the shop, among whom was Bernardino Manellini di Mugello. After advising them all to take proper care of my business, I said to Bernardino, "My friend, be careful to observe the method I have shown you, and use all possible expedition, for the metal will soon be ready. You cannot mistake: these two worthy men here will quickly make the tubes; with two such directors you certainly can contrive to pour out the hot metal by means of the mandriani or iron crooks; and I have no doubt that my mould will be filled completely. I find myself extremely ill, and really be-lieve that in a few hours this severe disorder will end my life." Thus I left them in great sorrow, and went to bed. I then ordered the maids to carry food and drink into the shop for all the men, and told them I did not

expect to live till morning. They encouraged me notwithstanding, assuring me that my disorder was only
the effect of overfatigue. In this manner did I continue
for two hours in a violent fever, which I every moment
perceived to increase; and I was incessantly crying out,
"I am dying, I am dying."

My housekeeper, Mona Fiora da Castel del Rio, one
of the most sensible and affectionate women in the world,
rebuked me for giving way to vain fears, and at the same
time attended me with the greatest kindness and care
imaginable. Yet, seeing me so very ill and terrified, she
shed a flood of tears, which she endeavored to conceal
from me. While we were both in this deep affliction, I
saw a man enter the room, who appeared to be as
crooked as a capital S, and began to express himself
in these terms, with a tone as dismal and melancholy
as those who exhort and pray with persons that are
about to be executed: "Alas! poor Benvenuto, your
work is spoiled, and the misfortune admits of no
remedy."

No sooner had I heard the words uttered by this messenger of evil, than I cried out so loud that my voice
might be heard to the skies, and got out of bed. I began
immediately to dress, and giving plenty of kicks and
cuffs to the maid servants and the boy as they offered to
help me on with my clothes, I complained bitterly in
these terms: "O you envious and treacherous wretches,
this is a piece of villainy contrived on purpose; but I
swear by the living God that I will sift it to the bottom,
and before I die, give such proofs who I am as shall
not fail to astonish the world." Having huddled on my
clothes, I went to the shop with a mind boding evil,
and I found all those whom I had left so alert and in
such high spirits, standing in the utmost confusion and
astonishment. I addressed them thus: "'Listen, all of
you to what I am about to say; and since you either

would not or could not follow the method I pointed out, obey me now that I am present. My work is before us, and let none of you offer to oppose or contradict me, for such cases as this require activity and not counsel." Hereupon one Alessandro Lastricati had the assurance to say to me, "Look you, Benvenuto, you have undertaken a work that our art cannot compass; it is not to be effected by human power."

Hearing these words, I turned in such a passion, and seemed so bent on mischief, that both he and all the rest cried out, "Give your orders, and we will all second you in whatever you command; we will assist you as long as we have breath in our bodies." These kind and affectionate words they uttered, as I firmly believe, in a persuasion that I was upon the point of expiring. I examined the furnace, and saw that all the metal in it was concreted. I thereupon ordered two of the helpers to step over the way to Capretta, a butcher, for a load of young oak, which had been more than a year drying.

As soon as he brought me the first bundles of it, I began to fill the grate. This sort of oak makes a brisker fire than any other wood whatever; but the wood of elder-trees and pine-trees is used in casting artillery, because it makes a gentle fire. As soon as the concreted metal felt the power of this violent fire, it began to brighten and glitter. In another quarter I made them hurry the tubes with all possible expedition, and I sent some of them to the roof of the house to take care of the fire, which through the great violence of the wind had acquired new force; and toward the garden I had caused some tables with pieces of tapestry and old clothes to be placed, in order to shelter me from the rain. As soon as I had applied the proper remedy to each evil, I cried out to my men to bestir themselves and lend a helping hand. When they saw the concreted metal melting again, the whole body obeyed me with such zeal and alacrity that every man did the work of three. Then I caused about sixty pounds of pewter to be thrown upon the metal in the furnace, which with the other helps, as the brisk wood fire, and stirring it sometimes with iron, and sometimes with long poles, soon became completely dissolved. Finding that, contrary to the opinion of my ignorant assistants, I had effected what seemed as difficult as to raise the dead, I recovered my vigor to such a degree that I no longer knew whether I had any fever, nor had I the least apprehension of death. Suddenly a loud noise was heard, and a glittering of fire flashed before our eyes, as if it had been the darting of a thunderbolt. On the appearance of this extraordinary phenomenon, terror seized all present, and on none more than myself. This tremendous noise being over, we stared at one another, and perceived that the stopper of the furnace had burst and flown off, so that the bronze began to run.

I immediately caused the mouths of my mould to be opened; but finding that the metal did not run with its usual velocity, and apprehending that the cause of it was that the fusibility of the metal was injured by the violence of the fire, I ordered all my dishes and porringers, in number about two hundred, to be placed one by one before my tubes, and part of them to be thrown into the furnace. All present then saw that my bronze was completely melted, and that my mould was filling; and they now with joy and alacrity assisted and obeyed me. I was sometimes in one place, sometimes in another, giving directions and assisting my men, before whom I offered up this prayer: "O God, I address myself to Thee, who, of thy divine power, didst rise from the dead, and ascend in glory to heaven. I acknowledge in gratitude this mercy that my mould has been filled. I fall prostrate before Thee, and with my whole heart return thanks to Thy divine majesty." My prayer being over, I took a plate of meat that stood upon a little bench,

and ate with a great appetite. I then drank with all my
journeymen and assistants, and went joyfully and in
good health to bed, for there were still two hours of
night, and I rested as well as if I had been troubled with
no manner of disorder.

My good housekeeper, without my having given any
orders, had provided a young capon for my dinner.
When I arose, which was not till about noon, she accosted me in high spirits, and said merrily, "Is this the
man that thought himself dying? It is my firm belief
that the cuffs and kicks you gave us last night, when you
were quite frantic and possessed, frightened away your
fever, which, apprehending lest you should fall upon it
in the same manner, took to flight."

So my whole poor family, having got over such panics
and hardships, without delay procured earthen vessels
to supply the place of the pewter dishes and porringers,
and we all dined together very cheerfully. Indeed, I
do not remember having ever eaten a meal with greater
satisfaction, or with a better appetite. After dinner,
all who had assisted me in my work came and congratulated me upon what had happened, returned thanks
to the Divine Being for having interposed so mercifully
in our behalf, and declared that they had in theory and
practice learned such things as were judged impossible
by other masters. I thereupon thought it allowable to
boast a little of my knowledge and skill in this fine art,
and, pulling out my purse, satisfied all my workmen for
their labor.

My mortal enemy, Pier Francesco Ricci, the Duke's
steward, was eager to know how the affair had turned
out; so that the two whom I suspected of being the
cause of my metal's concreting in the manner above related, told him that I was not a man, but rather a down-
right devil, for I had compassed that which was not in
the power of art to effect, with many other surprising

things, which would have been too much even for the
infernal powers. As they greatly exaggerated what had
passed, perhaps with a view of excusing themselves,
the steward wrote to the Duke, who was then at Pisa,
an account still more pompous, and more replete with the
marvelous than that which the workmen had given him.

Having left my work to cool for two days, I began
gradually to uncover it. I first of all found the Medusa's
head, which had come out admirably by the assistance
of the vents, as I had observed to the Duke that the
property of fire was to fly upward. I uncovered the rest,
and found that the other head, I mean that of Perseus,
had likewise come out perfectly well. This occasioned
me still greater surprise, because, as it is seen in the
statue, it is much lower than that of Medusa, the mouth
of that figure being placed over the head and shoulders
of Perseus. I found that where the head of Perseus
ends, all the bronze I had in my furnace was exhausted.
This surprised me very much, that there should not be
anything over and above what was necessary in casting.
My astonishment, indeed, was raised to such a degree,
that I looked upon it as a miracle immediately wrought
by the Almighty. I went on uncovering it with great
success, and found every part turn out to admiration,
till I reached the foot of the right leg, which supports
the figure, where I found the heel had come out. So
proceeding to examine it, and thinking the whole was
filled up, in one respect I was glad, in another sorry,
because I had told the Duke it would not have that
effect. Continuing, however, to uncover it, I found that
not only were the toes wanting, but part of the foot itself, so that almost one half was deficient. This occasioned me some new trouble; but I was not displeased
at it, because I could thereby convince the Duke that I
understood my business thoroughly; and though a great
deal more of that foot had come out than I thought

there would, the reason was, that in consequence of the several accidents, it was heated much more than it could have been in the regular course of business; especially as the pewter plates had been thrown into the furnace, a thing never done before.

I went to Pisa to pay my respects to the Duke, who received me in the most gracious manner imaginable. The Duchess vied with him in kindness to me; and though the steward had written them an account of the affair, it appeared to them much more wonderful and extraordinary when I related it myself. Upon my speaking to him of the foot of Perseus, which had not come out (a circumstance of which I had appraised his Excellency), I saw that he was filled with the utmost astonishment, and he told the affair to the Duchess in the same terms in which I had related it to him. Finding that these great personages were become so favorable to me, I availed myself of the opportunity to request the Duke's permission to go to Rome. He granted it in the most obliging terms, and desired me to return speedily, in order to finish my statue of Perseus. He at the same time gave me letters of recommendation to his ambassador, Averardo Serristori. This happened in the beginning of the pontificate of Pope Julio de Monti.

CHAPTER XLII

A CONFERENCE WITH MICHELANGELO

BEFORE my departure from Florence, I directed my men to proceed with the work according to the method I had taught them. The cause of my journey was this: having made a bust of Bindo Antonio Altoviti as large as the life, I sent it to him at

Rome; and he put it into a cabinet richly furnished with antiques and other things of value. This was an unfit repository for pieces of sculpture, or even for pictures, because the windows were under those fine works; so that, being placed in a wrong light, they did not appear to advantage. One day Bindo happened to be standing at his door, when Michelangelo Buonarroti the sculptor was passing by; and the former desired the latter to come in and take a view of his cabinet of curiosities. Michelangelo asked Bindo who was the artist that had taken his likeness in so masterly a manner? You must know," added he, "that I am highly pleased with this head, though there are very fine antiques near it; but if those windows were above, instead of underneath, the whole collection would be more conspicuous and show to much greater advantage, and your bust, even among so many noble pieces of antiquity, would claim a high degree of admiration."

Michelangelo, after leaving his friend Bindo, then wrote me a very polite letter to this purport: "My dear friend Benvenuto, I have many years known you for one of the ablest jewelers in the world, and I now find that you have equal abilities as a sculptor. You must know that Signor Bindo Altoviti showed me his bust in bronze, and told me it was done by you. I was highly pleased with the execution, but it gave me great uneasiness to see it placed in a disadvantageous light. Had it but been properly situated, it would have appeared to be the masterpiece it is."

This letter abounded with the most affectionate and most favorable expressions concerning myself; so, before I set out for Rome, I showed it to the Duke, who perused it with great pleasure, and said to me, "Benvenuto, I would have you write to him, and if you can prevail on him to come to Florence, I will make him one of the eight-and-forty.* Accordingly I wrote him a most affectionate epistle, expressing the Duke's sentiments, and saying a hundred times more than I had been commissioned to say. To avoid committing any error, I showed it to his Excellency before I sealed it, and told him that perhaps I had promised too much. He answered that I had done very right; that Michelangelo deserved still more than I had promised him, and that he purposed conferring on him more considerable favors. This letter of mine Michelangelo never answered, at which neglect the Duke was highly offended.

On my arrival at Rome I went to lodge at the house of Bindo Altoviti. He told me that he had shown his bust in bronze to Michelangelo, who had bestowed upon it the highest praises imaginable; so we talked of this affair for a considerable time. This man had in his hands one thousand two hundred crowns of mine, which he had borrowed to make up the sum of five thousand two hundred that he had lent to the Duke. Thus four thousand were his own, and mine were in his name. He regularly paid me the just interest for my share, which was the reason that I undertook to make his bust. When he first saw it in wax, he sent me fifty crowns. I did not choose to take the money, but sent it back by the messenger, and afterward told Bindo himself that it was sufficient for me if he would keep that money with the rest of mine in his hands, and let me receive the interest of it. But now I perceived that he had bad intentions, and instead of welcoming me according to custom, he behaved

---

* In the celebrated revolution at Florence, in 1532, by which Clement VII converted that republic into a duchy in favor of Alessandro de' Medici, were created three councils, one of two hundred, which in some measure represented the people, the other of forty-eight, called the Senate, in which the sovereignty was considered to reside, and which propounded the laws; and the third of four, chosen every three months from the forty-eight; to which, together with the Duke, was intrusted the execution of the laws.

quite rudely: though he entertained me in his house, he was never in a good humor. However, we settled the affair in a few words. I gave up my payment for making the bust, and even what the bronze had cost me; and agreed that Bindo should keep my money in his hands, and pay me fifteen per cent. during my natural life.

One of the first things I did at Rome was to go to kiss the Pope's feet. At that moment arrived Averardo Serristori, ambassador from our Duke. I talked for some time with his Holiness, and found him much disposed to favor me; nay, I verily believe that, disgusted with the difficulties I had to encounter at Florence, I should have settled again with his Holiness's consent at Rome, but I found that the Florentine ambassador thwarted me. I went to Michelangelo, and repeated to him the contents of the letter I had sent him from Florence by the Duke's orders. He told me he was employed in building St. Peter's church, and for that reason could not leave Rome. I then said to him that, since he had determined upon the model of the structure, he might leave his pupil Urbino in his place, who would punctually follow his directions, and at the same time I made him several new promises in the Duke's name. He looked at me attentively, and asked, with a smile, whether I myself was pleased with my situation at the court of Florence. Though I assured him I was perfectly well satisfied, and that I met with the kindest treatment imaginable, he seemed to be thoroughly acquainted with all my grievances; and his final answer was, that he could not think of leaving Rome.

After I had transacted my business with Bindo Altoviti so unsuccessfully as to lose my bust of bronze, and to entrust my money in his hands for life, I saw clearly what the principles of merchants are, and returned to Florence very much dissatisfied. I waited on his Excellency, who was then at the castle, on the bridge of Rifredi. By the way I met with Signor Pier Francesco Ricci, the steward, and when I made an offer to accost him with the civilities that custom prescribes, he exclaimed with the utmost surprise, "So you are returned!" His amazement still continuing, he clapped his hands and told me that the Duke was at the castle; then turned his back to me and marched off. I could not conceive why the fool behaved so oddly. I went, however, to the castle, and entered the garden where the Duke happened to be walking. At the sight of me he showed symptoms of great surprise, and signified to me by a nod that I might go about my business. I, who had flattered myself that he would compliment me rather more than at my departure, seeing him behave thus extravagantly, returned very much disgusted to Florence, and, resuming my business, endeavored to bring my works to a conclusion with all possible expedition. Not being able to conjecture the cause of the cold reception I had met with, I carefully observed in what manner I was looked upon by Signor Sforza, and others of the Duke's intimates; and I took it into my head to ask Sforza what was the meaning of this indifference. He answered laughing, "Benvenuto, endeavor to act the part of a man of honor, and fear nothing." Several days later he procured an interview for me with the Duke, who received me with a great many odd civilities, and asked what was doing at Rome. I gave him an account of the bust of bronze that I had made for Bindo Altoviti, with what happened on the occasion. I saw that he listened to me with the greatest attention imaginable; so I told him all that had passed between Michelangelo and me, at which he showed some resentment. He said the loss would be Michelangelo's, and not his. I made my bow and retired.

Now, gentle reader, thou art to hear of a most dreadful affair. I made all haste to finish my work, and in the evening went to the Duke's wardrobe, where I used to

assist the goldsmiths employed by his Excellency, most
of whose works were after my designs. The Duke took
great delight in seeing them busy, and in conversing with
me, which induced me sometimes to go there in the day-
time. One day when I happened to be in his wardrobe,
his Excellency came thither, as he often did, particularly
when he knew that I was there. He began to chat with
me, and I made myself so agreeable to him that he
appeared to be in a better humor than usual. All on a
sudden one of his secretaries entered the room, and
whispered in his ear, as if about some business of great
importance. The Duke rose, and they went together
into another apartment. As the Duchess had sent to see
what the Duke was doing, the page told her that he was
talking and laughing with Benvenuto, and we were very
merry. Her Excellency thereupon entered the wardrobe,
and, not finding the Duke, sat down by us. Perceiving
that it would be some time before we had done work, she
turned to me in great good humor, and, showing me a
fine string of large pearls, asked me what I thought of it.
I praised it highly. Her Excellency then said, "I wish
that the Duke would buy it for me; therefore, Benvenuto,
praise it in his presence as much as you possibly can."
Hearing the Duchess express herself in this manner, I
frankly told her my sentiments, with the most profound
respect, in these terms: "I thought that string of
pearls belonged to your Excellency, and it was proper
that I should say no ill of anything that was yours; but
at present I am under a necessity of speaking my mind.
You must then understand, that by my knowledge in
these matters I can discover many defects in these pearls,
and would by no means advise you to buy them." She
answered, "The merchant offers them to me for six thousand crowns; and if they had not some defects, they
would be worth twelve thousand." "If the string of
pearls," I replied, "were never so fine, I would not advise

any one to give more than five thousand crowns for it; because pearls, produced from fish, are not like jewels. In process of time they lose their value; but diamonds, rubies, emeralds, and sapphires are jewels that lose nothing by growing old, and therefore are a proper purchase." The Duchess, somewhat piqued, said she had a fancy for these pearls, therefore begged I would praise them to the Duke, and even make no scruple of telling an untruth to serve her, and I should find my acount in it.

I, who was always a lover of truth and an enemy to falsehood, being then under a necessity of telling lies, lest I should forfeit the favor of so great a princess, went with those unlucky pearls to the apartment to which the Duke had retired. As soon as he saw me, he said, "Benvenuto, what are you about?" I pulled out the string of pearls, and answered, "My Lord, I am come to show you a fine string of the choicest pearls;" then, bestowing the highest praises on them, I added, "Buy them, my Lord, buy them, by all means." The Duke told me he did not choose to buy them, as they were not perfect. To this I answered: "Excuse me, my Lord, these surpass all other pearls in beauty, and I do not believe there were ever so many such in one bunch." The Duchess was standing behind a door not far off, and could hear what I said; so I praised the pearls up to the skies. When the Duke first looked at them, he said he would not have them, as they were not nearly so good as I said; but as I maintained they were beautiful he said, "Benvenuto, I know you are an excellent judge of these things, and if the pearls are so very fine, I should not much mind purchasing them, as well to please the Duchess, as to have them in my possession for our children." As I had begun to tell lies, I plunged deeper and deeper into the mire, depending upon the Duchess, who, I hoped, would from time to time assist me. I was to receive two hundred crowns for making the bargain, for the Duchess had

hinted to me as much; but I resolved not to touch a
farthing of the money, lest the Duke should think I was
acting in this manner with an interested view. He
repeated to me again, that he looked upon me as a perfect
judge of such things, and begged that if I were the man
of principle he took me to be, I would simply speak the
truth. Thereupon the tears came into my eyes, and I
said to him, "My Lord, if I tell you the truth, I make the
Duchess my mortal enemy. I shall in consequence be
under a necessity of leaving this city; and my statue of
Perseus, which I promised the illustrious school of Florence, will become the scoff of my enemies. I therefore beg
your Excellency would consider my case." The Duke,
perceiving that I had spoken before by compulsion,
desired me to put my confidence in him and fear nothing.
I asked him how it was possible to conceal the affair from
the Duchess. He bade me tell her that the pearls were
eclipsed by a casket of diamonds. On his expressing
himself in that manner, I told him my real opinion of
the pearls, and declared that they were not worth more
than two thousand crowns.

The Duchess, perceiving that we were quiet, for we
lowered our voices as much as we could, came forward,
and said to the Duke, "My dear Lord, I beg you would
buy me that string of pearls, because I have taken a particular fancy to it. and your great artist, Benvenuto, says
he never saw a finer." The Duke told her he would not
buy it on any account. "Why, my dear Lord," replied the
Duchess, "will not your Excellency buy that string of
pearls to oblige me?" "Because," answered the Duke,
"I do not choose to throw away my money." "How is
it throwing away your money," replied the Duchess, "if
Benvenuto here, in whom you have so much confidence,
has assured me it would be cheap at more than three
thousand crowns?" The Duke then said, "Madam, Benvenuto has told me that if I buy it I shall throw away my

money, because these pearls are neither round nor equal, and there are many old ones among them.   To convince yourself that what I say is true, do but observe that pearl there, and that other; look there, and there again.   In a word, they are by no means for my purpose."   When he expressed himself in that manner, the Duchess gave me a very severe look, and, shaking her head with a menacing air, left the apartment.

I was now strongly tempted to hurry away to some other part of the world; but as my Perseus was in a manner finished, I could not think of neglecting to take it out of the mould.   The Duke had given orders to his servants to suffer me constantly to pass through the apartments, and to have access to his Excellency wherever he happened to be; and the Duchess now laid her injunctions upon the very same servants to turn me out whenever I came to the palace.   These fellows, as soon as they saw me coming, would quit their posts, and order me to turn back; but they took care to act thus unperceived by the Duke, for if his Excellency saw me first, he either called to me, or made me a sign to enter.   The Duchess sent for that Bernardone, of whose knavery she had so bitterly complained, and recommended the affair of the pearls to him in the same manner as to me.   Bernardone thereupon told her that her Excellncy might depend upon him.   The rogue went into the Duke's presence with the string of pearls in his hand.   But the Duke no sooner saw him than he ordered him to quit his presence. The knave, with his odd, affected tone of voice, with which he drawled through his nose in a ridiculous manner, said, "Ah, my dear Lord, buy that string of pearls for the poor lady, who cannot live without it."   He added many more foolish expressions; and at last he disgusted the Duke, who ordered him to be gone instantly, or he would give him a slap in the face.   The fellow knew very well what he was about; for if by means of flattery, or any other artifice whatever, he could prevail on the Duke to make that purchase, he was sure of gaining the Duchess's good graces, and of receiving several hundred crowns for the bargain. He continued therefore to fawn and flatter, and the Duke gave him several good sound boxes on the ear to make him quit the place. So smartly were the blows given that not only his cheeks became red, but the tears burst into his eyes. The fellow notwithstanding persisted in his importunities, and cried, "Ah, my Lord, your faithful servant would fain discharge his duty, and willingly submit to bear any severe treatment, provided the poor lady might be indulged in her desire." The Duke at last, quite tired of the man, being also wearied with cuffing him about, and no longer able to resist his love for the Duchess, whom he delighted to humor in everything, said to Bernardone "Get you gone and make a bargain for the pearls; for I am willing to do anything to please the Duchess."

CHAPTER XLIII

THE GREAT STATUE

ABOUT this time (1552) the war with Siena broke out, and the Duke, choosing to fortify Florence, consigned the gates of the city to the care of the most skilful engineers and architects. On this occasion, the gate leading to Prato, with the little gate of Arno, leading to the mills, fell to my share; to the Cavalier Bandinello was given the gate of St. Friano; to Pasqualino of Ancona, the gate of St. Pier Gattolini; to Guiliano di Baccio d'Agnolo, a carpenter, the gate of St. George; to Particino, a carpenter, the gate leading to St.

23

Nicholas; to Francesco da St. Gallo, the sculptor, surnamed Margolla, was consigned that which leads to
Croce; and to Giambattista, commonly called Tasso, was
given the Pinti gate; in like manner other bastions and
gates were distributed among other engineers.

The Duke, who was a man of abilities, and of a respect-
able character when uninfluenced by others, went his
rounds about the city; and after his Excellency had well
surveyed it, and determined upon his measures, he sent
for Lattanzio Gorini, his paymaster—an office in which
Lattanzio particularly delighted. His Excellency then
ordered him to draw plans of the methods he had determined on to repair the fortifications of his capital.
Accordingly Lattanzio sent each of us a plan of the gate
he was to fortify. When I received mine, perceiving
that the method was altogether defective, I took it to his
Excellency to show him my objections; but I no sooner
began to speak than he turned to me in a violent passion,
and told me he would readily allow me the superiority in
statuary, but in this business of fortification I must in my
turn yield to him; therefore I was to follow the plan he
had sent me. To this short admonition I answered in
the gentlest terms possible, and said, "My Lord, even with
regard to the method of making beautiful statues, I have
learned something from your Excellency, for we have
always had disputes on the subject; in like manner,
with regard to this article of fortifying your city, which
is a matter of much greater consequence than casting
statues, I beg your Excellency would vouchsafe to hear
me, that you may instruct me in what manner I am to
serve you." By these conciliatory expressions the Duke
was induced to enter into conversation with me. I made
it appear, by clear and convincing reasons, that his
method of fortifying would never answer; on which he
desired me to draw a plan myself. I drew two plans,
according to the right method of fortification, and carried

them to his Excellency, who then, distinguishing the true
from the false method, said with great good humor, "Go
and fortify the two gates in your own way; I have no
further objection." , I thereupon began the work with all
possible expedition.

There was on guard at the gate of Prato, a Lombard
captain, a robust, gigantic man who spoke in a very
rough, brutal manner, and was ignorant and presumptuous.   When he asked me what I was about, I, with
great mildness, showed him my plans, and found it very
difficult to make him conceive my method.   The stupid
mortal now shook his head, now turned himself one way,
and now another, often changed the position of his legs,
twisted his moustachios, which were very long, frequently
pulled the visor of his cap over his eyes, and uttered oaths
and imprecations, telling me he did not understand this
puzzling affair of mine.   Being at last tired of the fool,
I asked him to leave it to me, who did understand it; so
I turned my back on him, at which, being somewhat provoked, he cried out, "I say, sir, you and I must have a
tilt together." I immediately answered "It will be less
trouble to me to run you through the body than to make
the bastion for this gate." So we both at the same instant,
clapped our hands to our swords; but scarce had we
drawn when a considerable number of gentlemen, as well
Florentines as courtiers from other parts of the country,
interposed.   Most of them blamed my adversary, telling
him he was in the wrong; that I was capable of making
him pay dearly for what he did; and that if the Duke
learned what had passed between us the captain would
have reason to repent it.   He then went about his business, and I began to work at my bastion.

When I had settled in what manner it was to be erected,
I went to the other little gate of Arno, where I met with
a captain from Cesana, one of the politest men I ever knew
of his profession.   In his behavior he had all the gentle-

ness of a lady, and yet on occasion he showed himself to be one of the bravest and most formidable men living. This gentleman observed my manner of proceeding so attentively that I could not help taking notice of it. He asked to know what I was about, and I with great complaisance explained my plan to him. In a word, we vied with each other in politeness and civilities. When I had almost finished my bastions, Piero Strozzi's men made an irruption into the district of Prato, which threw the inhabitants into such a panic that they all instantly left it; on which account all the carriages of that country were loaded, every man removing with his effects to the city. Observing the great confusion, I ordered the guards at the gate to take care that no disturbance happened there, as had been the case at the gates of Turin, for if they should have occasion to let down the portcullis, it might possibly remain suspended on one of those carts. The fool of a captain of whom mention has been made above, hearing these words, began to give me abusive language. I answered him in the same style, so that we had a worse quarrel than before; but we were parted. Having completed my bastions, I received a good round sum of crowns that I little expected, and I returned to finish my Perseus.

About this time some curious antiquities were discovered in the district of Arezzo, amongst which was the chimæra, that lion of bronze, to be seen in the apartments next to the great hall of the palace. With it was found also a considerable number of small statues of bronze, covered either with earth or with rust, and each of them wanting the head, hands, or feet. The Duke took pleasure in cleaning these statues himself, with goldsmiths' chisels. I happened one day to have occasion to speak to his Excellency, when he put into my hand a small hammer, with which I struck the little chisels the Duke held in his hand, and in that manner the figures were separated from the earth and rust that covered them. While we thus passed several evenings together, the Duke employed me to supply the limbs that were wanting to the little statues; and he took such delight in these small labors of the chisel as to make me work even by day, and if I were tardy in going to him he would send for me. I several times gave his Excellency to understand that this made me neglect my Perseus, and would be attended with several bad consequences; the first of these was the length of time my work required would tire his Excellency, as it did in fact; the next was that I had several workmen, and my not being in the way gave rise to many inconveniences, for they not only spoiled my work but grew idle and negligent. The Duke therefore contented himself with my going to him after sunset.

About this time the new apartments were built toward the menagerie, so that his Excellency, desiring to retire to a private room, got a little chamber made up for him in these new buildings; and hither he ordered me to come to him through his wardrobe, which I did with the greatest privacy, by means of certain little secret passages on the other side of the great hall. But in a few days the Duchess deprived me of that privilege by causing all these passages to be closed, so that every evening that I came to the palace I was obliged to wait a considerable time, and, as she was ill, I never came without occasioning some inconvenience to her. She had taken such a dislike to me that she could not so much as bear the sight of my person. Though I had so much trouble, and received so many insults, I patiently continued my visits, and the Duke had given express orders that as soon as I knocked at those doors they should be opened to me. It sometimes happened that as I unexpectedly entered those apartments I found the Duchess engaged, when she would fly into such a passion with me that I used to be frightened, and she would constantly say, "Will you never have done mending those little statues? Your coming at present is very disagreeable to me." My answer was always couched in the gentlest terms: "My illustrious and only patroness, there is nothing I desire more than to serve you with fidelity and the most perfect obedience; and as these works, which the Duke has employed me on, will last several months, let me know, madam, whether it is your pleasure that I should come here no more. If it be, I will come no more on any account, let who will send for me; and even should the Duke himself send, I will say I am indisposed, and will not obey his order." Her reply was "I do not desire you to come no more, neither do I say you shall not obey the Duke; but I really think these works of yours will never have an end." Whether the Duke guessed something of this, or whatever else might be the cause, his Excellency again began to send for me at sunset, and the messenger told me to come without fail, for the Duke waited for me. I continued to struggle with these difficulties several weeks, and one evening, as I was entering according to custom, the Duke, who seemed to be engaged in some secret conversation with the Duchess, turned to me in the most violent passion imaginable, and I, being somewhat terrified, was for retiring at once, when he said suddenly; "Come in, my friend Benvenuto; go to your business, and I will soon follow you." As I was passing by, Signor Garzia, the Duke's son, then quite an infant, took me by the cloak, and played the prettiest tricks with me that were possible for such a child. The Duke expressed some surprise at this, and said: "How pleasant it is to see my very children so fond of you."

While my time was taken up in these trifling jobs, the princes Don Giovanni, Don Arnando, and Don Garzia every evening came into the room where I was at work, and, unknown to the Duke, began to play their tricks upon me. When I begged they would leave off, they said they could not; and I said to them, "You cannot, because you will not. Go your ways and leave me," at the same time the Duke and the Duchess began to laugh. Another evening, having finished the four little figures of bronze, which are joined at the base—I mean Jupiter, Mercury, Minerva, and Danaë, the mother of Perseus, with her little son Perseus sitting at her feet—I removed these small figures to the apartment where I worked in the evening, and placed them in proper order, raising them somewhat above the eye, so that they made a very pretty sight. The Duke, being apprised of this, came somewhat sooner than usual; and because the person that brought him the intelligence had represented them as something far beyond what they really were, affirming that they surpassed the works of the ancients, with other exaggerations, the Duke came with the Duchess, and talked to her in raptures of my works. I immediately rose and advanced to meet him. The Duke with a noble and striking gesture lifted his right hand, in which he held a fine large slip of a pear-tree, and said: "My friend, Benvenuto, put this pear-tree in your garden." I answered, "My Lord, are you in earnest when you desire me to put it in my garden?" The Duke repeated his words, and said, "In your garden, which is now your own, house and all, do you understand me?" I thereupon thanked both the Duke and the Duchess.

They then sat down before the little statues; for more than two hours they talked of nothing else, and the Duchess took such a liking to them that she said, "I will by no means suffer those figures to be lost by being placed upon that base down in the great square, where they will be in danger of being spoiled; on the contrary, I must get you to set them up in an apartment of mine, where they shall be taken particular care of, and kept in a manner suitable to their excellence." I opposed what she said by a variety of arguments; and, perceiving that she was determined that I should not place them on the base where they now stand, I waited till the day following. I then went to the palace about ten o'clock, and finding that both the Duke and the Duchess were gone to take an airing, as I had already properly prepared the base, I caused the statues to be brought down, and fixed them with lead in the position in which they were to stand. When the Duchess saw this, she was so highly provoked that, had it not been for the Duke, who took my part to his utmost, I should have come off worse than I did. In consequence of her resentment about the string of pearls, and for this affair, she did me so many ill offices that the Duke at last left off spending his leisure hours with me.

I returned to lodge at the house to which I had removed my Perseus, and went on with it under all the difficulties that I have enumerated; that is to say, without money, and with so many other cross accidents that half of them would have discouraged a man of the most determined resolution. When hearing mass at St. Piero Scheraggio, I saw Bernardone, the goldsmith whom the Duke had promoted to the place of purveyor to the Mint, as he was coming out of the church. Hardly had the wretch passed the doors when he committed a gross breach of good manners, which so provoked me that I accosted him with many opprobrious words, and then ran home for a cudgel; but Bernardone fled to the mint. I stood some time at my door, and ordered my boys to wait in the street and make me a sign as soon as they saw the brute. After I had waited a considerable time, I grew tired and resolved to take a different sort of revenge, and as this had happened within a day or two of the festival of our tutelary saint, St. John, I wrote some verses and pasted them up on the church of St. Piero Scheraggio.

These verses soon became known at the palace, the Duke and Duchess laughed heartily, and crowds gathered about the church, who were greatly diverted with the adventure. As they looked toward the mint, and fixed their eyes upon Bernardone, his son Baccio perceiving it, in a violent passion ran and tore the paper, and biting his finger, threatened the people with his shrill voice, which sounded through his nose, making a great clamor.

The Duke, being informed that my statue of Perseus would bear inspection as a finished piece, came one day to see it, and showed by many signs that it gave him the highest satisfaction imaginable; so, turning to some noblemen in his retinue, he said, "This work appears to me exceedingly beautiful; it ought likewise to be approved of by the people; therefore, my friend Benvenuto, before you have quite done with it, I should be obliged to you if you would for half a day throw open the gate before the large square, that we may see what the populace think of it; for there can be no doubt that, when it is viewed in an open place, it must make a very different appearance." I answered, "Depend upon it, my Lord, it will appear half as well again. Does not your Excellency remember having seen it in the garden at my house, in which spacious place it appeared to as great advantage as it could in the garden of the Innocents? Bandinello came to see it; and, notwithstanding his natural malevolence, put some constraint upon himself to praise my performance, though he never spoke well of anybody in his life before. I perceive that your Excellency listens too much to his insinuations." When I expressed myself thus, he smiled somewhat scornfully; and, still in the mildest terms, he begged me to oblige him. He left me, and I began to prepare to exhibit my statue; but it wanted a little gilding, varnish, and other things of the kind, which are usually left to the time of putting the last hand to a work. So, with great discontent, I exhibited my statue the next day.

But it so pleased God that as soon as my work was beheld by the populace they set up so loud a shout of applause that I began to be somewhat comforted for the mortifications I had undergone; and there were sonnets in my praise every day upon the gate, the language of which was extremely elegant and poetical. The very day on which I exhibited my work more than twenty sonnets were set up, containing the most hyperbolical praises of it. Even after I had covered it again, every day a number of verses, with Latin odes and Greek poems, were published on the occasion; for it was then vacation at the University of Pisa, and the learned men and scholars belonging to that place vied with each other in writing encomiums on my performance. But what gave me the highest satisfaction, and encouraged me to hope most from the Duke, was, that even those of the profession (I mean statuaries and painters) emulated one another in commending me; and among others the admirable painter Giacopo da Pontormo, whom I esteemed above all the rest, and his friend, the excellent painter Bronzino, whom I valued still more. The latter, not satisfied with causing several panegyrics upon me to be pasted up, sent them to my house. The Duke, though he had heard of the compliments paid me by this excellent school, said he was very glad that I had met with so favorable a reception from the public; but that I should not flatter myself, that when it was placed in such a manner as to be seen on all sides, the people would speak as advantageously of it as at present; on the contrary, they would then discover all the blemishes that it really had, and find many others that it had not; so that I must put

---

* This statue is now in the Loggia dei Lanzi, in Florence.

on the armor of patience. These words Bandinello said
to the Duke, when he spoke of the works of Andrea Ver-
rochio, who made the beautiful statues of Christ and San
Tommaso in bronze, which are to be seen in the front of
Orsanmichele, and of many other works, and even of the
admirable David of the divine Michelangelo Buonarroti,
declaring that they appeared to advantage only when
seen before; and when he afterward spoke of his own
Hercules, and the many satirical verses that were posted
up against him, and all the ill that was said of him by
the populace. All this made the Duke, who put too much
confidence in him, express himself in this manner concerning my statue. Once, when that villain Bernardone
the broker happened to be present, he, to add weight to
the words of Bandinello, said to the Duke, "You must
know, my Lord, that to make large figures is quite a different thing from working small ones; I do not say but
that Benvenuto has been happy enough in the latter, but
you will find his great statue will have different success."
With these insinuations he mixed many more equally
malicious.

At last I finished my work, and on a Thursday morning exhibited it fully. Just before the break of day so
great a crowd gathered about it that it is almost impossible for me to give an idea of their number, and they
seemed to vie with one another who should praise it
most. The Duke stood at a lower window of the palace,
just over the gate, and being half-concealed, heard all that
was said. After he had listened several hours he left the
window highly pleased, and turning to his favorite Signor Sforza, said: "Sforza, go to Benvenuto and tell him
from me that he has given me higher satisfaction than I
ever expected. Let him know, at the same time, that
I shall reward him in such a manner as will excite his
surprise, so bid him be of good cheer." During that
whole day the people showed me to one another as a sort

of prodigy.   There happened to be then in Florence two gentlemen who were sent from the Viceroy of Sicily to our Duke on business.   They came to me, with eagerness and animation, in the great square, where I was shown to them, and, cap in hand, made me a long harangue, which would have been too great a panegyric even for a pope.   I behaved as modestly as was possible; but they continued so long paying me compliments, that at last I begged they would leave the square, because the populace crowded about to stare at me more than at my statue of Perseus.   They even proposed to me to go with them to Sicily, telling me that I should have no objection to their terms; at the same time they told me that Brother Giovanangiolo, of the order of the Servi, had made them a fountain adorned with a variety of figures, which were vastly inferior to my Perseus, yet they had made his fortune.   I interrupted them and said, "I am very much surprised, gentlemen, that you should propose to me to quit the service of a Duke who is a greater lover and encourager of men of genius than any prince that ever lived; especially as I have at the same time the advantage of being in my own country, the first school in the world for the polite arts, and all works of ingenuity.   If the love of gain had been my ruling passion, I might have stayed in France, in the service of a great monarch, who allowed me a pension of a thousand crowns a year, and paid me for every piece of work I did for him besides, insomuch that annually I had more than four thousand crowns income and I left in Paris the work of four years." Thus I put a stop to their proposal, and returned them thanks for the praise they had bestowed on me.

Having let two days pass, and perceiving that my fame increased continually, I went to pay the Duke a visit, who said, "My friend Benvenuto, you have given me the highest satisfaction imaginable; but I have promised to reward you in such a manner as shall excite

your surprise, and, what is more, I am resolved not to
defer it so much as a day." On receiving these great
assurances, I raised all my mental and corporeal faculties
to the Almighty, and returned Him my hearty thanks;
at the same instant, I shed tears of joy, and kissing the
hem of his Excellency's garment, addressed him thus:
"My most noble Lord, liberal patron of the arts, and of
those that cultivate them, I beg it as a favor of your
Excellency, that you would give me leave to retire for a
week to return thanks to the Supreme Being; for I know
how hard I have worked, and am sensible that my faith
has prevailed with God to grant me His assistance. I
purpose going a pilgrimage for a week, to express my
acknowledgment to the Eternal Being, who ever assists
those who sincerely call upon Him." The Duke then
asked me whither I intended to go, and I said I should
go first to Vallombrosa, then to Camaldoli, and the wilderness, and afterward to the baths of Santa Maria, and
perhaps as far as Sestile, for I had been informed that
there were fine antiquities in that place. I should then
return by St. Francesco della Vernia, and should come
home joyfully to serve his Excellency. The Duke thereupon said, "Go, and return quickly. I am pleased with
your intention; but give me a couplet in remembrance of
you, and leave the rest to me." I immediately composed
four lines, in which I returned thanks for his promised
favors, and gave them to Signor Sforza, who put them
into the Duke's hand in my name. The latter, after
perusing them, gave them again to Signor Sforza, with
these words, "Be sure you show them to me every day;
for if Benvenuto should, on his return, find that I had
neglected his business, he would be the death of me,
beyond all doubt."

CHAPTER XLIV

A PILGRIMAGE

I LEFT Florence, singing psalms and saying many prayers to the honor and glory of God, during the whole journey, in which I had great pleasure, as it was then summer, and the weather very fine. So pleased was I with the country, in which I had never traveled before, that my delight proved equal to my wonder. My guide was a young man from the mountains of the Bagno, who worked in my shop, and whose name was Cæsar. I met with a kind reception at the baths from his father and the whole family, among whom was a man of more than seventy, a very agreeable companion, a physician and surgeon, who had a smattering of alchemy. This worthy man proved to me that the mountains of the Bagno contained a mine of gold and silver, and showed me several curiosities in that country; so that I never enjoyed greater pleasure than in his society. Being at last quite familiar with me, he told me one day that he could not help communicating to me a thought of his, which, if his Excellency would attend to us, he believed would be highly to our advantage; what he meant was, that near Camaldoli there was a pass so open that Piero Strozzi could not only pass through it with ease, but might surprise the castle of Poppi without difficulty; and, not satisfied with proving this to me in words, he took a leaf out of his pocket-book, upon which he had drawn so exact a plan of the whole country as showed but too plainly that the danger from that pass was not at all imaginary. I took the plan, and returned by the road of Prato Magno, and from St. Fransesco della Vernia arrived at Florence.

As soon as I had pulled off my riding-boots, I went to
the palace, and when I reached the abbey I met the Duke,
who received me most graciously, but at the same time
expressed some surprise, for he did not expect me that
week.   I answered that I had returned to serve his
Excellency.   "What business of importance," continued
the Duke, "has caused your speedy return?"   "My Lord,"
I replied, "I have something of great consequence to
show you;" so I went with him to the palace, where he
conducted me to a private apartment.   I told him all I
had heard, and showed him the sketch.   He appeared to
be highly pleased with my attention; and upon my
observing to his Excellency that it was absolutely necessary to find an immediate remedy for an affair of such
importance, the Duke seemed to muse for a while, and
then told me that he had concluded an agreement with
the Duke of Urbino, who would take care of that matter,
but this he desired me to keep to myself.   The next day
I made my appearance at the palace, and the Duke, after
a short conversation, said very pleasantly, "To-morrow
I will without fail despatch your business; so be of good
cheer."   Thinking myself sure of being provided for, I
with impatience waited for the morrow.   The wished-for
day being arrived, I went to the palace; but as it usually
happens that bad news are sooner communicated than
good, Signor Giacopo Guidi, his Excellency's secretary,
called me aside with his wry mouth and authoritative
voice, and, drawing himself up as stiff and formal as if he
had been frozen, told me that the Duke wished to know
from myself what I asked for my Perseus.   Quite surprised and disconcerted at this question, I answered that
it was not customary with me to set a price upon my
works, and that this request was not agreeable to the
promise his Excellency had made me a few days before.
The secretary, raising his voice, said he expressly commanded me in the Duke's name to tell what I expected

for my statue, on pain of totally forfeiting his Excellency's favor. I, who not only expected some considerable recompense, but likewise flattered myself that I had entirely gained the Duke's good graces, on meeting with this unexpected treatment, aggravated by the insolence of that waspish secretary, was incensed to such a degree that I declared if the Duke was to give me ten thousand crowns for my statue, it would be less than it was worth; and if I had expected to be bargained with in such a mercenary way, I never should have stayed at Florence. The spiteful secretary thereupon gave me a deal of opprobrious language, which I returned in the same style.

The very next day I went to pay my court to his Excellency, who told me, angrily, that cities and magnificent royal palaces might be built for ten thousand ducats. I bowed, and answered without hesitation, that his Excellency might find numbers of men capable of building cities and palaces, but perhaps he might not in the whole world find another artist able to make him such a statue of Perseus as mine; and I then departed. A few days later the Duchess sent for me, and desired me to make her arbitress of the dispute between the Duke and me, declaring that she would so contrive matters that I should have entire satisfaction. I answered that I never desired any higher reward for my labors than his Excellency's good graces; that he had promised me his favor, and it was unnecessary that I should then renew to their Excellencies the declaration I had made on the very day that I began to serve them. I added that, even if his Excellency had given me but twopence for my trouble, I should think myself happy if he did not deprive me of his good opinion. The Duchess, smiling, said, "Benvenuto, your best way would be to follow my advice;" and so she left me. Though the Duchess had had some difference with me, she was possessed of a great deal of good nature and certainly meant well.

At this time I was intimately acquainted with Girolamo degli Albizi, commissary to the militia, who one day
said: "Benvenuto, it appears highly expedient that we
should endeavor to find some method of settling this dispute between the Duke and you; and if you will put that
confidence in me, I dare say I shall find means to set all
to rights; for as the Duke is seriously offended, this may
otherwise turn out to your disadvantage; a word to the
wise is sufficient; I can say no more at present." As I
had been apprised of this, since the Duchess had the conversation with me, by one who perhaps had an ill intention in so doing, and who said he came by his information
accidentally, I replied in a passion, "I could for less than
twopence find in my heart to throw my Perseus away,
and that would completely put an end to the dispute at
once." However, on account of the suspicion I had of
the person from whom I had my information, I told
Girolamo degli Albizi that I left the whole affair to him,
and should readily agree to any proposal of his, provided
I might continue in favor with the Duke. This worthy
person, who was thoroughly acquainted with the profession of a soldier, but had no kind of taste for the polite
arts, told the Duke that I had left the whole affair to him,
and had requested him to speak to his Excellency in my
favor. The Duke replied, that he would also entrust
the whole affair to him, and abide by whatever he should
determine. Girolamo thereupon wrote a very ingenious
letter, in which he spoke greatly in my behalf; and his
determination was, that the Duke should give me three
thousand five hundred gold crowns, not as a gratifica-
tion for so elegant a piece of work, but toward my
present support, and that I should be satisfied with that
sum. The Duke subscribed to this with pleasure; but I
was very far from being satisfied.

When the Duchess heard of this, she said it would
have been better for me if I had left the affair to her,
24

for she would have procured me five thousand gold
crowns. And one day that I went to the palace, she said
the same thing to me in the presence of Signor Ala-
manno Salviati, and turned me into ridicule, telling me
that I deserved all the bad success I had met with. The
Duke gave orders that the money should be paid me
in monthly sums of a hundred gold crowns. Afterward
Signor Antonio de Nobili, who was commissioned to pay
me, began to give me only fifty, and after that again
he reduced his payments to five-and-twenty, and sometimes did not pay me at all. When I perceived these de-
lays, I mildly expostulated with Signor Antonio, and
begged to know for what reason he discontinued my
payments. He answered me civilly; but I thought that
in his answer he went a little beyond the bounds of
probability; for, first of all, he told me that the cause of
discontinuing my payments was, that money began to
be very scarce at court: but he added that as soon as he
had funds he would pay me. He at the same time loudly
declared that if he were to neglect paying me he should
be one of the greatest villains breathing. He promised
that he would pay me as soon as it was in his power;
but his actions proved quite contrary to his declarations.
Seeing myself thus hardly treated, I grew very angry,
and giving him a great deal of severe language, put him
in mind of all he had promised. He died soon afterward,
and now toward the close of the year 1556, five hundred
gold crowns still remain due to me. I then ceased to
receive any salary, and thought they would entirely
neglect to pay it, as nearly three years had elapsed. But
the Duke was about this time attacked by a dangerous
disorder, and, perceiving that remedies administered by
his physicians did him no service, he had recourse to
the Almighty, and thereupon ordered that all to whom
he was indebted should receive what money was due to

them. I was paid among the rest; but not the remainder of what was owing to me for my statue of Perseus.

I thought what I did was for the best, when I told the Duchess that I could not compromise what was not in my power; for I had assured the Duke that I should be satisfied with whatever his Excellency should think proper to give me. For a few days before he had made the agreement with Albizi he appeared to be very angry with me; and the reason was that, happening to complain to him of some ill usage that I had received from Signor Alfonso Quistello, and Signor Jacopo Polverino, who belonged to the treasury, and still more of Signor Giambattista Bandini of Volterra, I laid my charge against them with some appearance of warmth. I then perceived that the Duke was highly incensed, and threw out these angry expressions: "This puts me in mind of your statue of Perseus, for which you asked me ten thousand crowns. Interest has too much sway over you; I will get an estimate of its value, and pay you whatever it is rated at." I answered boldly, with some emotion: "How is it possible for a proper estimate to be taken of my statue, when there is not a man in Florence who is an adequate judge of its merit?" The Duke was still more provoked at this, and uttered a great many passionate expressions. "If there be a man in Florence," said he, "able to make one like it, that man must be capable of forming a proper estimate of it." When he said this, he had Bandinello in mind. "My Lord," said I, "your Excellency has given me an opportunity of executing, at the greatest school in the world, a noble and most arduous work, which has been more highly extolled than any other statue hitherto exhibited before that divine assembly; and what encourages me most is, that those excellent men who understand and profess the business, pass as favorable a judgment on my performance as the rest. For example, Bronzino, the painter, has written four sonnets on the occasion, using the most noble and sublime expressions that could possibly enter into his conception; and it is in consequence of the great encomiums bestowed on my work by this extraordinary person that the whole city has so greatly admired it; and I will venture to affirm that, if he were to cultivate sculpture as he cultivates painting, he would probably be able to equal it.   I must also inform your Excellency, that my master, Michelangelo Buonarroti, could likewise have made such a statue when he was younger than he is at present; it would, however, have cost him as much trouble as mine has cost me; but now that he has advanced in years, he is utterly incapable of producing anything like it, so that I do not think there is an artist living capable of equaling my work.   Thus has my performance received the greatest reward that it was possible for me to wish; and still more so as your Excellency has not only declared yourself satisfied with it, but has even bestowed upon it higher praise than anybody else.   What greater or more honorable reward could I possibly desire?   I will therefore affirm that you could not pay me in more glorious coin, nor with any sort of treasure equal to that; so that I am amply paid, and thank your Excellency with all my heart." "That is far from being the case," answered the Duke, "that you do not think I have treasure sufficient to satisfy you for your performance; but I assure you I will pay you much more than it is worth."   I replied, that I did not expect any further recompense from his Excellency, but thought myself amply rewarded by that which I received from the school of Florence; and with that I should presently depart, if it please God, without ever returning to the house his Excellency had given me, or ever more desiring to see Florence.

We were then at Santa Felicità, and the Duke was returning to his palace.   He turned to me and said angrily, "Don't go away; I say again, don't go away on any account." So that I accompanied him to the palace, somewhat frightened. He thereupon sent for Bartolini, the Archbishop of Pisa, and likewise for Signor Pandolfo della Stufa, and told them to order Baccio Bandinello, in his name, to examine my statue of Perseus, and value it, because he purposed paying me exactly according to its worth. The two worthy persons above named immediately found Baccio Bandinello, and delivered their message to him, who said he knew very well the value of the work, but as he had had many differences with me he did not choose to concern himself in my affairs. The two gentlemen then added, "The Duke has desired us to tell you that he commands you, on pain of his displeasure, to set a price upon the statue, and you may take two or three days to examine it attentively, if you think proper; after which you are to inform us what the artist deserves for his trouble." He answered that he had examined the statue attentively, and, as he could not avoid obeying the Duke's commands, was obliged to declare that the work had proved so admirable a masterpiece that, in his opinion, it was worth sixteen thousand gold crowns or more. The gentlemen immediately informed the Duke of this decision, who was highly displeased at it. They also told me of it; but I said I would by no means accept of the praises of Bandinello, as that man spoke ill of everybody. These words of mine were repeated to the Duke, and the Duchess again wished me to leave the whole affair to her.

The Duke gave me to understand, by Signor Lelio Torelli his auditor, that he wished me to represent certain historical pieces in a basso rilievo of bronze round the choir of Sta. Maria del Fiore; but as this choir was a work of Bandinello's, I was unwilling to ennoble his petty performances by my labors; though the plan of the choir was not his, as he had not the least knowledge of architecture, but that of Giuliano, the son of Baccio d'Agnolo, a carpenter, who spoiled the cupola. For these reasons I wished to decline being concerned in the work; though I humbly told the Duke that I was ready on all occasions to obey his commands. Soon after this he ordered the overseers of Sta. Maria del Fiore to talk to me about the affair; for he purposed to allow me only my salary of two hundred crowns a year; and in all other respects the overseers were to supply me out of the fund assigned for carrying on the work. I therefore went to the overseers, who told me the orders they had received; and as I thought I might freely acquaint them with all my reasons for disapproving the work proposed, I began to prove that so many pieces of history represented in bronze would occasion a prodigious expense, and that it would be squandering money. I laid before them all the causes that induced me to think so, and they were very capable of conceiving the full force of what I alleged. The first was that the manner in which the choir had been laid out was irregular, contrived without judgment, without the least appearance of art, convenience, gracefulness, or design; the other was, that the historical pieces, by being placed so low, would be beneath the eye, and would make a kennel for dogs, and be constantly defiled. For these reasons I declared that I did not choose, on any account, to be concerned in the work; that I ought not to lose the remainder of my best days without serving his Excellency, whom I was so ambitious to serve. Therefore if he wished to employ me, he should rather order me to make the middle door of the church of Sta. Maria del Fiore, which would be worth seeing, and would do him much more honor than the other. I added, that I was willing to enter into a contract that, in case I did not in the execution surpass the finest door of the church of San Giovanni, I should ask no reward for my trouble; but in case I finished it according to my promise, I consented that it should be valued, and even then I should be satisfied with a thousand crowns less than it was estimated at by those of the profession. The workmen, being highly pleased with what I proposed, went to speak of it to the Duke, and among others Piero Salviati attended. They thought that what they were going to propose would prove highly agreeable to him; but it proved quite the reverse; for he said I was for doing the very contrary of what he would have me do, so Piero left the Duke without coming to any conclusion.

When I heard what had passed between them, I waited on the Duke, who appeared to be somewhat offended with me. I begged he would condescend to hear what I had to say in my defence, and he promised me he would. So I began to give him an account of the whole affair, and used so many arguments to explain the nature of the thing, and convince him that to engage in such an undertaking would be only throwing away money, that I greatly softened him, and then took occasion to observe that, if he did not choose to have the door I mentioned, it was absolutely necessary to make two pulpits to the choir, and that they would be two noble works, and do him honor. I added that I would adorn them with historical pieces in basso rilievo of bronze, together with a variety of other embellishments. In this manner did I appease his Excellency, who gave me orders to begin the models without delay. I made a variety of models. Among others, I made one with eight faces more carefully than any of the rest, and thought it much better adapted to its purpose. I carried the models several times to the palace, and his Excellency at length ordered Signor Cæsar, his wardrobe-keeper, to ask me to leave them. I perceived afterward that the Duke had made choice of the very worst. One day he sent for me, and in some conversation concerning

these models, I proved to him that the model with eight
faces was the best calculated for the purpose, and by far
the most beautiful of them all.   The Duke answered that
he chose I should make it quadrangular, because he liked
that form best; he conversed with me, however, a long
time on the subject, with good humor.   Whether the
Duke at last became sensible that I spoke the truth, or
was resolved to have the thing his own way, a considerable time passed without his mentioning it to me again.

CHAPTER XLV

ATTEMPTED MURDER

ABOUT this time the great block of marble for a
statue of Neptune was brought up the river
Arno, and thence by the Grieve, and carried
through the road that leads to Poggio a Cajano, that it might be conveyed the more easily by that
level road to Florence, where I went to see it.   Though
I know to a certainty that the Duchess had by her interest procured it for the Cavalier Bandinello, yet, not
through any envy to that artist, but moved to compassion for the destiny of the unfortunate marble, I took a
view of it, measured its height and thickness every way,
and on my return to Florence made several little models
for it.   When we endeavor to preserve any great thing
from evil, it often meets with a worse fate than that
from which we rescued it; as was the case of this marble.
Having made the little models, I went to Poggio a
Cajano, where the Duke and Duchess were with the
Prince their son.   I found them all at table, and the
Duke dined in private with the Duchess, so that I began

to enter into conversation with the prince. As I talked with him a considerable time, the Duke overheard us, and sent for me, and as soon as I came into the presence of their excellencies, the Duchess began to converse with me with great good humor. I contrived to turn the subject of the conversation to the block of marble.

I observed that their ancestors had rendered the noble school of Florence so illustrious by exciting emulation among the men of genius in the different professions. It was this that produced the admirable cupola, the beautiful doors of the church of San Giovanni, and so many other noble temples and statues, reflecting such high honor on this city. The Duchess peevishly replied that she knew very well what I would be at, and asked me never to speak again of that marble in her presence, as nothing could give her greater offence. "I, then, offend you," said I, "madam, by becoming an agent for your Excellencies, and exerting myself to the utmost to have you well served. Consider seriously, that if your Excellencies are willing to permit every artist to produce a model of Neptune, even though you are resolved to give the preference to Bandinello's, this will excite him, for his own honor, to exert himself with more ardor in making a beautiful model than if he had had no competitor. Thus will your Excellencies be better served, and will avoid discouraging your excellent school, and will likewise see who applies closest to this admirable art—I mean in the grand style; and you will appear both to delight in it and be judges of its beauties." The Duchess then told me, in a passion, that I tired her patience; that she was resolved the marble should be Bandinello's; adding, that the Duke himself was determined that Bandinello should have it. When the Duchess ceased speaking, the Duke, who had continued silent, replied: "It is now twenty years since I caused this fine piece of marble to be taken out of the quarry on purpose for Bandinello, and therefore it is my pleasure that he should have it, and it shall be his."

I thereupon turned to the Duke, and begged it as a favor that he would give me leave just to say four words to him for his own advantage. The Duke bade me say whatever I thought proper, telling me that he would listen with attention. I then said: "You are to understand, my Lord, that the marble of which Bandinello made Hercules and Cacus was taken out of the quarry by the renowned Michelangelo Buonarroti, who made for it a model of Samson with four figures, which would have been one of the first pieces in the whole world; and your favorite Bandinello made of it only two figures, both ill executed, and put together in the most bungling manner. Therefore the admirable school of Florence still exclaims against the great injury that was done to that fine piece of marble. I really believe there were more than a thousand sonnets posted up to ridicule that wretched performance, and I am sure your Excellency remembers the thing very well. If, therefore, my worthy lord, the men to whose care that business was intrusted were so injudicious as to take so valuable a piece of marble from Michelangelo, and give it to Bandinello, who spoiled it, can you ever think of suffering the same person to spoil this much finer block, and not give it to some artist capable of doing it justice? Give orders, my Lord, for each artist to make a model, and let them all be laid before the Academy. Your Excellency will then hear its opinion concerning them, and with your usual judgment be able to choose the best. Thus you will avoid throwing away your money and discouraging a school that is now the most renowned in the world and reflects such honor on your Excellency." The Duke rose on a sudden from table, and said, "Go, my friend Benvenuto, make a model, and endeavor to win that fine piece of marble, for I am sensible that what you say is

just." The Duchess shook her head at me, and muttered
something as if she were angry; but I, bowing to their
Excellencies, made all haste to return to Florence, being
quite impatient to begin the model.

The Duke had no sooner arrived at Florence than, without giving me any notice whatever, he came to my house,
when I showed him two little models quite different
from each other. He praised them both, but added that
one of them pleased him much more than the other; and
bidding me finish that which he was pleased with, told
me I should find my account in it. As his Excellency
had seen those made by Bandinello and the other artists
he greatly preferred mine to the rest, for so I was informed by several courtiers who had heard him. Among
other circumstances worthy of being related, one was,
that the Cardinal di Santa Fiore being come to Florence,
the Duke took him with him to Poggio a Cajano. By
the way the Cardinal, seeing the piece of marble, praised
it highly, and asked who his Excellency intended should
work upon it. The Duke answered, "My Benvenuto,
who has drawn me an excellent model."

This was repeated to me by persons worthy of credit,
and on that account I waited on the Duchess, and carried her some pretty little trifles of my making, which
she liked very much. She asked me what I was at that
time about. I answered, "Madam, I have undertaken
one of the most laborious tasks in the world by way of
amusement. The task I mean is a Christ crucified, of
the whitest marble, on a cross of the blackest, and as
large as the life." She asked me what I purposed to do
with it, and I replied: "I assure you, madam, I would
not sell it for two thousand ducats; for no man ever took
so much pains with a piece of work; nor could I have
undertaken to make such a one for any nobleman, for
fear of revealing my want of capacity and being put to
confusion. I bought the marble with my own money,

and kept a young man about two years to assist me; and what with purchasing marble and tools, and paying him a salary, the work has cost me more than three hundred crowns, so that I again declare I would not give it for two thousand ducats. But if your Excellency will do me one favor, I will freely make you a present of it. All I desire is, that you will be neutral with respect to the models of a Neptune that the Duke has ordered to be made of the great marble." The Duchess answered with indignation, "It seems, then, you value neither my interest nor my opposition?" I replied, "You quite mistake me, madam; I know very well the consequence of both: why else do I offer you what I value at two thousand ducats? But I rely so much on my diligence and acquired knowledge, that I have good hopes of winning the prize, even if it were disputed with me by the great Michelangelo Buonarroti, from whom alone I learned all I know: and I would much rather that he who knows so much should make a model, than the others that know so little; for much honor might be won by entering the lists with my renowned master; but there can be very little in contending with inferior artists."

The Duchess rose angrily, and I returned to my model, working at it with all assiduity. As soon as I had finished it, the Duke came to see it, accompanied by two ambassadors, one from the Duke of Ferrara, the other from the republic of Lucca. My model gave high satisfaction, and the Duke said, "Benvenuto deserves the prize." Thereupon the noble personages complimented me highly, especially the ambassador of the republic of Lucca, who was a man of learning and had taken the degree of doctor. I retired to some distance, that they might speak their sentiments freely. When I found they were favorable to me, I approached, and, turning to the Duke, said, "My Lord, your Excellency should have recourse to another expedient, which is, to give orders that each artist should make a model of clay exactly of the same size as the marble statue; by which means your Excellency will be much better able to tell who deserves the preference. And I must further take the liberty to observe that, if you give the prize to an artist who is not deserving of it, you will not so much injure the person that has merit as yourself, for both loss and shame will result to you from such a decision; whereas, by a contrary conduct, that is, by giving it to him that is worthy of it, you will in the first place acquire great reputation; you next will lay out your money to advantage, and men of genius will think that you delight in the polite arts and are a judge of ability." When I had made an end of speaking, the Duke shrugged his shoulders; and, as he was just going, the ambassador from Lucca said, "My Lord, this Benvenuto of yours is a man of great spirit." The Duke replied, "He has more spirit than you are aware of; and it would have been well for him if he had less, for he would then have obtained many gratifications that he has missed." These words were repeated to me by the ambassador, who at the same time chided me for not acting the courtier better. I answered that I wished well to my lord, was his affectionate and faithful servant, but could not stoop to the arts of flattery and adulation.

Some weeks later, Bandinello died, and it was generally thought that, besides his disorder, his grief at losing the fine piece of marble, out of which the statue of Neptune was to be made, greatly contributed to hasten his death Bandinello had heard of my making the marble crucifix, of which I have spoken above. He thereupon took a small piece of marble, and made that figure of Piety which is to be seen in the church of the Nunziata.

As I had dedicated my crucifix to Santa Maria Novella, and had already fixed up the irons to fasten it upon, I wanted nothing further but to construct, on the ground under the crucifix, a little tomb to be buried in after my death. The monks told me they could not grant my request without asking leave of the overseers of the building. "Why, then," said I, "did you not consult the overseers before you permitted me to fix the irons in this place for setting up my crucifix?" For this reason, I resolved not to give my work to this church of Santa Maria Novella, though the overseers afterward came and made me an apology. I therefore went to the church of the Nunziata, and told the monks that I would make them a present of my crucifix, in the same manner that I had proposed giving it to the church of Santa Maria Novella; upon which the good brethren of the Nunziata bade me set up my crucifix in their church, and erect my tomb in whatever manner I thought proper. Bandinello, being informed of this, made all haste to finish his figure of Piety, and requested the Duchess to grant him the chapel formerly belonging to the Pazzi, which he at last with great difficulty obtained; and, as soon as he accomplished his desire, he erected his tomb in it, which was not completely finished when he died. The Duchess then said that she had befriended him during his life, and would continue her regard for him even after his decease; for though he was no more, Benvenuto must never expect to have the marble in his possession. Bernardone the broker, happening one day to meet me in town, told me that the Duchess had given away the marble, upon which I exclaimed, "O ill-fated stone! hard, indeed, was thy lot in falling into the hands of Bandinello! but it is a hundred times more deplorable now thou art in those of Ammanato!"

I had received directions from the Duke to make a model of clay, of the same size that the statue of marble was to be. At the same time he ordered me to be furnished with wood and clay, and a little partition to be erected in the apartment where I had made my Perseus.

He also paid the wages of a workman that was to assist
me. I set about my model with the utmost assiduity,
made the skeleton in wood with the greatest exactness,
and brought my work happily to a conclusion. I gave
myself no further trouble about making the statue; for I
knew the Duchess was determined that I should not have
the fine block of marble. But I promised myself that as
soon as I had finished it, the Duchess, who did not lack
discernment, would, after she had seen the work, be
sorry that she had done both the marble and herself so
much injustice.

Giovanni Fiamingo made one model in the cloisters of
St. Croce; another was made by Vincenzio Danti, of
Perugia, in the house of Signor Ottavio de' Medici; another was begun by the son of Moschino, at Pisa; and
still another was made by Bartolommeo Ammanato in
my working-room, which we had divided between us.
When I had well bronzed it over, and was about to finish
the head, the Duke came from the palace, with Giorgetto
the painter, to Ammanato's apartment, to view the statue
of Neptune, on which Giorgetto had worked several days
with his own hands, in conjunction with Ammanato and
all his journeymen. I was informed that, when his Excellency saw it, he appeared to be by no means satisfied;
and though Giorgetto, with his chatter, tried to persuade
him into a good opinion of the work, the Duke shook his
head, and, turning to Signor Giorgio Stefano, bade him
go ask Benvenuto whether his great model was in such
forwardness that he could let him have a sight of it.
Stefano thereupon delivered me this message, adding,
that if I did not think my work would yet bear inspection,
I might say so without reserve, as the Duke was well
aware that I had not been properly seconded in an undertaking of such importance. I answered that I should
be glad of the favor of his Excellency's presence; that
even if my work were not in any great forwardness, so

penetrating a genius as his could easily, from the specimen, form a judgment of what it would prove when finished. The gentleman delivered the message to the Duke, who came with great cheerfulness. No sooner had he entered the room, and cast his eye upon my work, than he appeared to be highly pleased with it. He examined it on all sides, fixing particularly upon the four principal points of view, just as a complete artist might have done; he then showed, by many gestures, that he was highly pleased with it, and said nothing further but, "Benvenuto, you have the last coat to lay on still." At length he turned to his attendants, and spoke of my performance in the most complimentary terms, declaring that the little model he saw at my house pleased him greatly, but this work of mine far surpassed the model.

As it pleased God, who makes all things coöperate to our advantage (I mean to the advantage of those who acknowledge and believe in his Divine Majesty), about this time an old rogue, from Vicchio, whose name was Pier Maria di Anterigoli, and his surname Sbietta, offered to sell me a farm for my natural life—that is, to sell me an annuity. This man followed the business of a grazier, and, as he was related to Signor Guido Guidi the physician, who is now chief magistrate of Pescia, I readily listened to his proposal. This farm I did not choose to go to see, being impatient to finish my model of the great statue of Neptune: besides, there was no occasion for my seeing it, as he sold me only the income of it, and had given me a written account of the measures of grain, wine, oil, corn, chestnuts, and other produce of the farm; all which, I took for granted, must, as times then were, be worth more than a hundred gold crowns; so I paid him six hundred and fifty crowns for them, including the taxes. After he had given me a writing, signed with his own hand, which imported that he would, during my natural life, take care to see me paid the in-

come of the farm, I thought it unnecessary to go and
take a view of it, but inquired whether the said Sbietta
and his brother Filippo were good men, such as might be
depended upon, and was assured by several of their acquaintances that I might feel perfectly secure. We
agreed to send for Pier Francesco Bertoldi the notary;
and the first thing I put into his hand was the written
account of what Sbietta was to make good to me, thinking it should by all means enter into the contract; but
the notary busied himself with two-and-twenty different
articles, which were mentioned to him by Sbietta, and,
as I thought, seemed to forget the main part of the contract, which was the payment of the annuity. While the
notary was writing, I worked on, and as he was several
hours in drawing the deed, in the mean time I made
a considerable part of the head of my Neptune. The
instrument being at last completed, Sbietta began to lavish compliments on me, as I in my turn did on him. He
made me presents of kids, cheeses, capons, cakes, and a
variety of fruits, till at last I began to be quite ashamed.
In return for these favors, every time he came to Florence
I took him home with me from his inn, and he was frequently accompanied by some of his relatives, whom
also I invited to my house.

One day he told me, in a jocular manner, that it was
a shame that after I had bought a farm, and several
weeks had passed since I made the purchase, I could not
discontinue my business for a few days, and go to see
it. Such an effect had his insinuations on my mind that
I at last, to my misfortune, did comply with his desire.
Sbietta received me with such courtesy and outward
ceremony that he could not have done more for a duke,
and his wife seemed to be still fonder of me than her
husband. This continued for a time, till what he and his
brother Filippo had concerted between them had taken
effect. At the same time I went on with my work, and

25

had already sketched out the whole with an exactness unknown to any artist before me; so that, though I was sure not to get the marble, I thought myself on the point of finishing and exhibiting the model in the public square. The weather was warm and pleasant, so that, being much importuned by the two villains above mentioned, I set out from my villa on Wednesday, which was doubly a holiday, for Trespiano. At the gate of Vicchio I met Filippo the priest, who seemed to know where I was going, and to be extremely fond of my company. He conducted me to Sbietta's house, where was his shameless wife, who seemed lavish of her compliments to me. I made her a present of a straw hat, and she declared that she had never seen a finer. Sbietta happened not to be then at home. Evening approaching, we all supped together very cheerfully; and when it was time to retire I was shown into a handsome apartment, where I slept in an exceedingly good bed, and my two servants were accommodated in a manner agreeable to their station. The same compliments were repeated when I rose in the morning. I went to take a view of my farm, with which I was highly pleased, and a certain quantity of corn and all sorts of grain were given to me. I then returned to Vicchio, and Filippo said to me at parting, "Benvenuto, though you have not received as much as was promised you, you must not be disheartened, for you will meet with an ample compensation, as you have honest people to deal with. I must, however, caution you against yon laborer, whom we have discharged because he is a rogue." This laborer, whose name was Mariano Rosselli, often said to me, "Take care of yourself, or you will know to your cost who among us is the greatest villain." When that country-fellow spoke to me in this manner, he smiled archly and shook his head, as much as to say, "You will one day find that I speak the truth."

I was guilty of an error in judgment, but was not at

all mistaken in what happened to me. Returning from my farm, which is about two miles from Vicchio toward the Alpi, I met Filippo the priest, who received me with his usual courtesy; so we breakfasted together. I then took a walk about the town of Vicchio, and the market was already open. I perceived that I was stared at by all the inhabitants, as an object they were not at all accustomed to; above all by a worthy man who had lived many years in the town, and whose wife made bread for sale. This honest person had, about a mile distant, some lands of his own, though he chose to live in that manner. He rented a house of mine in Vicchio, which fell to me with the farm known by the name of the Fountain. As we happened to fall into conversation, he said, "I live in your house, and will pay you your rent when it becomes due; or, if you choose to receive it beforehand you may, for I am resolved we shall have no disputes." While we were thus talking together, I perceived that the man several times fixed his eyes upon me attentively, so I could not help saying, "Dear Giovanni, why do you look at me with such earnestness?" The worthy man answered, "I will tell you with all my heart, if you promise upon your honor not to reveal your author." I solemnly promised him that I would not. He thereupon continued, "You must understand, then, this vile priest Signor Filippo a few days ago went about making his boasts of the great feats of his brother Sbietta, and declaring that he had sold a farm of his for life to an old man, who would never see the end of the year. You have villains to deal with; therefore take care of yourself, and be constantly upon your guard. I say no more."

In my walks up and down the town, I met Giambattista Santini, and he and I were invited to supper by the priest. It was then between five and six, and supper had been ordered at this early hour on my account, for I had declared my intention of returning in the evening

to Trespiano.   Supper was, therefore, prepared in all
haste, and Sbietta's wife was very active on the occasion, as was also one Cecchino Buti, a servant of theirs.
As soon as the salads were dressed, and the guests began
to sit down to table, the villain of a priest made a sort
of wry face, and said, "I must ask pardon of you all, but
I cannot possibly have the pleasure of supping with you,
for an affair of great consequence has since happened, in
which my brother Sbietta is concerned; and as he is not
here himself, I am under a necessity of supplying his
place." We all pressed him to stay, but were not able
to prevail on him to alter his purpose. So we sat down
to supper. As soon as we had eaten the salads off certain little dishes, the boiled meat was served about, and
porringers were distributed to the guests. Santini, who
sat opposite to me at a table, said, "They give you nap-
kins quite different from the rest. Did you ever see
finer?" I told him I had not perceived it. He then bade
me call to the wife of Sbietta, who, with Cecchino Buti,
ran up and down in a continual hurry, and ask her to sit
down at table. I used so many entreaties that I at last
prevailed on the woman to take her place. She was
sorry, she said, we did not like our supper, which appeared by our eating so little. After I had several times
praised the entertainment, assuring her that I never had
tasted anything better, or with a better appetite, I at
last told her I had eaten enough. I could not immediately guess why she pressed me so earnestly to eat.
When we had finished supper it was past eight o'clock,
and I had a mind to return that night to Trespiano, in
order to resume my business in the morning. So I set
out upon my journey.

I had hardly traveled three miles when I felt my stomach burn dreadfully, and was tormented with such
pangs that I thought it an age before I arrived at my
farm of Trespiano. I with great difficulty reached the

place that night, and immediately went to bed. The whole night I had no rest, my bowels being violently disordered. No sooner was it daylight than I felt my brain all on fire. I knew I had eaten something poisonous, and tried to think what it could be. I recollected the dishes and porringers that were given to me by Sbietta's wife, which appeared so different from those set before the rest of the company. I at the same time called to mind that the designing priest, Sbietta's brother, after taking so much pains to make me welcome, did not choose to sup with us. It further occurred to my memory that this priest had boasted of his brother's having made a fine bargain, in selling a farm for life to an old man who would never see the end of the year; for these words had been repeated to me by the worthy Del Sardella. So I concluded that they had given me in a porringer of sauce, which was very highly seasoned and extremely palatable, a dose of sublimate, as sublimate produces all the symptoms with which my illness was attended. I took two spoonfuls of the sauce in question, as it was extremely relishing; and I recollected that Sbietta's wife had several times pressed me to eat of it, as also that they had recourse to a variety of artifices to make me take the destructive sublimate.

Though I found myself thus disordered, I went to work at my great model of Neptune; but my illness in a few days so overpowered me that I was confined to my bed. As soon as the Duchess heard that I had been taken ill, she ordered the unfortunate marble to be put into the hands of Bartolommeo Ammanato, who sent me word that I might do what I pleased with my model, for he had won the marble. I did not, on hearing this, act like his master Bandinello, who was used to launch out into a superfluity of words. I contented myself with saying that I had always guessed it would turn out so; and desired Bartolommeo to exert his utmost efforts in showing himself worthy of the favor fortune had conferred on him. Thus I continued very ill, confined to my bed, and was attended by that skilful physician Signor Francesco di Monte Varchi, and by a surgeon named Raffaello de' Pilli. The sublimate had so burned my bowels that I could not retain my food a moment; but as Signor Francesco found that the poison had exhausted its power of hurting, for it was unable to subdue that strength of nature which he perceived to be in my constitution, he said to me one day, "Benvenuto, return thanks to God: you have got the better of your disorder. Be under no apprehension, for I am resolved to cure you in spite of the villains that endeavored to bereave you of life." Raffaello de' Pilli then cried out, "This will be one of the greatest and most difficult cures that ever were heard of. Do you know, Benvenuto, that you swallowed a whole spoonful of sublimate?" At these words Signor Francesco, interrupting him, said, "Perhaps there was some poisonous insect in it." I then told them that I knew to a certainty what kind of poison it was, and who gave it to me; and here we were all silent. They attended me more than six months, and it was more than a year before I was able to resume my business.

CHAPTER XLVI

INJUSTICE AND TREACHERY

ABOUT this time [October, 1560], the Duke went to Siena to make his public entry into that city, and Ammanato had gone thither some months before to erect the triumphal arches. On this occasion a natural son of Ammanato's, who continued to occupy the room where he worked, removed a sort of veil that I had thrown over my model of Neptune to keep it from being seen. I immediately went to make a complaint of this to Don Francesco, the Duke's son, who always appeared to be my friend. I represented to him that they had uncovered my figure, which was still imperfect, but that, if it had been finished, it would have given me no concern at all. To this the Prince answered, "Benvenuto, do not give yourself any trouble about covering the figure, for they think theirs much superior to yours; but if you require it to be kept covered, I will instantly give orders accordingly." To these words his Excellency added many more highly to my advantage, in the presence of several noblemen. I then requested him to give me an opportunity of finishing it, as I purposed making a present of it, as well as the little model, to his Excellency. He replied that with pleasure he accepted both, and would order all the conveniences to be given to me that I could require. So I subsisted upon this little favor, which in some measure restored my health; for so many ills and calamities had befallen me that I began to sink under them, but on this glimmering of princely encouragement I began to comfort myself with some hopes of life.

A year had now expired since my purchasing the farm of Fonte from Sbietta, and finding that, besides all the injuries he had done me, both by poison and by chicane, the farm did not produce what he had promised; and as I had, besides the contract, a writing signed by Sbietta's own hand, who had entered into an engagement before witnesses to pay me the yearly product of the farm; I addressed myself to the magistrates of the city of Florence. At that time, Signor Alfonso Quistello was living; he was superintendent of the treasury, and sat with the other councilors, among whom were Averardo Serristori and Federigo de' Ricci. Among them there was one of the Alessandri, and they were all persons of great distinction. When I had laid my case before those magistrates, they were unanimously of opinion that Sbietta should refund the money he had received from me, except Federigo de' Ricci, who at that time had connections with Sbietta. All the rest expressed their concern that Federigo de' Ricci should prevent them from deciding in my favor: among others, Averado Serristori was particularly clamorous on the occasion, as was also one of the Alessandri. Federigo having at last so protracted the cause that the magistrates put an end to the time of their sitting, the gentleman above mentioned came up to me one morning in the square of the Nunziata, when the magistrates had all left the court, and said with a loud voice: "Federigo de' Ricci has been too powerful for us all, so that you lost your cause in spite of us." Thus I lost my cause on account of a rich citizen, who employed the grazier from whom I had bought the farm.

The Duke being at Leghorn, I waited on his Excellency to solicit him to dismiss me, perceiving that I had entirely recovered my health and strength. I found myself out of employment and was displeased with a state of indolence; so I formed a resolution to go directly to Leghorn, where I found the Duke, and met with the most gracious reception. I made some stay in that town, and every day rode out with his Excellency, so that I had a fair opportunity of saying whatever I thought proper to him. The Duke used to ride several miles out of Leghorn by the seaside, where he was building a little fortress; and that he might not be troubled with too great a number of attendants, he chose to have me with him as a companion. One day, finding myself favored by his Excellency in a particular manner, I formed a resolution to turn the conversation to Sbietta, that is, Pier Maria of Anterigoli, and thus expressed myself: "My

Lord, I must lay before your Excellency a most extraordinary case, by hearing which you will know what
prevented me from finishing the model of Neptune. You
are to understand that I purchased a farm of Sbietta for
life." Here I gave the Duke a circumstantial account
of the whole transaction. When I came to the affair
of the poison I said that if ever my services had been
acceptable to his Excellency, he should, instead of pun-
ishing Sbietta and those who had administered the poison, confer some reward on them; for they had not given
me a sufficient dose to kill me, but just enough to remove a dangerous viscosity that I had in my stomach
and intestines; and it operated in such a manner that,
whereas in my former state of health I might have lived
only three or four years, this extraordinary physic had
produced such an effect that I reckoned upon having
gained a new lease of twenty years; in short, I found
myself better than ever, and returned thanks to the Almighty, being sensible that the saying I had so often
heard was verified, namely, that God afflicts us occasionally for our good.

The Duke listened with the utmost attention while we
rode more than two miles together, and only once exclaimed, "O the wicked people!" I concluded with observing that I was greatly obliged to them, and then
entered upon more agreeable topics of conversation. I
one day accosted him just at the right season, and finding him in a humor that suited my purpose, requested
his Excellency to dismiss me, that I might no longer lose
my time; adding that I was still able to work, and that,
as to what remained due to me for my Perseus, his Excellency might pay me whenever he thought proper. I
at the same time returned him thanks in a long speech,
and with much ceremony. He made me no answer, but
appeared to be highly offended. The day following, Signor Bartolommeo Concino, one of his Excellency's chief

secretaries, said to me in a sort of bravado, "The Duke declares that if you wish to be dismissed you may, but that if you choose to work he will employ you; and it were to be wished you could execute as much as his Excellency will please to order." I answered that I desired nothing more than to be employed, especially by his Excellency, whose service I preferred to that of any other great personage living, whether pope, emperor, or king; adding that I should be better pleased to serve him for a penny than another for a ducat. He replied that, if my sentiments were such as I represented them, I need say no more, for we were perfectly agreed. "Return," said he, "to Florence, and be of good cheer. The Duke wishes you well." Accordingly I then returned to Florence.

As soon as I arrived in this city, a person named Raffaello Schieggia, who worked in gold tissue, called at my house, and told me he wished to make up matters between me and Pier Maria Sbietta. I answered that the magistrates of Florence alone could settle affairs between us; and that Sbietta must not always expect to have upon the bench a Federigo de' Ricci, ready, for a present of two fat kids, to take his part, without fear of God or regard for his own honor, and shamefully violate justice and right. When I had uttered these words, with many others to the same effect, this Raffaello continued to remonstrate with me, that it was better to eat a thrush in peace than a large capon if it could not be had without broils and contention. He added that a lawsuit is often spun out to such length that it would be more for my interest to dedicate that time to making some elegant piece of work, by which I should acquire much greater reputation as well as emolument. As I was sensible that his observation was just, I began to listen to him; so that he soon compromised matters between us in the manner following: Sbietta was to take the farm, and pay me for it regularly seventy gold crowns per annum during my natural life. When we were ready to have the contract drawn up, which was to be done by Signor Giovanni di Ser Matteo da Falgano, Sbietta said that, in the manner we had settled it, the farm would produce more and could not possibly fail; therefore it was better that we should make the lease for five years, adding that he would adhere inviolably to his engagement, without ever giving occasion for another suit. The same promises were made in the most solemn manner by the rogue of a priest, his brother, so the contract was drawn up for the term of five years. During five years after making out the last lease, the two villains, instead of keeping any of their promises, were for returning me my farm, and did not choose to keep the lease of it any longer. I complained of this usage, and they had recourse to such chicanery with regard to the contract that I had no resource against their indirect proceedings. When I perceived this, I told them that the Duke and the Prince his son would not suffer them to do such flagrant injustice to a citizen of Florence. This menace so terrified them that they again sent to me the same Raffaello Schieggia, who had made up matters between us at first, to declare that they were not willing to pay the seventy gold crowns they had paid for five years past. I answered that I would take nothing less. Raffaello came to me and said, "My friend Benvenuto, you know very well that I am in your interest: they have all referred the affair to me." Thereupon he showed me a writing with their names signed to it. I, who was not aware that Raffaello was their near relative, thought myself in very good hands; so I left the management of the affair to him. This rogue came to me one evening, within half an hour of nightfall, in August, and made use of many arguments and persuasions to prevail on me to sign the contract while I was alone,

because he knew that if he deferred it till the morning
the trick would be discovered. So the contract was
signed, by which he engaged to pay me regularly sixty-
five crowns a year in two payments, during the course of
my natural life, and though I made a great stir about
the affair, and would by no means submit to such terms,
he showed the writing with my name to it, which made
all that saw it declare me to be in the wrong. The fellow at the same time affirmed that what he had done
had been for my good, and that he was entirely in my
interest; so, as neither the notary nor anybody else
knew of his being related to my adversaries, I was condemned by the general voice. I therefore gave up the
contest in time, and shall endeavor to do the best I can
for the future.

I committed another capital error in December of the
following year, 1566. I purchased half the farm of Poggio from them, that is, from Sbietta and the rest, for
two hundred crowns. This farm borders upon my other
of Fonte, and I let it to them for three years. Herein
I thought I acted wisely. I should become too prolix
were I to give a full account of all the ill-usage I received from these people. I therefore leave the whole
affair to the Almighty, who has always espoused my
cause against those who have injured me.

Having completely finished my marble crucifix, I
thought that if I raised it a few cubits above the ground,
it would appear to much greater advantage than if it
were placed immediately upon it; so I began to show
it to whomsoever had a mind to see such an exhibition.
The Duke and the Duchess, being informed of this, one
day, on their return from Pisa, came unexpectedly with
a grand retinue to my workshop, to see this image of
Christ on the cross. It pleased them so highly that
they, as well as all the nobility and gentry present, bestowed the highest encomiums on me. When I found

that it gave them such satisfaction, I said that the reason of my producing such a work was their having deprived me of the fine Neptune marble; and though I had undergone infinite labor in its execution, yet with pleasure I made them a present of it, thinking none more worthy of that fine piece of work than their Excellencies. I only requested that before they departed they would enter my humble habitation. At these words they rose with great complaisance, and, leaving the shop, entered my house, where they perceived my little model of Neptune and the fountain, which the Duchess had not seen before. So greatly was she affected by the sight that she burst into a loud exclamation of surprise, and, addressing herself to the Duke, said, "I declare, my Lord, I could never have formed a conception of anything so beautiful." The Duke answered her more than once, "Did I not tell you it would prove so?" Thus they talked a long time in praise of my abilities, and the Duchess seemed, as it were, to ask pardon for her treatment of me. She told me that it was her pleasure I should make choice of a piece of marble myself, and begin immediately to work upon it. To these kind words I answered that, if they gave me the means, I should, for their sake, cheerfully engage in so arduous an undertaking. The Duke replied, "Benvenuto, you shall have all the help you require, and I likewise shall give you some of my own contriving, which will be far more effectual than the others." Having expressed himself in these obliging terms, he withdrew, together with the Duchess, and left me highly pleased. But several weeks passed without my being taken any further notice of; insomuch that, seeing no orders given for furnishing me with what I wanted, I began to be in despair.

At this juncture the Queen-dowager of France despatched Signor Baccio del Bene to our Duke, to solicit a loan of money. The Duke in the kindest manner granted her request, at least, so it was generally reported. As Signor Baccio del Bene and I were intimate friends, we were very glad to see each other; and he gave me an account of all the favors conferred on him by his Excellency. On this occasion he asked me what works I had in hand. I mentioned the affair of Neptune and the fountain, and all the Duchess had done to injure me. He then told me that the Queen had a strong desire to finish the sepulchral monument of her husband, King Henry; and that Daniel of Volterra had undertaken to make a great horse of bronze for that purpose; but he was too far advanced in years, and the monument required a variety of ornaments; so that, if I chose to return to France, and again take possession of my castle, I should be abundantly supplied with whatever I wanted, in case I was willing to serve her Majesty. I asked Baccio to apply to the Duke, telling him that if his Excellency consented, I would return to France with pleasure. Baccio then told me, in high glee, that we should set out for France together, looking upon the affair as concluded. The day following he happened to have an interview with the Duke, when he took occasion to speak of me, and told his Excellency that, if it were agreeable to him, the Queen his mistress would take me into her service. The Duke answered: "Benvenuto is a man of great genius, as everybody knows; but now he chooses to work no longer." Thus the conversation was changed to other topics.

The next day I went to Baccio, who repeated all that had passed between him and the Duke. On which I began to be out of patience. "If," said I, "when his Excellency did not employ me, I of myself executed one of the most difficult pieces of work that ever were seen, which cost me more than two hundred crowns, what would have been the result in case his Excellency had set me to work? I must say he does me wrong; he has hurt me greatly." The gentleman repeated this answer of mine to the Duke, who declared that he had been jesting, and what he meant was to keep me in his own service. This provoked me greatly, and I had several times a great mind to decamp. The Queen of France did not care to propose the thing any more to the Duke, for fear of offending him; and I was obliged to stay, much against my will. About this time the Duke went on a journey with his whole court and his sons, excepting only the Prince, who was then in Spain. They traveled along the seacoast of Siena, and arrived at Pisa. The unwholesome air affected the Cardinal before any of the rest, so that he was attacked by a malignant fever, which in a few days put an end to his life. He was one of the Duke's chief supporters, and was highly beloved by him, being a person of great virtues and abilities; consequently his loss was severely felt. I let several days pass, till I thought their tears and grief must in some measure have subsided, and then I went to Pisa.

[Here ends Benvenuto Cellini's manuscript.]